Earthworks: a guide

N A Trenter

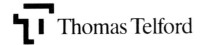
Thomas Telford

Published by Thomas Telford Publishing, Thomas Telford Limited, 1 Heron Quay, London E14 4JD.
URL: http://www.thomastelford.com

Distributors for Thomas Telford books are
USA: ASCE Press, 1801 Alexander Bell Drive, Reston, VA 20191-4400, USA
Japan: Maruzen Co. Ltd, Book Department, 3–10 Nihonbashi 2-chome, Chuo-ku, Tokyo 103
Australia: DA Books and Journals, 648 Whitehorse Road, Mitcham 3132, Victoria

First published 2001

Also available from Thomas Telford Books
A short course in soil and rock slope engineering. Noel Simons, Bruce Menzies and Marcus Matthews. ISBN 07277 2871 7
A short course in foundation engineering. Noel Simons and Bruce Menzies. ISBN 07277 2751 6

A catalogue record for this book is available from the British Library

ISBN: 0 7277 2966 7

Typeset by MHL Typesetting Limited, Coventry
Printed and bound in Great Britain by MPG Books, Bodmin, Cornwall

Contents

Acknowledgements

This book began as a *Design and Practice Guide*, one of a series produced by The Institution of Civil Engineers, and the early drafts on compaction were reviewed by a peer group comprising Mr F.R.D. Chartres, Professor B.G. Clarke, Mr L. Threadgold and Mr I.L. Whyte. Their patient and constructive assistance and the many suggestions made at that stage are greatly appreciated. The author would also like to express his thanks to his former colleagues at the Geotechnics Department at Halcrow Group Limited for their advice, particularly to Dr D.H. Beasley, Mr A. Andreou, Dr N.J. Burt and Dr R.A. Nicholls who made several valuable comments on the text, and to Mr J. Thrift who produced much useful material for the chapter on site safety. The Halcrow Group Librarian, Ms Julie Cordrey, always provided courteous and efficient help which is gladly acknowledged.

Appendices 2 and 3 were written by Mr P.C. Horner and are included with permission.

Preface

Earthworks are the most common product of civil engineering operations. Nothing can be built without some excavation and some transfer of soil (or rock) from one part of a site to another. Although normally seen as major structures such as earth dams, or cut and fill for airports, highways or railways, many earthworks are connected with minor civil works and building construction. Typically they comprise small scale cuts and embankments for diversions and widening schemes, together with site filling, levelling and estate road construction. In many cases, earthworks involve stripping sites of contaminated land or backfilling former quarries or open-cast mines. Whatever the type of work, the principles are the same.

It was not until relatively recently that earthworks were designed. The practical engineers driving roads, railways and canals across difficult terrain during the industrial revolution would build cuts and embankments at the slopes they believed appropriate on the basis of experience, cutting them back and slackening the slopes if failure occurred and using the same slopes for similar soils on the next occasion, if it did not. Thus maintenance engineering became accepted as part of earthworks in a way quite inappropriate for foundation engineering. Here, given the dangerous consequences of failure to a structure's occupants, the designer had to get things right first time. Even if a building did not collapse with life threatening consequences, an underpinning operation was hardly regarded as maintenance; on the contrary, it was (and still is) seen as an operation on a structure which had failed in its function in a way that most failed slopes had not.

As the volume of traffic using civil engineering infrastructure increased, this philosophy had to change. Today, failed earthworks are no longer a minor inconvenience but are seen as potentially dangerous by a public which expects higher standards of infrastructure facilities, yet is becoming more and more risk averse. There is every expectation that in the early decades of the twenty first century this situation will continue.

This book attempts to bring together topics usually considered as being essential to earthworks engineering. As a guide, it does not attempt to treat each exhaustively but to highlight what may be regarded as salient features. In particular, no attempt is made to establish technical proofs: this is amply dealt with in textbooks elsewhere. Instead, attention is paid to the practical consequences of the choices made by the engineer and to parameter selection, particularly in the matter of cut and embankment slope design. After a brief historical review (Chapter 1), the essential background to the compaction process is established (Chapter 2) and a description given of some fills commonly available, including some industrial materials (Chapters 3 to 6). There is a note on the nature of some current specifications (Chapter 7) and a description of design and construction control procedures (Chapter 8), noting that design and control in earthworks are intimately linked. The essential processes behind excavation, fill placement, cuttings and embankments are presented (Chapters 9 to 12), together with a brief note on site safety (Chapter 14).

A separate chapter (Chapter 13) is devoted to factor of safety of cuts and embankments. Developments in risk analysis and risk management suggest that the traditional approach, a lumped factor for all circumstances, may be inadequate and that more emphasis should be placed on the degree of risk to which the structure is likely to be exposed. Thus factor of safety may be regarded as a matrix in which risk to life on the one hand, and environmental and economic risk on the other all play a determining role. In this respect, the work of the Hong Kong Geotechnical Engineering Office in its Geotechnical Manual of Slopes (1984) is freely acknowledged. The interested reader will doubtless wish to consider the B. S. Eurocode 7 (1995) approach to factor of safety selection, as an alternative.

It is hoped that the guide will be a useful accompaniment to BS 6031: 1981 Code of Practice for Earthworks, the *Specification for Highway Works* (1998) and the various Advice Notes issued by *The Highways Agency*, particularly *Advice Note* HA 44/91. The readership is expected to include the chartered or near chartered civil engineer, who has a reasonable understanding of the essential soil mechanics vocabulary. It is also hoped that the geotechnical or engineering geologist specialist will find the material of interest, as will the University student. The intervention of suitably qualified and experienced specialists is considered essential in some matters of design and construction, especially in those topics dealt with in Chapters 11 to 13. The need for such intervention is occasionally stated, but in any doubt, specialist advice should always be sought. Likewise, there will be a need for a drainage engineer (for cuttings and embankment design and construction) and a rock mechanics engineer (for cuttings in rock). The involvement of the site safety engineer to augment the information given on safety is essential.

Developments not covered include the engineering of contaminated land. Another highly promising development, also not covered, is the use of vegetation to reinforce earthworks. As the public becomes more and more sophisticated in its expectations of the civil engineer in the environmental context, it is likely that there will be welcome progress in this field in the years ahead. Nevertheless, the requirement for information on the design and construction of conventional earthworks is expected to remain for a long time.

N A Trenter

1. Earthworks: an historical perspective

1.1 Highways

The origins of modern British earthworks lie in the Roman period, some two thousand years ago. The Romans constructed about 80 000 km of main roads, centred on Rome and extending outwards into the then Roman empire. Roads were graded into roughly five classes from the *Via*, constructed to allow the passage of two carriages and about 4.25 m wide, to the *Callais*, a mountain track. In their approach to road-building, the Romans demonstrated their understanding of one of the most important factors influencing the construction and maintenance of roads, namely drainage. This they did in two ways for their principal roads: first by drainage ditches either side of the carriageway; and second, by a layered construction, with a cambered surface, standing proud of the surrounding land. Water was not only shed off the road surface but the wearing course was protected from inundation by rising groundwater both by the adjoining open ditch drains and also by the elevated construction.

Roman roads radiated from London and probably formed the basis for Britain's main roads until the eighteenth century, although in the Middle Ages the Church took a keen interest in road and bridge maintenance for communications with churches and monastic institutions. With the dissolution of the monasteries in the sixteenth century, even this interest waned and roads in Britain deteriorated to a level probably not known before or since. In the seventeenth century, turnpikes were introduced, but their numbers grew slowly. By the time Macaulay wrote his *History of England* in 1848, there were only some 48 000 km of turnpike roads (Pannell, 1964), still over 30 000 km short of the total of main roads engineered by the Romans in their empire two thousand years previously.

With the establishment of turnpikes came the appointment of surveyors, salaried people who were paid to take a professional interest in highways. Standards of road-building began to improve in the late eighteenth and early nineteenth centuries, with Metcalfe, Telford and McAdam incorporating layered construction and drainage into road design. Although the design principles adopted by these pioneers are known, little information exists concerning their approach to earthworks as such. It is not known, for

Fig. 1.1 Earthworks in the Strand, London, 1851. Note the foreman in the foreground beating time (from Binnie, 1987).

example, whether the fill forming the embankments was systematically compacted or whether there was indeed any concept of suitable or unsuitable fill. However, highways hugged the contours to reduce cut and fill, and hence expense was kept to a minimum. Telford appears to have been aware of the problem of consolidation when he specified 'Where the height of the embankment shall exceed three feet, they are to stand from one to three months, in proportion as they increase in depth, as shall be determined by the inspector' (Pannell, 1964).

1.2   Railways

If large earthworks could be avoided with highway construction, they could not be avoided with railways, because of the small gradients employed. The London to Birmingham railway constructed by Robert Stephenson in the 1830s was probably one of the first modern examples of disastrous cost over-runs in British civil engineering. The final cost more than doubled from £2.4 million to £5.5 million, or some £50 000 per mile. The main reason appears to be Stephenson's wish to avoid large gradients, in railway terms, which meant that tunnels and deep cuttings had to be introduced. Also the London to Birmingham railway was one of the first major civil engineering structures to encounter the formidable problems posed by the London Clay, with the high retained cuttings between Camden Town and Euston and the Primrose Hill tunnel. Stephenson was also unfortunate enough to neglect the 'desk-study phase' of the site investigation for the Kilsby tunnel. The investigation failed to detect a 400 m length of 'quicksand', even though there was local knowledge of the feature. Eventually, it took thirteen pumps and some eighteen months to stabilize.

A completely different approach was taken by Locke with the Grand Junction railway, which connected the Manchester to Liverpool line to Birmingham. Locke accepted larger gradients (within the capabilities of the locomotives of the time) and made use of the terrain. He was therefore able to dispense with risk-laden tunnels and deep cuttings, at least to some extent, and the cost of the Grand Junction railway was reportedly only £19 000 per mile, roughly one third of the cost of the London to Birmingham railway. This approach demanded, at the same time, more earthworks including the the Penkridge bog crossing.

According to Skempton (1996), some 2 to 3 million yd^3 of earthworks per year were undertaken on each of the nine main railway lines under construction in England between 1834 and 1841. Thousands of men were employed, hundreds of horses, but only a handful of steam locomotives and stationary engines. This compares with the 7 million yd^3 per year during the construction of the early sections of the M1 motorway in the late 1950s, using modern construction plant (and producing well compacted fill). It is a tribute to the organizational and management skills of the early engineers that their productivity rivalled that achieved more than a century later. Although some of the fill placed would have been layered, especially at bridge abutments, this method would have proved too slow for the majority of construction. Most fill was end-tipped using teams of horse-drawn earth-wagons. Settlement would have been large but seems to have been accepted as an inevitable consequence of the construction method. Skempton reports that settlement effects would have been mitigated by speed restrictions and by packing ballast beneath sleepers until settlements had stabilized.

McGinnity and Russell (1995) describe some of the London Underground earth embankments (largely London Clay). Built 60 or 70 years after those of Stephenson and Locke, and still in use today, they were constructed with 'minimal, if any, effort at compaction'. The authors report that the large resulting settlements were made up by the addition of further clay fill and, once construction was complete, still further settlement would be made up using ash from the steam locomotives then in use; in other words, techniques very similar to those of the 1830s and 1840s.

The use of hand labour and horse-drawn wagons for earthworks in the early nineteenth century was replaced by steam-driven equipment in the latter half of the century, under the pressures of shortage of labour, now becoming increasingly organized, and the cost of money (Pannell, 1964). But even earlier, Robert Stephenson's Kilsby tunnel (referred to above) was rescued by steam pumps without which, according to some reports, tunnel completion may well have been impossible. Steam-powered winches were increasingly replacing the horse gin, the capstan and the treadmill, and steam-driven piling hammers were coming into use.

For a useful introduction to the history of road and railway construction in the UK, the reader is referred to Pannel (1964) and Upton (1975)

1.3 Canals and reservoirs

Canal construction in Great Britain commenced in about 1760 with the Bridgewater canal and was to continue for well over one hundred years. Between 1770 and 1830, over 2000 km of canals were built and by the end of the eighteenth century, the navigable Mersey, Trent, Severn and Thames rivers were all interconnected (Binnie, 1987). Although their construction may not be as celebrated as the later railways, they presented at least as many difficulties because canals had even more stringent vertical alignment criteria and had to be made leak-proof. This latter point alone demonstrates the intuitive skills of the eighteenth and early nineteenth century 'navvies'; with no theory to guide them, they must nevertheless have been intimately acquainted with the required fill properties. There was also more civil engineering, both design and construction, associated with lock building and with the reservoirs from which the canals drew their water.

The earliest example of an English earth dam for which engineering details survive is Grimsthorpe (Skempton, 1979). Constructed in 1748, the 18 feet high structure was not built to retain a canal reservoir but an ornamental lake and contained a central clay core. It exists to this day. The engineering details (dated 1766 and 1767) refer to a 25 feet high dam which was to have been built downstream of the original, also with a central clay core of clay 'well rammed and watered'. It is likely that these details also apply to the original structure. Interestingly, according to the records, the designer, Grundy, allowed 2 inches of settlement per foot of dam height and stated that the new dam would have to be built 29 feet high.

As is well known, earthworks for dam engineering require the highest degree of skill, both in terms of design, construction and also subsequent maintenance and, given the crude methods available at the time, it is surprising that so many of the old dams survive to this day. One of the early failures was the Blackbrook dam (1795–97), which failed twice and was rebuilt as a masonry structure a century later. The engineers for the later structure found that there had been no attempt to construct a puddle clay cut-off down to solid rock; only a narrow trench filled with 'riddled soil' had been constructed and founded in the debris covering the valley bottom. The dam shoulders were constructed from 'small lumps of rock mixed with soil, and were full of cavities' (Binnie, 1987).

Given the compaction techniques available, some form of puddle clay central core would have kept leakage to manageable proportions. This was not always the case. None of the dams built for the Rochdale canal (completed in 1804) had clay cores (Binnie, 1987). A reasonably high standard of compaction is therefore implied, with the fill well keyed into the underlying solid rock, especially since steep slopes were often employed. The 12.5 m high Blackstone dam built by Jessop was originally raised with side slopes of 1 in 1.5 which remained unaltered until 1878 (upstream) and 1925 (downstream), when they were flattened.

However, cases of bad practice were recorded. One observer noted 'such was the inattention of the engineer that he laid the foundation of the bank upon nothing but the moss and ling that covered the soil'. The 21 m high Slaithwaite dam for the Huddersfield canal was higher than any other built at the time (Binnie, 1987). It was reported to have leaked badly and the failure of the draw-off system points to large settlements of the embankment, no doubt due to poor compaction.

John Rennie's specification for the 10.5 m high Rudyard dam for the Leek canal exists, dated 1797. It is of historical interest to the earthworks engineer because it describes in some detail how the embankment should be raised, namely on solid ground in 'regular stratas throughout its whole length, none of which should exceed 2 ft thick'. The layers were required to dip towards the dam centre where a puddle core was provided to keep the puddle moist. No details of the fill are given except that it should comprise 'a good mixture of earth with few stones in it except small ones, that the whole may be solid throughout'. Of the puddle clay core, it was required to be placed on 'good ground both in the bottom and the sides of the vale'. It was to be 'made of good clay or clay and gravel mixed in the proportion of about 2 of the former to 1 of the latter', laid in 8 inch layers. Rennie specified that they should be covered with water 'until they (the layers) are dissolved, after which they must be well chopped and mixed, rising gradually with the bank'. The reference to 'chopping' means labourers working the puddle with spades. Despite the specification, the bank is reported to have leaked at both ends when the reservoir was raised above a certain level, probably because the cut-off trench was not founded on the 'good ground' specified by Rennie at the higher parts of the valley slope (Binnie, 1987).

Historically, large amounts of hand labour have always been employed in major earthworks. Penman (1986) describes how construction of embankment dams in India could involve 20 000 people excavating soil by hand, carrying it on the head, and then spreading it in thin layers to be watered and compacted underfoot. Evidently in Spain, a 28 m high dam was built by 1 500 convicts, 200 labourers, 400 beasts of burden and (only) four steam engines. Compaction was by herds of animals driven backwards and forwards across the placed fill, a common construction expedient before the advent of mechanized plant.

The collapse of the Dale Dyke dam in 1864 with the loss of 250 lives and involving much damage led Victorian engineers to re-examine the traditional embankment dam designs, particularly the puddle clay cut-off. This feature was liable to intense erosion in fissured and fractured ground such as Carboniferous Limestone. Developments were introduced, including concrete and brickwork linings and grouting, in order to secure the cut-offs. Another innovation, of major importance to the earthworks engineer, was the introduction of zoning of earth banks with the finer material placed in the shoulders adjacent to the core. This was a consequence of the failure of the Bilberry dam in 1852. This measure was introduced to control differential settlement between the shoulders and the core, by providing a more uniform decrease in stiffness when progressing from the outer slopes to the central core. However, it also introduced a filter effect, which dam engineers later discovered was of great importance to the stability and safety of their structures.

Probably the greatest earth-moving operation in Britain in the nineteenth century was the Manchester Ship Canal, constructed in the 1880s, which involved excavating and removing over 53 million cubic yards of material of which 12 million was sandstone rock. The majority of the excavation was performed in the dry by nearly one hundred steam excavators, backed up by over six thousand spoil wagons drawn by over one hundred and seventy steam locomotives. The Ruston and Dunbar Steam Navvy was the most popular piece of excavating equipment at the time and comprised a self-propelled rail-mounted wrought iron frame with the engine and boiler at one end and the crane at the other. Equivalent to today's face shovel, the machine had a capacity of 1 000 cubic yards per day.

An outstanding account of the history of early dam construction in the UK is provided by Binnie (1987).

1.4   Design developments

The theory of earth pressures was formulated in Great Britain by William Rankine (1820–72); in France, Collin (1808–90) investigated the stability of both undisturbed and remoulded soils (such as are found in earthworks) by a study of slope failures in railway cuttings and embankments, and in earth dams. However, the extent to which these studies were taken into account in earthworks engineering later in the nineteenth century is not clear. The massive slope failures which accompanied the construction of the Panama Canal prompted the formation of a committee by the American Society of Civil Engineers in the first decade of the twentieth century to investigate the problem. At about the same time, in Sweden, a state commission was established to examine the reason for failures in railway embankments and cuttings, which had claimed over forty lives, and was to lead to the development of the Swedish method of slices for the solution of slope stability problems. Research into stability problems also commenced in Germany following the construction of the Kiel Canal, where failures had been common. Again it is not clear to what extent the results of these studies were adopted as routine in earthworks engineering at the time.

The large-scale mechanization of earthmoving equipment in the United States in the 1920s and 1930s created the need for rational design methods for earthworks compaction and a rapid means of control. The work of Proctor (1933) and Porter (1938) in California in the 1930s led directly to major improvements in these areas of earthwork engineering. Proctor developed the concept of 'optimum water content' for soil compaction when he was involved in the construction of earth dams, while Porter developed another (static) compaction test for the California Division of Highways. This was designed for use with an important innovation in pavement design, the California Bearing Ratio (CBR) test.

The outbreak of the Second World War in 1939 provided impetus for simple methods of classifying soils for military airfield and road making purposes. The Casagrande system of soil classification was published in 1942 and drew heavily on the concept of a soil's plasticity index as formulated by Atterberg in Sweden in the early years of the century. This classification was used as a basis for British classification schemes to follow. Shortly after the war, work at the Road Research Laboratory (later to become the Transport Research Laboratory) was to have a major influence on earthworks engineering, by relating soil compaction qualities to the nature of compaction plant, amongst other developments. The culmination of much of the research was the introduction in the UK of the Department of Transport 'Specification for Highway Works' (current edition dated 1998), which simplified the tendering process and made compaction supervision much easier, because of a uniform approach to compaction techniques.

2. The compaction process

2.1 Introduction

Compaction is the process by which soil particles are forced together by reduction of the air voids content. It has the following effects on most materials:

- increase in density
- increase in shear strength
- reduction in compressibility
- reduction in permeability.

2.2 Phase relationships

Soil or rock fill comprises three components or phases:

- solid (soil or rock particles)
- water (leachate or other fluid)
- air (or other gases).

The classic vehicle for understanding the relationship between these three phases is the phase diagram (Fig. 2.1). From this diagram, certain important relationships can be written down and the following formulae derived:

$$\text{Degree of saturation } S_r = \frac{wG_s}{e} \qquad (2.1)$$

where w is the water (moisture) content, G_s is the specific gravity of the soil and e is the void ratio.

$$\text{Dry density } \rho_d = \frac{G_s\rho_w}{1+e} \qquad (\text{Mg/m}^3) \qquad (2.2)$$

$$\text{Bulk density } \rho = \frac{(G_s + S_r e)}{1+e}\rho_w \quad (\text{Mg/m}^3) \qquad (2.3)$$

where ρ_w is the water density.

In BS 1377 (1990), the term particle density (the product of the specific gravity and the water density ρ_w) is used instead of specific gravity but, as pointed out by Craig (1997), it is advantageous to use the dimensionless specific gravity when deriving relationships from Fig. 2.1.

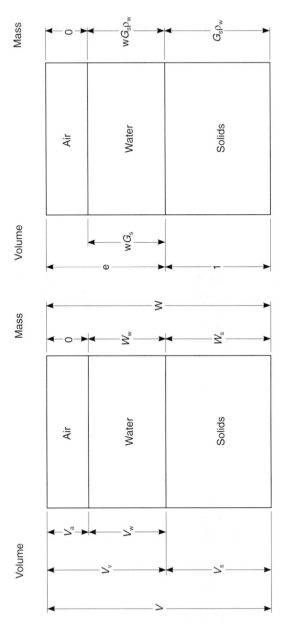

Fig. 2.1 Phase diagram for establishing properties of compacted fills (from Craig, 1997)

Bulk density and dry density are related via the water content, as follows:

$$\rho = \rho_d(1 + w) \quad (\text{Mg/m}^3) \tag{2.4}$$

Air voids content is the ratio of the volume of air to the total volume and is written:

$$A_v = \left(1 - \frac{\rho_d}{G_s \rho_w}[1 + wG_s]\right) \tag{2.5}$$

Degree of saturation S_r and air voids content A_v are expressed in terms of void ratio by:

$$\frac{A_v}{1 - S_r} = \frac{e}{1 + e} \tag{2.6}$$

Void ratio may be expressed in terms of specific gravity, water density and dry density from equation 2.2, as follows:

$$e = \frac{G_s \rho_w}{\rho_d} - 1 \tag{2.7}$$

2.3 Optimum water content and maximum dry density

If a soil is subjected to the same compactive effort over a wide range of water contents, a curve such as the one shown in Fig. 2.2 (curve *a*) results. At low water contents, the dry density is low but, as the water content increases, the soil particles are softened and lubricated which facilitates air void reduction. Dry density increases as a consequence.

When the water content increases above a certain value, water and air in combination begin to resist further close packing of soil particles. The addition of more water only increases the total voids in the soil and the dry density begins to fall as a result. The water content at which this occurs, for the given compactive effort, is termed the *Optimum Water Content* (OWC) and the corresponding dry density is termed the *Maximum Dry Density* (MDD).

According to Vaughan (1982), when the degree of saturation exceeds about 90 per cent, usual for most UK soils wet of optimum, air is occluded and the soils can sustain positive pore pressures; below this percentage saturation, air is continuous and pore-water pressures will be sub-atmospheric or negative. Thus the degree of saturation of the excavated soil will control, in part, the (undrained) behaviour of the fill when placed and compacted, unless special measures are taken to condition the soil (see Section 10.5).

2.4 Effect of compactive effort

Curve *a* shown in Fig. 2.2 is just one of an infinite number which could be produced for a given soil, depending on the compactive effort. If the compactive effort is increased, the apex of the curve moves upwards and to

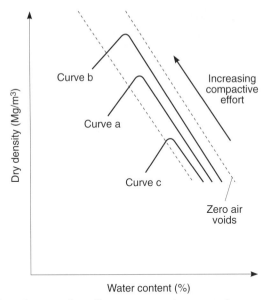

Fig. 2.2   Effect of compactive effort on compaction properties

the left (curve *b*); if it is decreased, the apex moves downwards and to the right (curve *c*). Also shown in Fig. 2.2 is the zero air voids content. At water contents in excess of OWC, the air voids content does not change significantly, whatever the compactive effort employed.

The orientation and packing of the soil particles change with water content and compactive effort. For a given compactive effort, the soil texture varies from disaggregation at low water content to more and more particle orientation until at OWC the compacted soil takes on a more homogeneous and orientated texture. At water contents well dry of OWC, the fill, particularly clay fill and uniform fine sands, can be unstable, as will be shown in later chapters.

The OWC varies with compactive effort as illustrated in Fig. 2.2; it is not a fundamental property for a given soil, as is sometimes supposed.

In UK practice there are two levels of compactive effort to which soil compaction properties are usually related. Both tests employ rammers to compact the soil; the rammers are of different masses (2.5 and 4.5 kg), fall from different heights and are applied to different numbers of soil layers in the mould. The tests are, respectively, BS 1377: 1990: Part 4: Test 3.3 and Part 4: Test 3.5. A third test, less often performed, uses a vibrating hammer of known weight, vibrating at a known frequency for a known time period (Part 4: Test 3.7). The Moisture Condition Value test (Part 4: Tests 5.4 and 5.5), commonly used in earthworks (see Section 8.4.5), can be regarded as a compaction test but one in which the soil sample is compacted to refusal and not to a specified level of compactive effort, as with the tests mentioned above.

2.5 Effect of initial fill water content

Simply because a heavier compaction specification is adopted, higher dry densities will not necessarily follow. The initial water content of the fill (usually the natural water content of the soil at the borrow, allowing for any changes in handling and placing) has a major influence on the maximum dry density as illustrated in Fig. 2.3. At water contents at or dry of optimum (water content *a*), there is a large difference between the dry densities achievable for the two compactive efforts. At water contents well wet of optimum (water content *b*), the corresponding difference between the dry densities is small. Hence, the use of high compactive efforts wet of optimum water content will not be particularly productive in terms of denser fill and, in the case of clay fill, could lead to the construction problems of 'mattressing' (see Section 3.4.4).

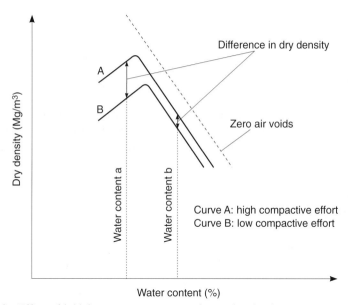

Fig. 2.3 Effect of initial water content on maximum dry density

Note should also be taken of the effect of initial water content on the suction (negative pore pressure) existing in the compacted soil. If a clay fill is compacted well dry of optimum, there will be a substantial suction and consequently a marked affinity for water, which could affect fill stability (volume change) during service. Clay fill compacted at or above optimum will show much smaller suctions, with a correspondingly reduced affinity for water. Working with a sand-bentonite mixture, Dineen *et al.* (1999) showed that at optimum water content (2.5 kg rammer), suctions of about $200\,kN/m^2$ existed, whereas at 2 per cent *dry* of optimum, the suctions had more than doubled to $550\,kN/m^2$. At 2 per cent *wet* of optimum, suction had reduced to about $150\,kN/m^2$.

Also noteworthy in the Dineen *et al.* test series was the increase in suctions measured between optimum water content for the 2.5 kg rammer test (about $200\,\text{kN/m}^2$) and the 4.5 kg rammer test (about $1000\,\text{kN/m}^2$). Compacting to a heavier specification does not always produce a more stable fill. This matter is discussed in more detail in Section 8.3.4.

2.6   Compaction of fill with over-size particles
2.6.1   Effect on dry density

The maximum particle size which can be treated with the BS rammer tests is 20 mm, unless a California Bearing Ratio (CBR) mould is employed. In this case, a maximum particle size of 37.5 mm may be adopted; however, the proportion between 20 and 37.5 mm should not exceed 30 per cent of the total. Reference should be made to BS 1377: 1990: Part 4: Test 3.4 for the 2.5 kg rammer and to Part 4: Test 3.6 for the 4.5 kg rammer methods.

There are three common methods used to correct dry density where particle sizes in excess of 20 mm have been removed:

- the elimination method
- the adjusted maximum dry density method
- the substitution method.

Elimination method

The dry weight of the portion larger than 20 mm (the 'stones') in the sample is measured and the ratio F is determined, where F is the fraction of the stones to all particles by dry weight. The total dry density ρ_t of the fill is then:

$$\rho_t = \frac{\rho_m \rho_w G_s}{\rho_w G_s (1 - F) + F \rho_m} \quad (\text{Mg/m}^3) \tag{2.8}$$

where ρ_m is the dry density of the matrix (smaller than 20 mm), ρ_w is the water density and G_s is the specific gravity of the stones. Head (1992) recommends that F should be less than 0.25, but Day (1989) adopts an F value of less than 0.5.

Adjusted maximum dry density method

This method (NAVFAC DM 7.2, 1982) is written in terms of maximum dry density of the soil matrix only, and:

$$\rho_t = \frac{1 - 0.05F}{\dfrac{F}{2.6} + \dfrac{1 - F}{\rho_m}} \quad (\text{Mg/m}^3) \tag{2.9}$$

where F is as defined above. A maximum value of F of 0.6 is recommended by NAVFAC.

Substitution method

This method (ASTM D 1557–91, 1997) is valid for two ranges of F only:

- Method C when $0.07 < F < 0.1$
- Method D when $0.10 < F < 0.3$

When $F > 0.3$ the substitution method cannot be used.

Method C requires that all the stones be removed and no correction made, i.e. $\rho_t = \rho_m$.

For method D, the amount of material passing the 76 mm sieve and retained on the 20 mm sieve is replaced by the same weight of material passing the 20 mm sieve and retained on the 5 mm sieve. The compaction test is then performed on the substituted sample in the normal way. Winter *et al.* (1998) suggest that method D should be restricted in application to $0.05 < F < 0.1$ rather than the range recommended by ASTM.

In an attempt to quantify the results of the above three methods, Fig. 2.4 was prepared for a soil having a maximum matrix dry density ρ_m of 2.0 Mg/m^3 and a specific gravity G_s of 2.65. It will be seen that, for a given value of F, the elimination method gives the largest maximum dry densities and the adjusted maximum dry density method the least: the substitution method (method D) produces results below the mean of the two sets of values. The elimination method, often termed the 'scalping' method, is frequently used because of its simplicity. However, the fact that its results are not conservative (i.e. it produces higher values of dry density for a given value of F than the other two methods) should be borne in mind.

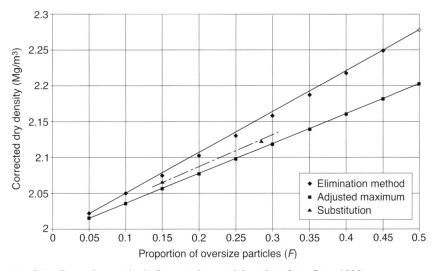

Fig. 2.4 Correction methods for oversize particles (data from Day, 1989)

2.6.2 Effect on water content

Head (1992) proposed that the total water content of the whole fill w_t may be related to the matrix water content w_m by the relationship:

$$w_t = w_m([1 - F] + w_s F) \tag{2.10}$$

where F is the fraction of the stones to all particles by dry weight and w_s is the water absorption content of the stones. According to Winter *et al.* (1998), w_s is often taken to be zero or a very small value.

Removing the oversize material during testing changes the water content and dry density as well as the particle size distribution. If the performance of the fill is to be measured in any of these terms, care should be taken to see that the specification refers to the relevant property, e.g. w_m rather than w_t, or ρ_m rather than ρ_t. Likewise, if corrections are made to the tests at the design stage, the identical correction methods should be employed during control testing. It is essential that like be compared with like.

2.7   Use of correlations to obtain compaction data

The repetitive nature of earthworks testing, particularly control testing, has generated attempts to correlate essential compaction properties, like optimum water content and maximum dry density, with the results of simple and inexpensive tests like the Atterberg limit tests. Not only does this decrease expense when performing large test programmes for earthworks projects, but results based on the readily performed Atterberg limit tests are quickly obtained, which is of major benefit to the control function.

An attempt to correlate the compaction characteristics of a large number of United States and Iraqi soils was made by Al-Khafaji (1993). Charts were drawn up using curve fitting procedures which allowed both the optimum water content and the maximum dry density to be calculated, provided that the liquid and plastic limits were given. It is not known the extent to which these correlations will apply and, in particular, whether they are relevant to British conditions. The charts predicted a very similar value of maximum dry density for liquid and plastic limits of 40 and 20 per cent, for both the US and Iraqi soils, but the optimum water content values predicted differed significantly. This suggests that cross correlations with British or other soils may not always be acceptable. Nevertheless, for a major earthworks project it may be worthwhile testing the Al-Khafaji method and assessing its applicability, perhaps modifying where appropriate for site specific conditions.

A more fundamental approach was put forward by Pandian *et al.* (1997). They demonstrated linear relationships between water content and liquid limit for given degrees of saturation, both wet and dry of optimum and, by equating these relationships, they calculated the optimum water content and the maximum dry density. The soil tested in the compaction test is substantially coarser than in the liquid limit test (up to 20 mm against 0.425 mm). By making allowances for this factor, the authors were able to produce a set of curves of dry density v water content for a wide range of liquid limits. Knowing a soil's liquid limit and just one point on the density-water content relationship, it is claimed that the whole dry density v water content relationship can be predicted for that particular soil. The relationships were based on tests made on Indian soils. Again, it is not known to what extent they are applicable to British conditions. However, like the method described above, the Pandian *et al.* approach would seem worthwhile trying for a major earthworks project.

For further details of both methods, the original references should be consulted.

2.8 Paez plotting method for compaction test results

The compaction test can be difficult to interpret because the plots of water content v dry density are curved. Unless there are data points close to and either side of optimum, deciding upon the optimum water content can be difficult. If the optimum water content cannot be accurately established, neither can the maximum dry density nor the air voids content; this makes for problems with both design and control, when the compaction test is adopted (see Section 8.4.3).

By use of a simple transform (Paez, 1980), both legs of the compaction curves plot as clusters of straight lines. The wet leg lines plot parallel with the air voids (also now a cluster of straight lines) while the dry leg clusters plot at an obtuse angle. The lines for both legs intersect at a point which gives the optimum water content; hence the maximum dry density and the air voids content are also established.

From the relationships in Fig. 2.1, it may be shown that for zero air voids:

$$\frac{G_s}{\rho_d} = 1 + \frac{w.G_s}{\rho_w} \tag{2.11}$$

$$\text{Putting } x = \frac{w.G_s}{\rho_w} \tag{2.12}$$

$$\text{and } y = \frac{G_s}{\rho_d} \tag{2.13}$$

Equation (2.11) now becomes $y = x + 1$ and is the line corresponding to the zero air voids.

The line $y(1 - A_v) = x + 1$ is the line corresponding to A_v air voids.

Data for several different soils are plotted using the above approach in Fig. 2.5. Undoubtedly, there is additional work involved in the Paez plotting procedure, but the time and expense is justified by the accuracy obtained. As with all methods of plotting which rely on air voids content, the accuracy of

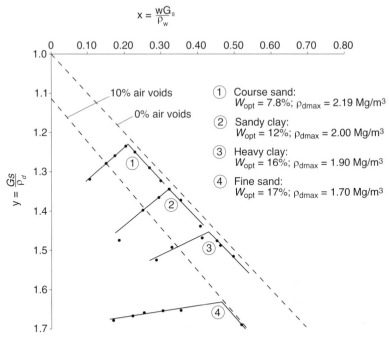

Fig. 2.5 Examples of use of alternative plotting method. From Paez (1980), (data from *Soil Mechanics for Road Engineers*, 1951)

the specific gravity value used directly affects the accuracy of the results. Note should be taken of the comments in Section 8.4.3 on the difficulties in measuring the specific gravity of some materials, particularly colliery discards and chalks.

3. Some characteristics of clay (cohesive) fill

3.1 Introduction

There is a wide range of clay soils which vary in particle size distribution and in plasticity characteristics. Text books on soil mechanics (e.g. Craig, 1997) demonstrate two types of clay for consideration in British conditions: normally consolidated and overconsolidated clays. Normally consolidated clay exists under effective stresses which have never been exceeded, whilst overconsolidated clay currently exists under effective stresses lower than those experienced in the past. The reduction of effective stresses could have been caused by erosion, by changes in ground water level(s) or by other geological factors. The 'overconsolidation ratio' may vary, e.g. lightly overconsolidated, heavily overconsolidated. Whether or not a clay is overconsolidated has a major impact upon its behaviour as fill because it controls both shear strength and water content with respect to the soil's plastic limit and optimum water content.

A further problem with overconsolidated clay is the low (sometimes negative) pore pressures it may contain, particularly when excavated from depth, and the likelihood of swelling over the long term if used as fill. Overconsolidated clay can be regarded as a distinct clay fill type, difficult to work in many circumstances.

3.2 Description and classification

3.2.1 General

Central to selecting soil for fill purposes is its proper description and/or classification. There are two approaches: *description*, using conventions established in BS 5930 (1999), illustrated in Fig. 3.1, and *classification*, using laboratory test procedures. The former approach has the advantage that the proposed fill can be described and evaluated immediately, without awaiting the results of laboratory tests which can take several days. This makes the descriptive approach attractive when, for example, a borrow pit has to be extended during construction and immediate decisions are called for. The classification approach is essential for the *Specification for Highway Works* (1998) and its use with this document is prescribed.

Fig. 3.1 Identification and description of soils (from BS 5930: 1999)

soil group	Density/compactness/strength		Discontinuity		Bedding		Colour	Composite soil types (mixture of basic soil types)		Particle shape	Particle size	PRINCIPAL SOIL TYPE
	Term	Field test										
Very coarse soils	Loose	By inspection of voids and particle packing	Scale of spacing of discontinuities		Scale of bedding thickness		Red	For mixtures involving very coarse soils, see 41,4,4,3		Angular		BOULDERS
	Dense		Term	Mean spacing mm	Term	Mean thickness mm	Orange	Term	Approx.% secondary	Sub angular	—200 —60	COBBLES
Coarse soils (over 65% sand and gravel sizes)	Borehole with SPT N-value		Very widely	Over 2 000	Very thickly bedded	Over 2 000	Yellow Brown	Slightly (sandy a))	< 5	Sub rounded Rounded	Coarse —20 Medium	GRAVEL
	Very loose	0 - 4	Widely	2 000 to 600	Thickly bedded	2 000 to 600	Green Blue			Flat	—6 Fine	
	Loose	4 - 10	Medium	600 to 200	Medium bedded	600 to 200	White	(sandy d))	5 to 20 b)	Tabular	—2	
	Medium dense	10 - 30	Closely	200 to 60	Thinly bedded	200 to 60	Cream Grey			Elongated		
	Dense	30 - 50	Very closely	60 to 20	Very thinly bedded	60 to 20	Black etc.	Very (sandy d))	> 20 b)	Minor constituent type	Coarse —0.6 Medium	SAND
	Very dense	>60	Extremely closely	Under 20	Thickly laminated	20 to 6				Calcareous, shelly, glauconitic, micaceous etc. using terms such as: Slightly calcareous calcareous very calcareous	—0.2 Fine —0.06	
	Slightly cemented	Visual examination: pick removes soil in lumps which can be abraded	Fissured	Breaks into blocks along polished discontinuities	Thinly laminated	Under 6		SAND AND GRAVEL	about 60 b)		Coarse —0.02 Medium —0.006	SILT
Fine soils (over 35% silt and clay sizes)	un-compact	Easily moulded or crushed in the fingers	Sheared	Breaks into blocks along polished discontinuities	Inter-bedded	Alternating layers of different types prequalified by thickness term if in equal proportions. Otherwise thickness of the spacing between subordinate layers defined.	Light Dark Mottled	Term	Approx.% secondary c)		Fine —0.002	
	Compact	Can be moulded or crushed by strong pressure in the fingers	Spacing terms also used for distance between partings, isolated beds or laminae, dessication cracks, rootlets etc.					Slightly (sandy e))	> 35			CLAY/ SILT
	Very soft 0-20	Finger easily pushed in up to 25mm			Inter-laminated					% defined on a site or material specific basis or subjective		
	Soft 20-40	Finger pushed in up to 10mm						(sandy e))	35 to 65 a)			
	Firm 40-75	Thumb makes impression easily										
	Stiff 75-150	Can be indented slightly by thumb										CLAY
	Very stiff 150-300	Can be indented by thumb nail						Very (sandy f))	> 65 a)			
	Hard (or very weak mudstone) Cu>300kPa	Can be scratched by thumb nail, see A1.2.2										

Organic soils					Transported mixtures	Colour						
	Firm	Fibres already compressed together	Fibrous	Plant remains recognizable and retains some strength	Slightly organic clay or silt Slightly organic sand	Gray as mineral	Contains finely divided or discrete particles of organic matter, often with distinctive smell, may oxidize rapidly. Describe as for inorganic soils using terminology above.					
					Organic clay or silt Organic sand	Dark grey Dark grey						
	Spongy	Very compressible and open structure	Pseudo-fibrous	Plant remains recognizable. strength lost	Very organic clay or silt Very organic sand	Black Black						
					Accumulated in situ							
	Plastic	Can be moulded in hand and smears fingers	Amor-phous	Recognizable plant remains absent	Peat		Predominantly plant remains, usually dark brown or black in colour, distictive smell. low bulk density. Can contain certain disseminated or discrete mineral soils.					

Fig. 3.1 Continued

PRINCIPAL SOIL TYPE	Visual identification	Minor constituents	Stratum name	Example descriptions
BOULDERS	Only seen complete in pits or exposures	Shell fragments, pockets of peat, gypsum crystals, flint gravel, fragments of brick, rootlets, plastic bags etc.		Loose, brown very sandy sub-angular fine to coarse flint GRAVEL with small pockets (up to 30mm) of clay. (TERRACE GRAVELS)
COBBLES	Often difficult to recover whole from boreholes			
GRAVEL	Easily visible to naked eye; particle shape can be described; grading can be descibed.	using terms such as: with rare	RECENT DEPOSITS, ALLUVIUM, WEATHERED BRACKLESHAM CLAY,	Medium dense light brown gravelly clayey fine SAND. Gravel is fine (GLACIAL DEPOSITS)
SAND	Visible to the naked eye; no cohesion when dry; grading can be described.	with occasional with abundant/frequent/ numerous	LIAS CLAY, EMBANKMENT FILL,	Stiff very closely sheared orange mottled brown slightly gravelly CLAY. Gravel is fine and medium of rounded quarzite. (REWORKED WEATHERED LONDON CLAY)
SILT	Only coarse silt visible with hand lens; exhibits little plasticity and marked dilatancy; slightly granular or silky to the touch; disintegrates in water; lumps dry quickly; possesses cohesion but can be powdered easily between fingers	% defined on a site or material specific basis or subjective	TOPSOIL, MADE GROUND OR GLACIAL DEPOSITS? ETC.	Firm thinly laminated grey CLAY with closely spaced thick laminae of sand. (ALLUVIUM)
CLAY/ SILT	Intermediate in behaviour between clay and silt, slightly dilatant			
CLAY	Dry lumps can be broken but not powdered between the fingers; they also disintegrate under water but more slowly than silt; smooth to the touch; exhibits plasticity but no dilatancy; sticks to the fingers and dries slowly; shrinks appreciably on drying usually showing cracks.			Plastic brown clayey amorphous PEAT. (RECENT DEPOSITS)

NOTES

a) Or described as coarse soil depending on mass behaviour

b) Or described as fine soil depending on mass behaviour

c) % coarse or fine soil type assessed excluding cobbles and boulders

d) Gravelly or sandy and/or silty or clayey

e) Gravelly and/or sandy

f) Gravelly or sandy

Unfortunately there is little similarity between the BS 5930 (1999) and the *Specification for Highway Works* (1998) in the way that soils are described. This is made clear in *The Highways Agency Advice Note* HA 44/91 which states (para 2.8) that '... soil descriptions provided in ground investigation documents to BS 5930 (1981 version) may not accord with descriptions resulting from classifications in accordance with *Specification for Highway Works*, Table 6.1. Designers should ensure that where descriptions and classifications of materials are given the system used is clearly described.'

BS 5930 (1999) objects to the term 'cohesive' because it does not accurately describe the properties of fine soils. For example, and as is well known, an unsaturated sand (a coarse soil) can exhibit an apparent cohesion because of the negative pore pressures it contains, whilst the long term behaviour of a clay (a fine soil) is controlled by its frictional effective shear strength properties. Thus in BS 5930 (1999) 'cohesive' and 'granular' are suppressed in favour of the more accurate 'fine' and 'coarse'. Although these objections are scientifically sound, the terms 'cohesive' and 'granular' are so well established in the earthworks vocabulary, particularly their adoption in the *Specification for Highway Works* (1998), that their removal would appear to offer no particular advantages and would only increase the confusion which the differences between the descriptive BS 5930 (1999) and the classificatory *Specification for Highway Works* (1998) approaches inevitably produce. Consequently, these terms have been retained in this book, along with the term 'clay', to describe fill types.

3.2.2 Description

Section 6 of BS 5930 (1999) defines 'fine soils' as having at least 35 per cent finer than 0.06 mm particle size and includes silts (0.002 to 0.06 mm) and clays (finer than 0.002 mm). Coarse granular materials, sands and gravels, may be present to greater than 65 per cent. This appears at first sight anomalous because it would not appear possible to have greater than 65 per cent coarse material and for the soil to remain 'fine grained' as defined. However, BS 5930 (1999) qualifies the use of the 35 per cent figure by reference to the soil's 'mass behaviour'; the geotechnical engineer or engineering geologist must therefore decide, irrespective of percentage quantities, whether behaviour is more appropriate to fine or to coarse grained soil. The above quoted measurements are made on material from which the larger sizes 'cobbles' (60 to 200 mm) and 'boulders' (larger than 200 mm) have been removed. These latter soils are termed 'very coarse' in BS 5930 (1999).

Unlike granular soils whose particle sizes and distributions and to some extent shapes can be estimated by the naked eye, particle sizes within fine soils cannot readily be identified; consequently, the scope for description as opposed to classification with clay fill is much more limited. Many descriptors are applied to the structure or fabric of clays, with such terms as fissured, laminated and slickensided being common. As fabric is partially or totally destroyed during compaction, fabric descriptions are of limited use for clay destined for fill, although they can be of critical importance for undisturbed clay soils revealed in cuts or in embankment foundations (Chapters 11 and 12).

Section 6 of BS 5930 (1999) provides a basis for soil description. The way the description is written demonstrates the proportion of particle sizes present: materials written in upper case constitute more than 35 per cent of the total (after the removal of any cobbles and boulders) and the lower case qualifiers indicate the nature and amount of any subordinate materials. For example:

slightly sandy CLAY (sand-size particles present up to 35 per cent)
sandy CLAY (sand-size particles present between 35 and 65 per cent)
very sandy CLAY (sand-size particles present in excess of 65 per cent)

The term 'gravelly' is used in the same way when gravel, rather than sand, predominates in the granular fraction. Silts are defined in the same manner: thus a silt containing greater than 65 per cent sand is described as a 'very sandy SILT'. As already noted, percentage quantities are regarded as a guide and, according to BS 5930 (1999), it is the soil's engineering behaviour in the mass which determines the soil's description.

BS 5930 (1999) does not permit the use of 'silt' as well as 'clay' in the same description; therefore, there is no such thing as 'silty CLAY' or 'clayey SILT'. This could have consequences for earthworks where silt can be a problem because of frost heave. No information on its potential performance in frost heave terms will be conveyed by the description 'CLAY' even though the material concerned may in fact contain a large percentage of silt. Great care is therefore necessary when confronting the term 'CLAY' in borehole records. Laboratory tests should be conducted if there is any room for doubt. See Section 3.5.3 for the frost-heave susceptibility of clay fill.

The use of descriptors to indicate the size of the gravel particles, e.g. 'fine gravel' or 'fine to medium gravel' is optional. The descriptor 'coarse' is helpful because coarse gravel starts at 20 mm, the size which is excluded from the BS compaction and Moisture Condition Value (MCV) tests (unless a CBR mould is used for the former). The amount of coarse gravel in any sample of potential fill therefore provides the geotechnical engineer preparing the laboratory test programme with an indication of the nature of the compaction tests which will have to be performed (whether using a standard or a CBR mould or whether the corrections as described in Chapter 2 are necessary).

3.2.3 Classification
The *Specification for Highway Works* (1998) subdivides cohesive fill into several classes. However, the names themselves convey only the broadest

indication of the nature of the fill (e.g. wet cohesive material, dry cohesive material, stony cohesive material) and give no indication of its likely performance. Some of the properties involved in classifying clay or cohesive fill are given in the next section.

3.3 Properties

3.3.1 Plasticity and water content

Plasticity is normally denoted by the plasticity index, the difference between the liquid and plastic limits. The plasticity of some British clays is given in the form of a Casagrande chart in Figure 3.2.

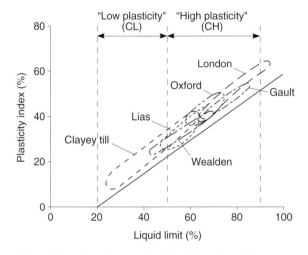

Fig. 3.2 Plasticity relationships for some British clays (from Vaughan *et al.* 1978)

The relation between the water content (w), the plastic limit (PL) and the plasticity index (PI) is defined by the liquidity index (LI), where:

$$LI = \frac{w - PL}{PI} \tag{3.1}$$

Thus the liquidity index is a measure of a clay's water content with respect to its plasticity characteristics. In practical earthworks conditions, the water content can vary from close to the clay's liquid limit to several percentage points below its plastic limit. Depending upon the type of clay and the conditions at the borrow, a liquidity index varying from close to unity to zero and below (i.e. a negative value) may be expected.

An alternative method of presenting the information given in equation 3.1 is use of the consistency index (CI), where:

$$CI = \frac{LL - w}{PI} \tag{3.2}$$

The advantage of using this expression is that a negative *CI* is a clear warning that the water content of the fill is greater than the soil's liquid limit, and that great difficulty can be expected in handling.

A clay mineral's liquid and plastic limits vary depending upon the complexity of its structure, including the nature of the exchangeable ion. Table 3.1 shows data relating to three of the commonest clay minerals, montmorillonite, illite and kaolinite: Illitic clays are probably the most common in the UK, kaolinitic clays less so. Fortunately, the high plasticity montmorillonite is not common in British conditions, although by no means absent.

Table 3.1   Atterberg limits of some clay soils (from Lambe and Whitman, 1969)

Clay mineral	Exchangeable ion	Liquid limit (%)	Plastic limit (%)	Plasticity index (%)
Montmorillonite	Na	710	54	656
	K	660	98	562
	Ca	510	81	429
Illite	Na	120	53	67
	K	120	60	60
	Ca	100	45	55
Kaolinite	Na	53	32	21
	K	49	29	20
	Ca	38	27	11

From the results given in Table 3.1 it could be concluded that where there are widely varying plasticity results exhibited by clay soils, the cause is the presence of several different clay minerals or one clay mineral with several different exchangeable ions. In fact it may have little to do with the type of clay mineral or the exchangeable ion present. Plasticity tests are performed on soil passing the 0.425 mm aperture sieve, which is in the middle of the medium sand range; consequently, depending upon the grading of the sample, plasticity tests may be performed in part on granular soil, as well as silt and clay.

Work by Dumbleton and West (1966) showed that plasticity varies with the granular content of the mixture. Fig. 3.3 illustrates this point for various mixtures of a kaolinitic clay and natural quartz sand. They also showed that plasticity varies with the nature of the granular component: whether it comprised well rounded or angular particles, or whether uniform or well graded. Substantial scatter may therefore be expected in the results of any set of plasticity determinations. However, this scatter may be due to the type, nature and amount of the granular material (and silt) present within the otherwise clay soil, rather than to variations in the plasticity characteristics of the clay minerals themselves.

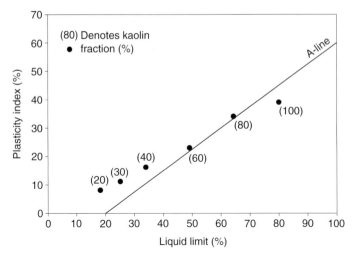

Fig. 3.3 Relationship between index properties and clay content for various mixtures of clay and sand (modified after Dumbleton and West, 1966; with adaptations after Trenter, 1999), reproduced by kind permission from CIRIA

3.3.2 Undrained shear strength
Factors affecting the undrained strength of clay fill

Work of major practical importance in understanding the behaviour of clay fill in undrained shear was reported by Vaughan (1978a) and Vaughan *et al.* (1978). They distinguished between high plasticity clay (liquid limit in excess of 50 per cent or CH) and low plasticity clay (liquid limit less than 50 per cent or CL):

High plasticity clay   Vaughan *et al.* (1978) show that at the relatively low rate of loading which controls stability in an embankment, pore pressure redistribution is important and it depends upon the compacted structure of the fill. The undrained strength mobilized in the field may be some 20 per cent lower than the corresponding strength measured in the conventional unconsolidated undrained triaxial test (BS 1377: 1990: Part 7: Test 8). The opposite effect is likely with trafficability. Here the strength mobilised by plastic clay fill on the point of rutting is substantially in excess of the strength measured in the conventional triaxial test, perhaps by a factor of some 50 per cent.

Low plasticity clay   The nature of the compacted structure of a sandy clay fill is considered by the authors to have a negligible influence on its undrained strength. Reliable indications of undrained strength in these materials can be obtained by the conventional undrained triaxial test. However, the authors note that if these strengths are employed in embankment stability analysis, unacceptably large deformations may occur at otherwise apparently satisfactory factors of safety.

Strength correlations

According to Whyte (1982), there is a simple relationship between liquidity index and undrained shear strength of remoulded clay soil, as illustrated in Fig. 3.4.

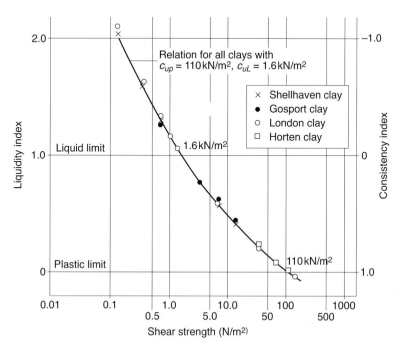

Fig. 3.4 Variation of remoulded undrained shear strength with consistency index (from Whyte, 1982)

The figure shows that at high water contents (liquidity index close to unity), the undrained shear strength is about $1.6 \, \text{kN/m}^2$; at low water contents (liquidity index close to zero), the undrained shear strength is about $110 \, \text{kN/m}^2$. From this figure, it is possible to estimate a remoulded clay soil's undrained shear strength using:

$$c_u = 1.6e^{4.23(1-LI)} \ (\text{kN/m}^2) \tag{3.3}$$

Whyte also proposed the simple relationship between compression index C_c and plastic index PI, as follows:

$$C_c = 1.45 \, PI \tag{3.4}$$

Use of these two expressions permits a relationship between strength, compression index and consistency index (numerically equal to $1 - LI$ and written as a number and not a percentage) as given in Table 3.2.

Table 3.2 Suggested relationship between shear strength and consistency

Strength classification	Consistency index $(1 - LI)$	Undrained shear strength (kN/m^2)
Hard	> 1.15	> 300
Very stiff	1.05 to 1.15	150 to 300
Stiff	0.92 to 1.05	75 to 150
Firm	0.82 to 0.92	40 to 75
Soft	0.60 to 0.82	20 to 40
Very soft	< 0.60	<20

The plastic limit (necessary to calculate the liquidity and consistency index) is difficult to measure accurately; for this reason, equations 3.3 and 3.4 together with Table 3.2 should be used with caution. Note that the above relationships are for remoulded clays, such as clay fill; undisturbed materials which contain structure and/or cementing material may not behave in the manner described.

It may be undesirable to mix clay and granular soils when forming fill. Diagram (a) in Fig. 3.5 illustrates the effect on undrained shear strength of adding sand to a remoulded clay soil whilst diagram (b) shows the effect of adding gravel. The shear strength curves become steeper (i.e. more sensitive to the addition of water and hence more difficult to employ as a fill) as the granular component in the mixture increases. Vaughan (1978a) also concludes that mixing poor fill with a better one is unlikely to be effective. See also Section 10.3.

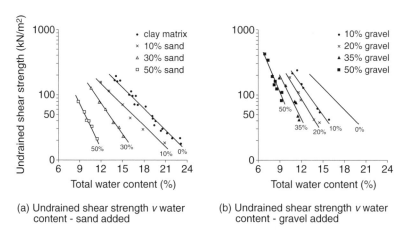

(a) Undrained shear strength *v* water content - sand added

(b) Undrained shear strength *v* water content - gravel added

Fig. 3.5 Variation of remoulded undrained shear strength with total water content for clay soils with various proportions of granular materials (from Barnes and Staples, 1988)

Dennehy (1978) suggested performing undrained shear strength tests on remoulded samples of fill and plotting the results on a graph of water content

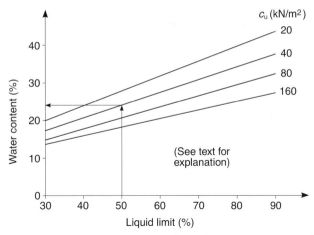

Fig. 3.6 Contours of undrained shear strength for various water contents and liquid limits (adapted from Dennehy, 1978). Proceedings of international conference of clay fills, ICE. N.B.: Graph indicative only

against liquid limit (Fig. 3.6). For fill of a given liquid limit, the shear strength corresponding to the fill water content may be read off the graph. Thus for a fill having a liquid limit of 50 per cent, a water content in excess of about 24 per cent should not be exceeded if a shear strength of $40 \, kN/m^2$ is required for trafficking. For preliminary purposes, equation 3.3 could conveniently be employed for calculating shear strengths. The above approach demonstrates neatly the effect of plasticity characteristics on trafficability (see below) and its dependence on weather conditions. Low plasticity clays, including glacial till, can rapidly slurry on mixing with water. Thus a site whose fill water content was acceptably low during a dry spell could become a quagmire after rain.

3.4 Behaviour of clay fill: temporary works

3.4.1 General

There are four principal construction problems with clay fill: trafficability (instability), under-compaction, mattressing and shear surface formation. They are influenced by the fill's initial water content and plasticity characteristics. The likelihood or otherwise of their occurrence during the main works should be investigated during compaction trials (see Section 8.5).

3.4.2 Trafficability (instability)

A layer (current and previous) may exhibit significant and permanent deformation (rutting) under the weight of compaction or construction plant. The root of the problem is the fill's undrained shear strength, which is too low for the weight of the plant in operation. Bearing capacity failure occurs, giving rise to the permanent deformation which is typical. Corrective methods include lighter compaction plant, reducing tire pressure of pneumatic tired equipment, and/or drying by fill conditioning (see Section 10.5).

Based on the observed performance of various construction plant on a number of British soil types, Parsons and Darley (1982) calculated the minimum MCV values required to permit trafficking. Soil types included alluvium, glacial till, terrace gravels, overconsolidated clay, Old Red Sandstone, Chalk Marl, Lower and Middle Coal Measures. Regression analysis (correlation coefficient 0.90) permitted the estimation of the MCV values quoted in Table 3.3, where brief details of the plant are also provided:

Table 3.3 Summary of minimum MCVs for effective operation of plant (adapted from Parsons and Darley, 1982)

Type of machine (power)	Struck capacity (m^3)	Mass of machine loaded (empty) (Mg)	Calculated minimum MCV loaded (empty)
Small twin engined scraper (214 kW)	11	45 (24)	5.5 (3)
Medium twin engined scraper (450/530 kW)	16–18	78 (43)	7 (3)
Large twin engined scraper (700 kW)	25	110 (63)	9 (3.5)
Small dump truck – rigid chassis (170/200 kW)	8	24–27 (10–11)	7.5 (6)
Medium dump truck (300 kW)	17	59 (27)	9.5 (6)
Large dump truck (360 kW)	22	74 (33)	10 (5.5)

A wide range of shear strengths is quoted in the literature in connection with trafficability. An undrained shear strength of some 60 kN/m^2 is often regarded as the strength above which most plant can be satisfactorily manoeuvred and instability (rutting) avoided, although machines such as heavy motorised scrapers or dump trucks may require strengths substantially above this figure. For example, Farrar and Darley (1975) found that the following shear strengths were necessary for scrapers:

- towed and small scrapers ($<15 \text{ m}^3$ capacity): most efficient operation 140 kN/m^2; feasible operation 60 kN/m^2
- medium and large motorised scrapers ($>15 \text{ m}^3$ capacity): most efficient operation 170 kN/m^2; feasible operation 100 kN/m^2

Some specialist plant, such as bulldozers with extra low contact pressure facilities may also perform on fills having substantially lower strengths

(Parsons, 1978; Threadgold, 1978). It is quite possible that the wide range in quoted strengths derives, at least in part, from the different ways in which shear strength was measured in the various trials referred to. For this reason, it is suggested that the shear strength figures should be used as a guide only.

3.4.3 Under-compaction

For hard clay, mudstone or siltstone fill, uniform compaction may be difficult if not impossible to achieve at normal borrow pit water contents and much will be excavated as large chunks. The shear strength of the chunks is likely to range from 150 to 200 kN/m^2 (*The Highways Agency Advice Note HA 44/91*) and, as a consequence, the fill cannot be kneaded into a dense uniform and homogeneous whole. In this connection, Greenwood *et al.* (1985) stated that for water contents less than 1.1 times the fill's plastic limit uniform compaction will not occur for overconsolidated clay. Whyte personal communication, 2000) suggests that an MCV value greater than from 13 to 15 would be sufficient for under-compaction. Corrective treatment would include the procedures outlined in Section 10.5.

3.4.4 Mattressing

Unlike over-compaction, which results in permanent deformation due to bearing capacity failure, 'mattressing' is for the most part recoverable deformation, due to high pore pressures set up in the current and previous layers of clay fill. When mattressing occurs, it is a sign that the fill has been compacted to refusal at its particular water content and that the pore pressures induced by the compaction plant are preventing the fill particles from adopting a closer packing arrangement. The most effective treatment, if still closer packing (higher density) is necessary, is to reduce the water content; using lighter plant will not usually assist because pore pressures are still set up which prevent the soil particles from forming a denser packing (see Section 10.5).

3.4.5 Compaction induced shear surfaces

At water contents well wet of optimum, roughly horizontal shear surfaces may be produced in the more plastic clay fills and some weak mudstones by the action of compaction plant (Whyte and Vakalis, 1988). Depending upon their continuity, these shear surfaces may hinder vertical drainage and reduce the efficacy of any horizontal drainage layers installed to reduce pore pressures and to increase the stability of wet clay fill (see Section 10.5.6). The surfaces will usually be of lower shear strength than the surrounding fill which could be serious because of the possibility of the formation of failure surfaces along them. Vaughan (1994) reports that part of the slide which formed in the weak mudstones comprising the Carsington embankment dam occurred parallel to construction surfaces and the possibility exists that it coincided with at least some of them.

Should shear surfaces form, they should be removed by appropriate scarification before the next layer is placed. This is especially necessary at the embankment edges where the possibility of these surfaces contributing to instability is greatest; if not, a reduction in design strength for the embankment fill may be necessary. Vaughan (1994) also reports that the risk of formation of such surfaces decreases as the layer thickness increases. Compaction using sheepsfoot rollers may also inhibit their formation (see Section 10.4.2).

3.5 Behaviour of clay fill: permanent works

3.5.1 Heave and settlement

Clay fill can heave and settle just as natural clay soil, depending upon external agencies such as climatic variation or vegetation growth. Unlike most naturally occurring clay soil in north-west Europe, clay fill can exhibit 'collapse settlement' if placed dry of optimum. Natural soil exhibits this phenomenon in arid lands because it is frequently unsaturated. In such environments, collapse settlement may occur in response to a rising water table, often provoked by construction works in which proper drainage design was overlooked. It is unusual with natural soils in north-west Europe which are normally saturated because of the climate. However, the phenomenon is common with some clay fill compacted dry of optimum water content and with some weak rocks (see Section 4.5.3).

Whether a clay fill of given plasticity will exhibit heave or settlement depends upon the following factors:

- the initial water content (or air voids)
- the compactive effort applied
- the confining pressure (i.e. the pressure due to overlying fill and foundation loads).

The relationship between the above factors is summarized in Fig. 3.7. For a clay fill of given plasticity, compacted to a low compactive effort and dry of optimum, collapse settlement may be expected at high confining pressures; the trigger mechanism usually being inundation by groundwater rising in the base of the fill (Fig. 3.7a). If a clay fill of given plasticity is compacted to a high compactive effort, dry of optimum, heave may be expected at low confining pressures; the trigger mechanism again being water (Fig. 3.7b). Because confining pressures are low, the water source is often shallow depth run-off.

The propensity for swelling or heaving of clay fill *increases with plasticity*: for this reason, clay soils with a liquid limit in excess of 50 per cent are not recommended as fill in areas where heave could be a problem (see Section 8.3.4). There is a comprehensive discussion of clay heave and settlement in Cox (1978).

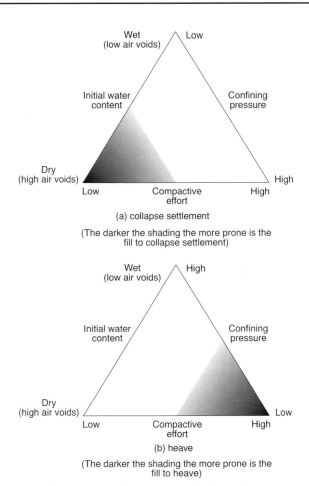

Fig. 3.7 Relationship between critical factors affecting collapse settlement and heave for clay fill of given plasticity

3.5.2 Chemical attack by sulphur-bearing minerals
General

Sulphur bearing minerals contained within overconsolidated clay, argillaceous rocks (Chapter 4) and some industrial waste fills (Chapter 6) may have the following deleterious effects on earthworks:

- chemical attack of any buried concrete or other construction materials
- expansive reaction of finished earthworks, with consequences for overlying structures
- volume reduction of finished earthworks, with consequences for overlying structures
- chemical attack of limestone with the possible formation of noxious carbon dioxide.

Many British clays of Tertiary age and older contain significant quantities of sulphur-bearing minerals. The two most common forms in Britain are iron pyrites (iron sulphide) and gypsum (hydrated calcium sulphate) but other more soluble salts such as magnesium and sodium sulphates also occur. Iron pyrites and gypsum may be present as nodules or concretions or they may be finely disseminated within the soil. Leaching often ensures that sulphates are absent in the first metre or so, but concentrate at some 2 or 3 m depth, reducing in concentration at greater depths. The reason for their concentration at this depth interval may also be the oxidation (during weathering) of the sulphides. Therefore, low sulphide contents may be expected to some 3 m depth, but possibly increasing in concentration below. Trial pits (or trial excavations) are the best means of examining the soils in the borrow areas and of mapping sulphur-bearing minerals. Securing representative samples of soil at the borrow for chemical analysis is notoriously difficult because, as noted above, sulphur-bearing minerals may be concentrated at certain depths and locations. Unless there is careful mapping of the trial pits to locate the sulphur-bearing minerals it is easy to come to the wrong conclusion on the correct chemical content for design purposes.

Further difficulties may arise if soil samples are not correctly preserved and tested as soon as possible after retrieval from the ground. With time, sulphates in soil samples oxidize with the formation of sulphuric acid, thus lowering the pH value. Hawkins and Wilson (1990) found that over a five month period, a significant increase in the laboratory acid soluble sulphate content of certain Lias clay samples occurred, sufficient to raise the aggressivity of some of the samples by one class of the (then) BRE classification. Undesirable chemical changes may also be reduced, if not avoided, by keeping samples in air-tight containers at as low a temperature as practicable until testing is performed.

Assuming its presence, groundwater, over time, will have permeated relatively large volumes of soil in the borrow area, thus providing the opportunity for groundwater samples to take up a more representative sulphate content than individual soil samples. Consequently, there is usually less scatter in the groundwater test results. For this reason, greater emphasis is often placed upon groundwater test results than upon those of the corresponding soils, but care must be taken to see that the groundwater samples themselves are not contaminated by surface water during sampling. This is often difficult to accomplish during conventional cable tool boring and a more reliable method may be to sample from standpipes, after having air-lifted the water column in the standpipe several times to remove surface water or any water used during boring or drilling. Note that the solubility of magnesium and sodium sulphates is markedly higher than that of calcium sulphate (150 and 250 times more soluble, respectively). Therefore the sulphate concentrations measured in groundwater samples may relate more to the magnesium and sodium sulphates than to the calcium variety.

BRE Digest 363 (1996) suggests that, when analysing the results of chemical tests on groundwater samples, the highest value recorded should be used for design purposes. Where the results of a large number of soil samples are to hand, the Digest recommends adopting the mean of the highest 20 per cent. For more details see BRE Digest 363 (1996).

Attack of buried construction materials

Protection of buried concrete is normally secured by the correct mix design. This in turn depends upon the amount and type of sulphur bearing minerals and the pH of the surrounding fill and/or groundwater. Reference should be made to BRE Digest 363 (1996) for full details. Note that the Specification for Highway Works (1998) requires that fill with water soluble sulphate content exceeding 1.9 gm of sulphate (expressed as SO_3) per Litre, when tested in accordance with BS1377: 1990: Part 3: Test 5, shall not be deposited within 500 mm (or other suitable distance) of concrete, cement bound or other cementitious material or stabilised capping forming part of the permanent works. Materials with water soluble sulphate contents (as above defined) exceeding 0.25 gm/L shall not be deposited within 500 mm (or other suitable distance) of metallic items forming part of the permanent works.

Chemical attack involving the formation of the mineral thaumasite has been observed in bridge and other foundations surrounded by a mixture of weathered and unweathered Lower Lias clay backfill in the west of England (Wallace, 1999). The cause was believed to have been the oxidation of pyrites contained in the backfill, which, with the formation of sulphuric acid, reacted with the carbonate in the clay to form gypsum. Slater (personal communication, 2000) reported that low temperatures and the presence of groundwater, sulphate and carbonate produced conditions favourable to the formation of the expansive mineral thaumasite within the concrete. In all cases, the concrete of the affected structures contained a proportion of carbonate aggregates; the addition of chloride rich de-icing agents probably exacerbated the problem of the bridge foundations. Thaumasite attack has also been identified in buried concrete surrounded by burnt colliery discard fill, and in grout between tunnel linings surrounded by a sand lense at the base of the London Clay. The possibility must exist that this form of chemical attack could occur elsewhere in the country where the Lower Lias outcrops or indeed where any of the clays of Tertiary age or older are present and where burnt colliery discard is employed as fill.

Expansive reaction of finished earthworks

Any fills containing sulphur-bearing minerals which could undergo expansive reaction in-service are suspect; they include some Tertiary and older clays, pyritic shales, colliery discard and some of the other materials discussed in Chapter 6 (e.g. steel slag). Swelling of coal shale fill (by up to 70 mm) has been put down to the expansive alteration of sulphides to sulphates by Caldwell *et al.* (1984). Similar problems occur with soils or weak rocks in situ. Quigley *et al.* (1973) described how an area of black pyritic shale (above the water table and near heating ducts) heaved up to 76 mm, while other areas below the water table (and consequently out of the oxidizing environment) showed no movement. The opportunity for oxidation (by excavation during basement construction) and heating (by the presence of boilers in basements) appears to play a major part in expansive reactions, and situations such as these are typical of some domestic, commercial and industrial structures. Quigley *et al.* (1973) also noted that heave of black pyritic shales was greatly reduced by gunite or bitumen coatings which helped to prevent oxidation of the pyrite. Hawkins and Pinches (1987) record structural damage to a hospital due to gypsum growth in black pyritic mudstones.

Lime-stabilized soils are amongst those most at risk from volume changes of this sort. Sulphate and lime react in an expansive manner causing the stabilized layer to heave or crack. Snedker (1996) describes how heave of up to 60 per cent of the initial layer thickness and an increase in water content to some 60 per cent occurred for Lower Lias clays and mudstones. Proposals to use lime stabilization in clay fill from any Tertiary age or older clays, or any industrial fill should be accompanied by thorough investigation of the sulphur-bearing minerals present. Investigation should also determine whether fresh sulphate growth could be produced by the changing conditions (particularly oxidation) caused by construction itself.

Volume reduction of finished earthworks

Volume reductions can occur due to the dissolution of calcite (or other soluble carbonate) in argillaceous rocks containing pyrite in finely divided form. Following oxidation of the pyrite, the carbonates are attacked with volume reduction as a consequence. Pye and Miller (1990) believe that there was a volume loss of up to 10 per cent of part of a Derbyshire dam, constructed of Carboniferous mudstones, which could have occurred in this way. Although collapse settlement is a possible alternative explanation, it would nevertheless be prudent to keep the possibility of such occurrences in mind when using fill of the type Pye and Miller describe.

Attack of limestone

Limestone is frequently employed as rockfill, capping layers and drainage blankets and surrounds. As such, it may come into contact with fills containing sulphur minerals. The chemical reaction between oxidizing sulphur minerals and the limestone could produce carbon dioxide in significant quantities. In most circumstances, the carbon dioxide vents to the atmosphere and little harm is done, but there have been tragic fatalities, such as those in inspection chambers at the downstream toe during construction of the Carsington dam in Derbyshire, UK (Bromhead, 1992).

Great care should be taken where limestone and sulphur-bearing fills are concerned. A risk assessment of the consequences to operatives and maintenance workers should always be undertaken, particularly with man-access points to underground works.

3.5.3 Frost-heave susceptibility

According to Croney and Jacobs (1967), clay fill may be regarded as being non frost-heave susceptible provided that its plasticity index exceeds 15 per cent for well drained materials (groundwater greater than 600 mm from the formation) or 20 per cent for poorly drained materials (groundwater within 600 mm of the formation). They also noted that the susceptibility of clay fill to frost-heave decreased as the degree of compaction increased.

Frost-heave has been recorded in lime stabilized fill, depending upon the fill type, the amount of lime employed and the stage in the treatment (see Section 10.5.2).

3.6 Clay fill as landfill liner

3.6.1 Required properties

There has been heightened interest in the use of clay fill for landfill liners in the past decade because it provides the low permeability necessary to restrict leachate egress. There is also evidence that the clay minerals in the liner absorb certain ions from the leachate, depending upon the pH of the system, an alkaline environment being beneficial. Tests with the organic chemicals which may occur in leachates are reported to bring about clay mineral flocculation and an increase in liner permeability; however, most tests use much higher concentrations of chemicals than occur in practice in domestic leachates and consequently the representativeness of these test results may be questioned.

There are limits for the suitability of clays used in landfill liners and they were brought together by Murray (1998) in the following:

Table 3.4 Engineering property limits for clay fill for landfill liner purposes (Murray, 1998)

Engineering property	Reference	Limit/criterion
Plasticity	DETR (1995)	30% > plasticity index > 10%
	Daniel (1993)	Plasticity index > 7 to 10%
	NRA (1992)	Liquid limit < 90%
		Plasticity index < 65%
	Murray *et al.* (1992)	Plasticity index > 12%
	Gordon (1987)	Plasticity index > 15%
	Williams (1987)	Plasticity index > 15%
Percentage fines	Daniel (1993)	Clay and silt > 20 to 30%
	NRA (1992)	Clay > 10%
	Gordon (1987)	Clay and silt > 50%
Activity	DETR (1995)	> 0.3
Percentage gravel	Daniel (1993)	Gravel (> 4.8 mm) < 30%
Maximum particle size	Daniel (1993)	< 25 to 30 mm

Table 3.4 shows that the use of a plasticity index above the range 12 to 15 per cent would appear appropriate for landfill liners in the UK. There is differing advice for fines content (<0.06 mm), varying from at least 20 per cent to 50 per cent and over. The minimum percentage clay (<0.002 mm) is 10 per cent according to the National Rivers Authority (NRA) which should be compared with an activity of greater than 0.3 recommended by the Department of the Environment, Transport and the Regions (DETR); assuming a plasticity index of 15 per cent, this implies a clay content above 50 per cent, substantially in excess of the NRA figure. Murray (1998) reports that permeability of clay fills increases rapidly at a gravel content of about 50 to 60 per cent. It is worth noting that the maximum particle size quoted by Daniel (1993) is close to the lower limit of the medium gravel range as denoted by BS 5930: 1990. Therefore, the 30 per cent limit quoted applies to a smaller particle size range than is normally used in the UK. This should be borne in mind when assessing the maximum gravel percentage based on Daniel's criterion.

According to Privett *et al.* (1996), the United States Environmental Protection Agency (USEP, 1991) requires a suite of soil properties in order to achieve a minimum permeability of 10^{-9} m/s, as follows:

percentage fines (*passing the 0.075 mm sieve*) $\geq 20\%$
plasticity index $\geq 10\%$
percentage gravel $\leq 30\%$
maximum particle size   50 mm

Note that the minimum percentage fines recommended by USEP is expressed in terms of the 0.075 mm sieve, rather than the 0.063 mm sieve. Depending upon the actual particle size distribution, this means that the USEP requirement of a minimum of 20 per cent fines becomes a minimum of roughly 16 per cent fines using the alternative definition. The plasticity index is also a little low, when set against the recommendations of Murray *et al.* (1992), Gordon (1987) and Williams (1987). The percentage gravel accords with the recommendation of Daniel (1993), although the maximum particles size is larger (50 mm against 30 mm). Site and laboratory trials should help to determine which of the above specifications to adopt for the particular circumstances at hand.

Murray *et al.* (1992) demonstrated that permeability of clay fill at optimum water content (OWC) decreased as the plasticity index increased. A maximum permeability of 10^{-9} m/s is often specified (NRA, 1992) and they found that clay fill having a plasticity index lower than 12 per cent could not be relied upon to produce permeability values of this magnitude (see Table 3.4). They also showed that permeability decreased as OWC increased.

In some cases, clay soils at the borrow within economic haul distance do not have the desired properties for liner formation and the use of Bentonite Enhanced Sands (BES) as a liner material may be considered. The ability to add sodium (or sodium-activated) bentonite in varying proportions (usually 5 to 20 per cent) means that the important properties of strength and permeability may be 'tailor made' for the particular engineering requirements of the facility. Kraus *et al.* (1997) determined that BES is less frost susceptible than compacted clay and according to Dixon *et al.* (1985) suffered less shrinkage on drying.

A study of the engineering properties of BES has been reported by Stewart *et al.* (1999).

3.6.2 Aspects of liner construction

Murray (1998) suggested compacting to the 4.5 kg rammer specification for low plasticity clays and to the 2.5 kg rammer for high plasticity clays, if the desired permeability characteristics (usually 10^{-9} m/s) were to be met. As far as practicable, clay layers for landfill liners should be placed in parallel rather than horizontal lifts (Fig. 3.8). In this way, a defective layer will have no immediate access for leachate migration. Privett *et al.* (1996) recommended 1 (vertical) in 3 (horizontal) side slopes for landfill liners but, in practice, the characteristics of the compaction plant as well as the fill must be taken into account in determining the side slopes which can be safely and effectively placed and compacted.

(a) Defective material is confined in slope-parallel
    construction method

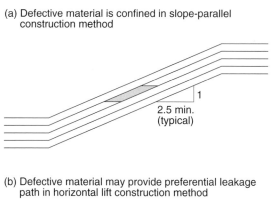

(b) Defective material may provide preferential leakage
    path in horizontal lift construction method

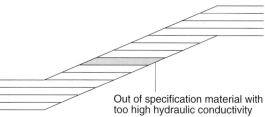

Fig. 3.8   Placing fill for landfill liners (from Privett *et al.* 1996)

As noted, overconsolidated clays such as the London, Gault and Lias and weak rocks such as shales and mudstones may be particularly difficult to compact. Recent work suggests that water or permeant flows between 'clods' of hard, poorly compacted, cohesive fill. The more these clods are broken down, the more homogeneous and uniform will be the fill and the lower the overall fill permeability. A rotavator can reduce clods to more manageable sizes (see Section 10.5.3). Compaction using thin layers may then produce a more uniform, homogeneous and impermeable fill.

Settlement or heave of the liner should be considered. Settlement of a soft clay foundation could be sufficient to disrupt the integrity of the basal clay liner under the weight of the overlying landfill, causing cracking and permitting leachate egress. Where present, artesian or sub-artesian water pressures could lift the basal clay liner, particularly at the early stages of operation and before the weight of landfill increases the effective stress on the liner foundation, again with cracking as a consequence. Liner sides should also be checked. Failure mechanisms for steep-sided liners, such as would be employed to line existing quarries or pits, include, for example, bulging of the liner into the fill. Bearing capacity failure of a soft soil foundation supporting the liner sides is also possible. Both mechanisms could cause cracking of the liner. Cracking could also result from the differential movement between the liner side wall and the waste contained within it. For a more complete discussion, see Edelmann *et al.* (1999).

As with any earth built water retaining structure, clay liners can erode. Fills most at risk are silts and uniform silty sands; clays of low plasticity such as some glacial tills, dry of optimum; and weathered argillaceous rocks such as siltstones and silty mudstones. Dispersivity tests should be performed to assess the material's suitability (Murray, 1998, Table A1 and BS 1377: 1990: Part 5: Test 6).

4. Some characteristics of granular and weak rock fill

4.1 Introduction

Normally free-draining, granular soils are much easier to work than cohesive soils. Apart from uniformly graded sands, silty sands, and some weak rocks, commented upon further below, they are relatively trouble free when employed as fill.

Weak rocks are defined here as material falling within the 'ripping' range shown in Fig. 9.1 (Chapter 9) although, in some cases, material falling within 'hard digging' also qualifies. Not only the mudstones, siltstones and sandstones of the British Coal Measures apply, but also some older weathered rocks. Thus sedimentary rocks of Devonian or older could be included, together with igneous and metamorphic rocks of any age. Harder chalks (see Section 5.3) may also be classified as weak rocks.

4.2 Description and classification

4.2.1 General

In Section 6 of BS 5930 (1999), 'coarse soils' are defined as having at least 65 per cent coarser than the 0.06 mm particle size and include sand (0.06 to 2 mm) and gravel (2 to 60 mm). Therefore, coarse soils have less than 35 per cent fines. In the *Specification for Highway Works* (1998), less than 15 per cent fines constitutes 'granular fill'. Consequently there is no direct correlation between 'coarse soils' in BS 5930 (1999) and 'granular fill' in the *Specification for Highway Works* (1998).

As already noted, the above quoted measurements are made on material from which 'cobbles' (60 to 200 mm) and 'boulders' (larger than 200 mm) have been removed.

4.2.2 Description

A satisfactory description for a granular soil destined to be used as a fill should contain at least:

- the mineralogy, particle sizes and particle shapes (important factors for determining compressibility characteristics, see Section 10.6.4)
- the particle size distribution.

As with fine soils, Section 6 of BS 5930 (1999) provides a basis for such estimates. The way that the description is written indicates the proportion of particle sizes present: materials written in upper case constitute more than 65 per cent of the total (not including any cobbles and boulders) and the lower case qualifiers indicate the nature and amount of any subordinate materials. For example:

- *Slightly sandy GRAVEL* (sand-size particles present up to 5 per cent)
- *Sandy GRAVEL* (sand size particles present between 5 and 20 per cent)
- *Very sandy GRAVEL* (sand-size particles present in excess of 20 per cent).

Again, and as discussed in Section 3.2.2, the percentage figures are qualified in BS 5730 (1999) by the mass behaviour of the soil.

An estimate of the particle size distribution of a granular soil can be made by attaching the qualifiers 'well graded', 'uniformly graded' and 'gap graded' to the above. 'Well graded' means particles reasonably evenly distributed throughout the particle size range; 'uniformly graded' has the overwhelming proportion of its distribution in one (or more) restricted size; and 'gap graded' has a marked lack of particles in one or more size range. For example:

- *Sandy GRAVEL*; well graded (material roughly equally distributed between the sand and gravel sizes)
- *Slightly silty fine SAND*; uniformly graded (sand restricted to the fine sand range, containing up to 5 per cent silt)

Although adopted in *Soil Mechanics for Road Engineers* (1951) and the previous edition of BS 5930 (1981 version), the qualifiers 'well graded', etc. are not used in BS 5930 (1999) because it is considered that there may be a misunderstanding of the terms. Their use is retained in this book because they provide a link to the *Specification for Highway Works* (1998) which also uses these qualifiers (see below). Nevertheless, the geotechnical engineer or geologist should be aware of the possibility of confusion and should always define terms clearly, if necessary by reference to Fig. 4.1. The particle shape is valuable information which may readily be obtained for most granular soils using a hand lens. Section 6 of BS 5930 (1999) provides examples of both angularity and form.

4.2.3 Classification

The alternative to the descriptive approach is given in the *Specification for Highway Works* (1998), where granular soils are classified in terms of certain laboratory tests. Acceptable limits are quoted within which the results must fall. The soils are subdivided into classes and the names of the classes themselves are general, conveying only a broad indication of the nature of

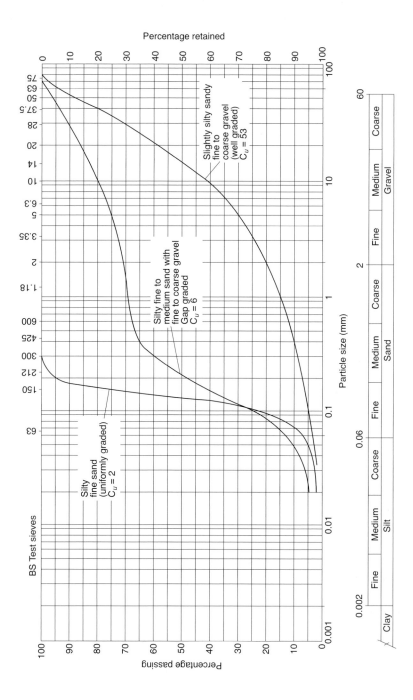

Fig. 4.1 Particle size distribution of granular soils and the terminology used to describe them (from BS 5930: 1981)

the fill (e.g. well graded granular material, uniformly graded granular material, coarse granular material, etc.). Uses for the fill classes are also given in general terms.

As already noted, one of the major differences between the descriptive approach of BS 5930 (1999) and the classificatory approach of the *Specification for Highway Works* (1998) is the difference between the limits adopted for 'coarse soils' and 'granular fill', i.e. maximum of about 35 and 15 per cent fines, respectively. The different maximum fines content adopted in the *Specification for Highway Works* (1998) is probably a response to the fact that, at fines contents greater than about 15 per cent, the soil is no longer free draining.

An important classifier used in the *Specification for Highway Works* (1998) is the soil's uniformity coefficient:

$$C_u = D_{60}/D_{10} \tag{4.1}$$

Reference to Fig. 4.1 demonstrates limitations to its use: the gap-graded nature of the particle size distribution of the example illustrated cannot be identified, although it could have a significant effect on its performance as a fill. Consequently, C_u has to be used with care; blind adherence can mislead. A visual description of a representative hand specimen made by an experienced geotechnical engineer or engineering geologist can often be at least as useful a device as the uniformity coefficient.

Which approach to adopt, whether descriptive or classificatory, depends upon the personal preferences of the engineer since there is no right or wrong method. It goes without saying that if the *Specification for Highway Works* (1998) is adopted, the classificatory approach must also be followed.

4.3 Properties

4.3.1 Particle size distribution

The following points apply:

- well graded granular fill has the best engineering properties. Abundant particle contacts reduce inter-particle stresses and accompanying breakage; furthermore, by filling void spaces, the smaller particles help to increase density.
- uniformly graded fill has relatively few particle contacts and demonstrates poorer engineering properties than its well graded counterpart. This is illustrated in Fig. 4.2, where there is a markedly lower density for a given water content and compactive effort.
- gap graded fill excavated from some glacial tills may not always possess the mix of particles necessary for the best engineering performance.
- for rocks, Vaughan (1994) describes how ripping fills the interstices between the larger particles with smaller grains, forming a relatively

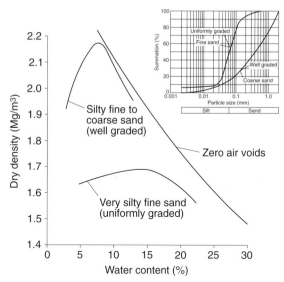

Fig. 4.2 Dry density v. water content relationships for well graded and uniformly graded granular soils (from *Soil Mechanics for Road Engineers*, 1951)

well graded fill with abundant particle contacts. Blasting produces a more uniformly graded assortment of blocks or particles, with a relatively small component of fines, and a more uniform fill. Vaughan referred to these two types as 'filled' and 'underfilled', respectively. The 'filled' and 'underfilled' materials may be expected to have characteristics broadly similar to those of 'well graded' and 'uniformly graded' granular fills. Because of the high stresses produced at the few particle contacts, underfilled material may not always reflect the higher strength and hardness of the rock from which it was composed.

4.3.2 Effect of large particle sizes

Section 2.6 described methods of correcting for oversize particles or stones (greater than 20 mm) when determining dry density in the standard compaction test mould. However, there is still a problem in determining how strength and compressibility properties of granular fill are affected by oversize material. Winter and Suhardi (1993) suggest that provided the proportion of the soil having particles larger than 20 mm is smaller than between about 45 and 50 per cent of the total (F less than 0.45 or 0.5 in Section 2.6), then the properties of the matrix (i.e. the material finer than the stones) will control those of the fill as a whole.

If the proportion of the stones rises significantly above 45 to 50 per cent of the total, then the results of strength and compressibility tests may not be representative and some form of large scale testing, including *in situ* test equipment built for the purpose, may be necessary. This was done by Bolton and Lee (1993) who demonstrated that for a given relative density, the angle of shearing resistance ϕ increased as the maximum particle size increased. It was suggested that large particle sizes acted as reinforcement as the smaller particles flowed around them. Large scale tests are seldom practicable for most projects and the results of tests on matrix materials or correlations (see below) are normally accepted for design purposes.

The work of Winter and Suhardi (1993) also showed that, as the stones increased above the 45 to 50 per cent level, the density began to decrease. This might seem at first sight anomalous in that an increasing content of coarse particle sizes might be expected to result in increasing, not decreasing, densities. However, as the stone content increases, so does the opportunity for the large particles to rub together and even crush. Much of the energy applied during compaction is lost due to the friction between, and crushing of, the larger particles and therefore a smaller proportion of energy is available to reduce the void spaces between the particles. Substantially heavier equipment and/or more passes and/or thinner fill layers are necessary to secure high levels of compaction in coarse granular fills than in their finer grained, or matrix dominant, counterparts. Recognition of this fact means that many specifications require a maximum particle size no greater than two thirds of the layer thickness in order to reduce the amount of compactive effort absorbed in handling the large particle sizes.

Although mixing fills is seldom advantageous with soils (see Section 3.3.2), Marsal and Fuentes de la Rosa (1976) demonstrated that the addition of finer granular material ranging from 20 to 50 per cent by weight to an otherwise uniform basalt rockfill improved compaction performance significantly under vibrating rollers. They also found that when some 30 to 40 per cent of finer granular material was added to the rockfill, grain breakage and compressibility were reduced.

4.3.3 Shear strength

McGown (1975) suggested that there was an optimum proportion of fines (less than the 0.06 mm particle size) which would produce the minimum void ratio and the maximum angle of shearing resistance ϕ for granular fill; work by McGown and others indicated that this optimum proportion varied from about 20 to 40 per cent (Fig. 4.3). Similar results were established by Irfan and Tang (1993) who tested Hong Kong soils; these authors found that shear strength increased sharply if the coarse fraction increased above about 30 per cent. This suggests in turn that provided coarse material does not amount to more than say 25 per cent of the test specimen, its removal should not significantly affect the measured shear strength of the remainder.

Most shear strength testing devices available in commercial laboratories are capable of testing triaxial specimens no larger than 100 mm in diameter and 60 mm square for the shear box. A ratio specimen size to maximum particle size no smaller than six is usually regarded as being appropriate for

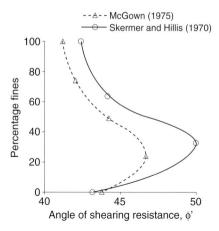

Fig. 4.3 Variation of angle of shearing resistance ϕ with percentage fines <0.06 mm (from McGown, 1975)

shear strength testing purposes. This is approximately the figure adopted by Irfan and Tang in their tests. For such a ratio, the maximum particle sizes which can be tested as routine in commercial testing laboratories are small, even allowing for the removal of a proportion of the coarser soils. For this reason, when designing granular fill for strength purposes, correlations between shear strength and properties such as the relative density are usually relied upon.

Relative density D_r may be expressed as:

$$D_r = \frac{\rho_{d\,max}}{\rho_d} \cdot \frac{(\rho_d - \rho_{d\,min})}{(\rho_{d\,max} - \rho_{d\,min})} \tag{4.2}$$

where ρ_d is the dry density of the fill, as measured in situ (see Section 8.4.3), ρ_{dmax} is the corresponding maximum and ρ_{dmin} the corresponding minimum dry densities of the fill, both measured in the laboratory (BS 1377: 1990: Part 4: Tests 4.2 to 4.5). Usually expressed as a percentage, D_r obtained by this means may be used to find the angle of shearing resistance ϕ by employing a correlation such as that by Parkin (1988). This correlation is reproduced in Fig. 4.4, where ϕ *(triaxial)* values corresponding to different granular soil types are given. The ϕ values obtained this way are applicable to normally consolidated material. It is likely that most compacted granular fill will be overconsolidated, at least throughout most of the layer thickness, so conservative results will be produced when using this correlation.

Care should be taken to see that relative density tests are done on representative samples. If corrections were made when performing the maximum dry density tests (see Section 2.6), the corresponding changes to the particle size should also be made to the materials used in the other tests which have to be performed to calculate D_r.

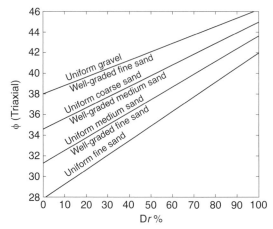

Fig. 4.4 Variation of angle of shearing resistance ϕ (triaxial) with relative density D_r for normally consolidated granular soils (from Parkin, 1988), reproduced with kind permission from the publisher Balkema

Charles and Watts (1980) proposed a non linear relationship between shear strength τ and normal effective stress σ', as follows:

$$\tau = A(\sigma')^b \; (\text{MN/m}^2) \tag{4.3}$$

where A and b are constants. Tests were performed on sandstone, slate and basalt fill compacted in a large diameter triaxial device. It is likely that a relationship of this form also applies to coarse and very coarse granular soil fill as well as rockfill. In a test series involving crushed basalt, Al-Hussaini (1983) found that measured ϕ values increased with sample relative density and also deduced evidence that ϕ increased as the coefficient of uniformity increased (equation 4.1), i.e. strength was larger for well graded as opposed to uniformly graded materials, when tested under the same conditions.

Shear strengths of a number of weak rocks are illustrated in Fig. 4.5 (Vaughan, 1994); the ratio shear strength to normal strength varies strongly with normal stress. This implies in turn a strongly non-linear failure envelope.

4.4 Behaviour of granular and some weak rock fills: temporary works

4.4.1 General

Because of its free draining properties, granular fill does not normally suffer from the construction problems already described for cohesive fill (see Section 3.4.). However, and as noted in Section 4.3.1, uniform fine grained soil, when used as fill, demonstrates a markedly lower density for a given compactive effort than other granular soils and a common problem during construction with such soils is 'overstressing'. Because the normal

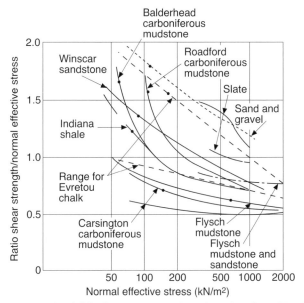

Fig. 4.5 Shear strength of fills from strong and weak rocks (from Vaughan, 1994), reproduced with kind permission from the publisher Balkema

stress at the top of the current layer is low, the shear strength of the granular soil is also low; therefore, under the action of some compaction plant, loosening of the layer surface may occur as the shear strength is exceeded by the applied shear stress. The problem can be reduced, if not avoided, by limiting the applied shear stresses, for example by switching off the vibratory component of a vibrating roller for the initial passes or by using lighter equipment.

4.4.2 Construction settlement

The maximum internal self weight settlement ρ of a wide body of granular fill of height H occurs at mid-height and is (Charles, 1993):

$$\rho = 0.25 \frac{\gamma H^2}{D} \text{ (m)} \tag{4.4}$$

where D is the constrained modulus ($1/m_v$).

On the basis of field measurements, Charles and Penman (1988) proposed modifying equation 4.4 to the following relationship:

$$\rho = 0.30 \frac{\gamma H^2}{D^*} \text{ (m)} \tag{4.5}$$

where D^* is the constant equivalent constrained modulus. Typical values of D^* are given in Table 4.1 for a variety of fills, including a clay fill, and for three different embankment heights:

Table 4.1 Typical values of constant equivalent constrained modulus D^* for various fill types and embankment heights (Charles, 1993)

Fill type	D^*		
	$H = 10\,m$	$H = 30\,m$	$H = 100\,m$
Sandy gravel $(D_r = 80\%)$	50	90	170
Sandy gravel $(D_r = 50\%)$	30	50	90
Sandstone rockfill $(D_r = 80\%)$	15	25	45
Sandstone rockfill $(D_r = 50\%)$	6	10	20
Clay (plasticity index, 15%;			
liquidity index, 0.1)	6	10	18

Most practical engineers are not so much interested in the maximum internal self weight settlement as the total self weight settlement, since this will yield the amount needed to top up at the end of construction. Simple integration will show that the total self weight settlement is:

$$\rho_t = 0.50 \frac{\gamma H^2}{D} \text{ (m)} \tag{4.6}$$

where the symbols have the significance previously defined. It is suggested that the values of D^* quoted in Table 4.1 be adopted when using equation 4.6.

For granular fill used as a foundation, Charles (1993) proposed the use of a secant constrained modulus D_s. Values of this property, based on the results of large one metre diameter oedometer tests over a stress range from 30 to 130 kN/m², are reproduced in Table 4.2 (the vertical strain ε_v is also quoted):

Table 4.2 Typical values of secant constrained modulus D_s (stress increment from 30 to 130 kN/m²)

Fill type	D_s (MN/m^2)	ε_v (%)
Sandy gravel $(D_r = 80\%)$	50	0.2
Sandy gravel $(D_r = 50\%)$	25	0.4
Sandstone fill $(D_r = 80\%)$	12	0.83
Sandstone fill $(D_r = 50\%)$	6	1.67
Colliery spoil (compacted)	6	1.67
Colliery spoil (uncompacted)	3	3.3

Note that the secant constrained modulus depends heavily on the relative density (D_r). Increasing D_r from 50 per cent to 80 per cent doubles the modulus of the fill concerned. However, note also that heavy compaction plant and relatively thin layers may be necessary to produce a relative density of 80 per cent in very coarse granular or rock fill, depending upon the maximum particle sizes. The values quoted in Table 4.2 will not necessarily hold for different stress increments; Charles (1993) gives empirical formulae which may assist in such cases. Methods of estimating settlements using Standard Penetration Test (SPT) data have been proposed by Burland and Burbridge (1985).

The compression of some weak rocks is illustrated in Fig. 4.6 (Vaughan, 1994). As might be expected, there is a non-linear relationship between vertical compression and vertical effective stress. It is worth noting the range for mudstones, from relatively low for Balderhead to high for Carsington. Use of these data for the appropriate stress range, together with equation 4.6, may help in estimating construction settlements. Such settlements can be of value to a contractor who may wish to know how much extra material to haul to the bank to achieve design elevation.

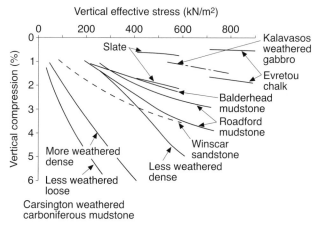

Fig. 4.6 Variation of compression with vertical effective stress for weak rocks-grading filled or near filled (from Vaughan, 1994), reproduced with kind permission from the publisher Balkema

4.5 Behaviour of granular and some weak rock fills: permanent works
4.5.1 General
During the working life of the structure (the permanent works condition) creep and collapse settlement may occur. Erosion can be a threat, particularly with poorly compacted granular fill or fill having a uniform particle size distribution. These phenomena are commented upon below.

4.5.2 Creep settlement
Experience indicates a linear relationship between creep settlement and the logarithm of time elapsed since construction. This takes the form:

$$\alpha = \frac{100\Delta_s}{H\log(t_2/t_1)} \tag{4.7}$$

where Δ_s is the settlement between times t_1 and t_2 since completion of construction, and H is the embankment height at the end of construction. The relationship is normally expressed as a percentage.

In a study of creep settlement for a variety of British Coal Measures open-cast fills, Hodgetts *et al.* (1993) and Hills and Denby (1996) found that a 'full scheme of backfill compaction' produced an α factor of about 0.2 per cent; 'partial backfill compaction' about 0.4 per cent; and 'uncompacted backfill' about 0.8 per cent. Values of α varying from 0.2 to 1.0 per cent were reported for rockfill dams in the United States (Charles, 1993) and Sharp (1996) published values of 0.34 and 0.48 for rockfill used in the construction of quays in the Gulf and in Ghana, respectively. Care must be taken in interpreting these data because the value of α may not simply be related to the nature of the fill, but also to its method of placing. For the United States examples, the smallest values of post construction settlement (and hence α) were obtained when the fill had been sluiced during compaction (Charles, 1993).

4.5.3   Collapse settlement

Collapse settlement can occur with some weak rocks as well as with cohesive fills. If there is any likelihood of water rising up in the base of the fill, monitoring is essential and construction at the surface should be postponed for as long as possible to reduce the possibility of volume change during the in-service period. Hills and Denby (1996) measured the collapse settlement response of a number of Coal Measures open-cast fills, largely from the same study areas as discussed under creep settlement above, and proposed a relationship between collapse settlement and air voids. They proposed that collapse settlement increased non-linearly as air voids content increased and suggested that a site compacted to air voids contents between 0 and 10 per cent would represent full backfill compaction; between 10 and 15 per cent partial backfill compaction; and greater than 15 per cent uncompacted backfill.

This work was extended by Blanchfield and Anderson (2000). On the basis of laboratory tests and field measurements made on a site in the English Midlands, they considered that collapse settlement was related not only to air voids content but also to the magnitude of the overburden pressure acting on the fill (as proposed in Section 3.5.1). Their relationship is illustrated in Fig. 4.7. Most available records for collapse settlement in the UK concern open-cast materials but the results obtained are likely to be applicable to other weak rocks.

It should not be assumed that collapse settlement is entirely restricted to water rising up in the base of fill. There is evidence (Charles, 1993) that

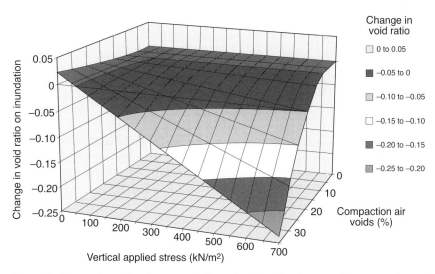

Fig. 4.7 Three dimensional representation of void ratio change with compaction air voids and vertical stress at inundation (from Blanchfield and Anderson, 2000). Proceedings of the Institution of Civil Engineers, Geotechnical Engineering, 143

surface water entering open trenches during construction may be sufficient to cause such settlement, albeit locally. More severe consequences may be expected from leaking mains and drains or the careless and ill-considered location of soakaways. Attention should always be paid to the performance of engineering structures such as these, both during construction and over the long term permanent works condition.

4.5.4 Erosion

Erosion can be a major problem with uniform fine grained granular fill; in part, this is due to the low dry densities achievable with fill formed from these materials (see above) but also because the few particle contacts generated by its uniform particle size distribution mean that individual grains are poorly anchored one to the other and are easily disturbed by flowing water. Where the use of such fill is inevitable and erosion is a risk, such as with river training, canal works, adjoining drains or soakaways, some form of geotextile protection should be considered.

Where adequate bearing capacity for road sub-bases is needed, or to support low rise foundations, it may be worthwhile experimenting with some form of soil stabilization, provided that full mixing of the constituents can be assured. *Soil Mechanics for Road Engineers* (1951) suggests that cement stabilization can be adopted economically for granular soils having the following characteristics:

Maximum size: 76 mm
Passing 5 mm: >50%
Passing 0.425 mm: >15%
Passing 0.075 mm: <50%
Liquid limit: <40%
Plasticity index: <18%
Organic matter: <2%

Most uniform fine sands in this country will not meet the coarser end of this particle size distribution requirement (greater than 50 per cent passing the 5 mm sieve), which is why some experimentation may be necessary.

4.5.5 Frost-heave susceptibility

Croney and Jacobs (1967) found that uniformly graded silts and silty sands were amongst the materials most prone to frost heave. They should not be used within 450 mm of finished work (*The Highways Agency, Advice Note 44/91*).

Otherwise, granular fill may be regarded as non frost-heave susceptible provided that 10 per cent or less passed the 0.075 mm sieve (i.e. the silt content was small). Croney and Jacobs also noted that the degree of compaction did not significantly affect frost-heave susceptibility for the granular soils tested. Lambe (1962) remarked that frost susceptible soils (such as silty fine sands) were not necessarily made less frost susceptible by treatment with cement. This advice was not confirmed by Croney and Jacobs who believed that a small proportion of cement (or bituminous) additive was sufficient to prevent heave in such soils. However, they stated that the effect of repeated freezing and thawing on such stabilised materials needed investigation.

Limestone gravels produced much greater heave than occurred with sandstone or flint gravels in the tests conducted by Croney and Jacobs. They noted that all Oolitic and Magnesian limestones having an average saturation water content (SWC) in excess of 3 per cent must be regarded as frost-heave susceptible and that the percentage passing the 0.075 mm sieve had little influence on likely heave. 'Hard' limestones (minimum dry density reported as $2.05 \, \text{Mg/m}^3$) with less than 2 per cent average SWC and with 10 per cent or less passing the 0.075 mm sieve may be regarded as non frost-heave susceptible.

5. Some characteristics of other natural deposits

5.1 Mercia Mudstone

The Mercia Mudstone (formerly Keuper Marl) is a series of red-brown mudstones with subordinate siltstones and sandstones of Triassic age. In the UK it outcrops on both sides of the Pennines, in the Midlands and extends to the Bristol Channel. There are also outcrops in the Cheshire Plain and in the Mersey area. Only highly weathered Mercia Mudstone has soil-like consistency and engineering properties. Chandler (1969) produced a descriptive classification grading the material into five zones, depending upon the degree of weathering. This scheme is reproduced in Table 5.1, where it has been supplemented with index properties for various Mercia Mudstone zones published by Chandler and Davis (1973).

Zone 1 may behave like weak rock, along with any unweathered siltstones and mudstones. It is likely that the slightly weathered and drier Zone 2 material will show some granular compaction characteristics, giving way with weathering to the cohesive properties of Zone 4. This latter material may be expected to display the compaction characteristics of similar cohesive fill having a similar consistency index (see Section 3.3.2).

Chandler and Davis (1973) performed compaction tests on compacted Mercia Mudstone of widely varying plasticity. The amount of heave was found to depend upon what was termed the placement moisture deficiency (liquid limit less the placement water content). The greatest heave occurred with the samples of highest plasticity and with the highest placement moisture deficiency. The authors recognized that the heave resulted from residual suctions prior to wetting. Their work was expanded by Cox (1978). The comments on heave (Sections 3.5.2 and 8.3.4) apply here.

5.2 Glacial deposits

5.2.1 General

Four types of glacial (glacigenic) deposits have been identified (e.g. Trenter, 1999):

- glacioterrestrial (glacial till or 'boulder clay')
- glaciofluvial (glacial outwash)

Table 5.1   A Classification for Mercia Mudstone (from Chandler, 1969 and Chandler and Davis, 1973)

Zone	Number and description	Notes	Water content (%)	Plasticity index (%)	Con-sistency index
Fully weathered	**4b** Matrix only	Can be confused with solifluction or drift deposits but contains no pebbles. May be fissured	18–35	17–35	<1.1
	4a Matrix with occasional claystone pellets less than 3 mm dia, but more usually coarse sand size	Little or no trace of original Zone 1 structure though clay may be fissured			
Partially weathered	**3** Matrix with frequent lithorelicts up to 25 mm. Lithorelicts become less angular with weathering	Water content of matrix greater than that of lithorelicts	12–20	10–18	1.4–1.1
	2 Angular blocks of un-weathered marl with little if any matrix	Speroidal weathering. Matrix starting to encroach along joints: first indications of chemical weathering	5–15	10–15*	2–1.5
Un-weathered	**1** Mudstone often fissured	Water content varies depending on depositional conditions			

* May be non-plastic.

- glaciolacustrine (glacial lake-clays)
- glaciomarine.

Glacioterrestrial deposits are formed without significant amounts of water, whilst glaciofluvials comprise sands and gravels deposited by water from a wasting glacier; they often interdigitate with glacioterrestrial tills. Glaciolacustrine deposits are the laminated silty clays formed within ice-dammed lakes and are also frequently found in close proximity to glacioterrestrial tills. Glaciomarine deposits are found at the margins of landmasses (as they were in glacial times) and comprise a combination of glacial detritus and marine sediments. They are seldom widely distributed onshore in the UK and are not considered further.

Some 60 per cent of Great Britain is believed to have been covered by the Devensian, the youngest and most extensive of the three glaciations which are thought to have occurred between some 500 000 and 10 000 years ago. The characteristic of glacial deposits is their variability, not only between the four generic types listed above, but within each of the four types themselves. This variability depends on the nature of the terrain invaded by the glaciers, on the terrain elevation and on other factors. Thus tills can vary from clay of medium plasticity (commonly found in English lowland areas) to coarse granular deposits containing cobbles and boulders and only small amounts of fines (commonly found in upland areas). Outwash deposits vary from coarse gravel to silt and sand. The extent of the variation inherent in glacial deposits makes them amongst the most difficult to engineer; this is particularly the case with earthworks for linear structures such as roads and railways which, stretching over tens of kilometres, may traverse several glacial deposits and many different soil types.

Although demonstrating great variability, most glacial deposits fall under the headings of granular and cohesive soils, discussed in previous Chapters. In some terrains, particularly in the Scottish Highlands, relatively little clay mineral was produced by glacial action on the igneous and metamorphic rocks traversed by the glaciers and is replaced instead by quartz and feldspar 'rock-flour'. Glacial tills containing this material are of low plasticity and difficult to handle when wet. The performance of glacial deposits as fills is summarized in Table 5.2:

Table 5.2 Performance of glacial deposits as fill

Generic type (commonly called)	*Typical range of soil types*	*Typical problems encountered*
Glacioterrestrial (tills)	Low to medium plasticity clays, often containing sand pockets, varying gravel content, occasional cobbles and boulders (lowland areas)	Easily slurry-up on contact with water; either surface or groundwater contained within sand pockets or lenses Can be very hard when dry
	Gravel and cobble mixtures, with only a small proportion of fines (upland areas)	Groundwater common and pumping or other forms of control frequently necessary
Glaciofluvial (outwash deposits)	Sands and gravels of widely varying particle sizes; silt pockets frequent	Groundwater common; proximity to more clayey tills can mean perched water tables and slurrying-up of the tills on excavation
Glaciolacustrine (glacial lake clays)	Laminated silty clays	Usually too plastic for routine use in earthworks; silty layers may be water bearing; avoid mixing with otherwise suitable fill; notoriously unstable in cut slopes

5.2.2 Construction problems with tills

Some glacial tills can be amongst the most difficult to work. Blasting has been adopted to loosen clay tills prior to working (Johnstone, 1975) and damage to construction plant has been caused by these materials when hard (Hertford, 1985). However, in wet weather as noted in Table 5.2, low plasticity till can slurry up on excavation and transport, making it almost impossible to place and compact. The presence of water bearing silt and sand pockets and layers, so typical of some glacial tills, only aggravates the difficulties in handling these materials and should be searched for during site investigation.

5.3 Chalk

5.3.1 General

The Upper Chalk occurring in the south, south-east and east of England is a fine grained porous and remarkably pure limestone of Upper Cretaceous age. It should not be confused with the Lower Chalk which, whilst containing much calcium carbonate, also contains much clay giving it engineering properties more akin to the cohesive soils already described, than to the Upper Chalk. For brevity the Upper Chalk will be referred to simply as 'chalk'.

Chalk porosity can vary, giving rise to a wide range of water contents, densities and strengths; 'hard grounds' are reported, where the void ratio is as low as 0.1, making excavation difficult without special equipment. For the more normal lower strength materials, water released on excavation, subsequent handling and trafficking can make them difficult to work; for this reason, double handling should be avoided, especially with the softer higher water content chalks. Because of its porosity, chalk is also frost-heave susceptible (see Section 5.3.4) and should not be used close to the surface of finished earthworks, basements or other structures.

In addition to its finely porous structure, chalk contains discontinuities which account not only for its high permeability *in situ*, but also facilitate its break down on excavation to fragments from boulder to sand- and gravel-sizes. Free water which may be contained within the discontinuities also contributes to the water released on breakdown. Chalk weathers along discontinuities, frequently widening them to solution features filled with collapsed material (see Section 10.6.6). Weathering breaks down its porous structure, resulting in the formation of 'putty chalk', which has a structure and consistency quite unlike the intact chalk from which it was derived. Thus, far from being the uniform substance, which a glance at a quarry or borrow pit would suggest, chalk can be highly variable in its consistency and its engineering properties.

5.3.2 Chalk specification in the UK

Current British practice as described by the *Specification for Highway Works* (1998) employs the properties saturation water content (BS 1377:

1990: Part 2: Test 3.3) and chalk crushing value (BS 1377: 1990: Part 4: Test 6). The latter test measures the susceptibility of the chalk to crushing and is taken as the rate at which a 1 kg sample of single size chalk lumps (passing the 20 mm and retained on the 10 mm aperture sieves) contained in a 100 mm diameter mould crushes under the impact of a 7 kg rammer, falling from a height of 250 mm (Ingoldby, 1978). Using this test, a classification system for chalk earthworks involving four classes 'A' to 'D' was developed (Fig. 5.1). A flow chart for use of chalk as fill, is given in *The Highways Agency Advice Note* HA 44/91, together with recommendations for the compaction method to be used in Table 6/4 of the *Specification for Highway Works* (1998).

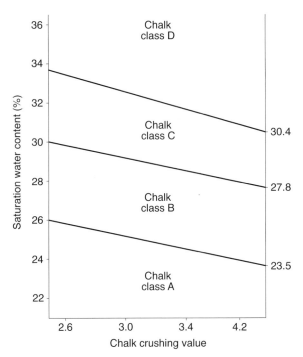

Fig. 5.1 Chalk classification chart for use with the *Specification for Highway Works* (1998) (from Advice Note HA 44/91)

Greenwood (1993) drew upon continental experience and recommended the relationship given in Fig. 5.2, which relates earthworks properties to water content and dry density. Greenwood also related his scheme to the compaction methodology quoted in the *Specification for Highway Works* (1998) and given in Table 5.3.

Greenwood also offers a flow-diagram to facilitate the use of his approach. Whilst Greenwood's method appears to offer advantages,

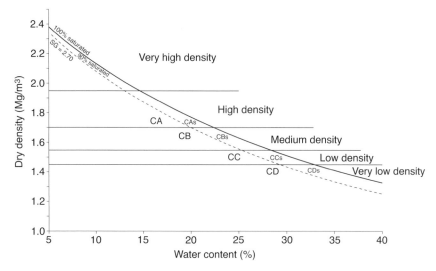

Fig. 5.2   Proposed classification chart for chalk fill (from Greenwood, 1993)

Table 5.3   Guidance on chalk compaction (Greenwood, 1993)

Chalk class	Preferred compaction method	Likely excavation plant	Instability	Workable in light rain
CA	2	Any	Not expected	Yes
CA$_S$	2	Any	Not expected	Probably
CB	1$^{(1)}$	Any	Not expected	Yes
CB$_S$	1	Face shovel	Unlikely	No
CC	1$^{(1)}$	Face shovel	Unlikely	Possibly
CC$_S$	4	Face shovel	Probable	No
CD	4	Face shovel	Possible	No
CD$_S$	4$^{(2)}$	Face shovel	Expected	No

Notes: 'Preferred compaction method' relates to *Specification for Highway Works* (1991), Table 6.4.

(1)   amend to compaction method 2 if water content ≤22%

(2)   use may not be economical in embankment fill

particularly because of the few tests necessary to perform the classification, a check against the existing *Specification for Highway Works* (1998) procedures would be prudent, particularly for larger projects.

Whichever the system adopted, the aim of the earthworks engineer is to produce a workable material and in practice this must be done by selecting the right combination of layer thickness and equipment to suit the particular chalk water content and hardness (or density). In this respect, chalk is no different from other materials the earthworks engineer has to handle, but the consequence of getting the combination wrong are probably more severe with chalk than with most other substances. Site trials are therefore considered essential (see Section 8.5).

5.3.3 Construction problems

Great care is needed placing poor quality Class C and D chalks. The following, taken in part from the *Specification for Highway Works* (1998), are suggested precautions:

- no earthworks to take place in winter (and in frost or periods of heavy rain)
- excavating and/or mixing poor (Class C and D) with better quality (Class A and B) chalks to be avoided
- trafficking by heavy (greater than $15\,m^3$ struck capacity) construction plant to be avoided
- trafficking in winter months only if covered by protective layer with layer trimming delayed by at least four weeks
- at the end of each working day, the work to be sealed by two passes of a 2100 kg roller
- no stockpiling or multiple handling
- work to be halted if temporary instability occurs
- trials to determine how long it may take for poor quality chalks to harden after initial disturbance, and such times written into the contract documents
- use of a face shovel (or back-acter) for excavation to produce the minimum amount of tracking and hence the minimum amount of breakdown, with the machine chassis stationary whilst working and swinging to excavate and unload.

Site trials may be of great assistance in determining what precautionary measures are necessary. It may be found, for example, that for the particular chalks encountered, not all the above precautions are relevant; on the other hand, some precautions may be necessary in handling better quality Class A and B materials.

The length of time necessary for wet chalks to dry-out and to harden can be critical to a construction contract. Measurements of the water content loss with time were made by Heath (1966) on wet chalk fill delivered to the site of the M40 High Wycombe Bypass during dry sunny weather, when the temperature was reported as varying from 24 to 28°C. After one hour the water content of the top fill layer reduced by about 3 percentage points, after two hours by about 4 and after four hours by about 6.5. Wet weather can of course cause the opposite effect.

Although rightly regarded as a potential problem, high water content chalks need not be a deterrent to successful earthworks, provided that the appropriate site trials are undertaken and there is strict site control throughout. Designated as Class 3 on the *Specification for Highway Works* (1998) classification, Rail Link Engineering were able to handle chalk with water contents varying from 20 to 28% for one of the Channel Tunnel Rail Link contracts (Andreou, personal communication, 1999). It was also possible to use chalk as engineered fill with water contents up to 30 per cent by placing and compacting at a controlled rate which lowered its water content and reduced instability (rutting) to an acceptable level. Air voids contents of 8 per cent or lower were reportedly achieved.

To minimize problems in compacting wetter and finer chalks, large layer thicknesses have been used with little compaction. However, substantial collapse settlement can occur with improperly compacted chalk fill. Clayton (1980) observed settlements up to 6 per cent of embankment height because of this mechanism. Careful mapping and classification of the chalk during site investigation should help to identify the higher water content and potentially unstable chalks and to permit planning of excavation and compaction during the main works. This is especially important when construction in autumn is expected. As demonstrated in the Rail Link Engineering example quoted above, site trials are essential, especially where wetter chalks are in contention.

The use of lime (or cement) stabilization procedures may be considered for wet chalks (say water content in excess of 28 per cent). Lime (to improve handling) and cement (to increase strength) of chalk is frequently adopted in France and Mudet (1993) and Puiatti (1995) may be consulted for French experience. Further details on British techniques in handling chalk may be obtained from *The Highways Agency Advice Note* HA 44/91, the *Specification for Highway Works* (1998) and from Greenwood (1993).

5.3.4 Frost-heave susceptibility

All crushed chalks were found frost-heave susceptible by Croney and Jacobs (1967) and the magnitude of frost-heave increased linearly with the saturation water content of the chalk fragments. The authors reported that neither the water content nor the size of the chalk fragments nor the degree of compaction had much influence on frost-heave susceptibility.

6.   Some properties of industrial fill

6.1   Introduction

In the last decade, there has been considerable interest in the use of industrial materials as fill for engineering purposes. Re-using industrial materials instead of excavating and hauling natural soils and rocks to site is obviously appealing because of the environmental benefits. In some cases, the industrial materials concerned may be only a short haul from the works, so additional environmental benefits accrue. Unfortunately, industrial materials may themselves be unsuitable by virtue of their chemical or physical properties and so what appears to be an excellent environmental solution brings many other engineering problems in its train. Nevertheless, provided that the necessary comprehensive test programme is performed, industrial materials may offer an attractive solution when used as engineered fill.

Reference should be made to BS 6543 (1990): *Use of industrial by-products and waste materials in building and civil engineering*. A review of industrial materials used in road building is given by Sherwood (1995)

6.2   Colliery discard (minestone)

6.2.1   General

There are large quantities of colliery discard or 'minestone' forming spoil heaps or tips both in former and in existing coal-mining areas of the United Kingdom. It normally comprises shales, mudstones, siltstones with some sandstones and arises from both coal face working, roadway and heading construction, drift and shaft sinking. The two latter operations may involve penetrating rocks younger than the Coal Measure horizons from which the coal was extracted, and a variety of rock types, often referred to as 'run-of-mine' or 'development dirt', may be introduced into the discard as a consequence.

Colliery discard is the coarse by-product of the colliery workings and ranges predominantly from sand- to cobble-sizes. Fine discard is a washery by-product, either a slurry (fine coal particles) or tailings (fine rock particles), and was deposited in lagoons either on the colliery discard spoil heap or on adjacent land. Care should be taken, when taking delivery of colliery discard for fill purposes, that quantities of fine discard from lagoons on the spoil heap have not become mixed with the coarser material.

Many old tips were constructed loose and at their angle of repose and the coal content in some of the discard was high. Firing was common, sometimes caused by the negligence of operatives and sometimes due to the heat caused by the oxidation of pyrites present in the discard. Large quantities of 'burnt shale' or 'red shale' were produced as a result. This material has somewhat different properties from the unburnt colliery discard.

Coal content is one of the main factors affecting the performance of unburnt colliery discard. Organic carbon can vary from virtually zero to 40 per cent, with the specific gravity varying from 2.65 to 1.7 as a consequence (Taylor, 1984). The plasticity indices of several hundred coarse unburnt colliery discards from all over the UK were measured and the results are given in Fig. 6.1 (Taylor, 1984); the majority of the plasticity indices fall below about 20 per cent, indicating low plasticity clay behaviour, but a substantial minority fall above 20 per cent. Note that the plasticity indices are measured on a fine grained particle range but in many instances the coarse discards break down to fine particle sizes during placement and compaction, so these data may be significant for design purposes.

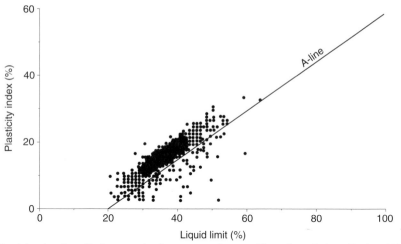

Fig. 6.1   Atterberg limit properties for coarse unburnt colliery discard (from Taylor, 1984)

The natural water content with respect to optimum is of practical use for design and construction using colliery discard (both unburnt and burnt). Average data from the results of a large number of tests (Taylor, 1984) are plotted in Fig. 6.2.

The average water contents (i.e. as received) of both the unburnt and the burnt colliery discards are dry of the average optimum, as illustrated in Table 6.1, particularly so for the burnt material. Significant addition of water may be necessary when using these materials as fill, especially in the dry season.

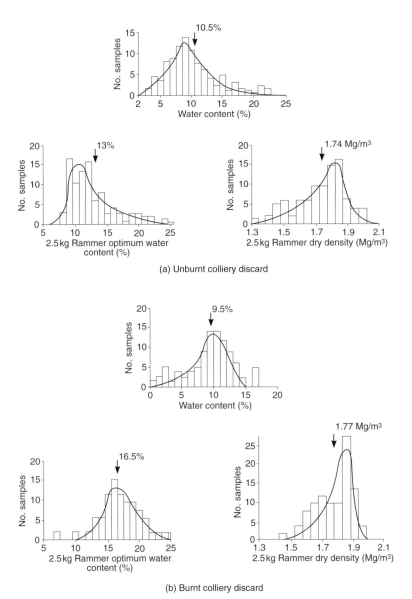

Fig. 6.2 Compaction characteristics of coarse colliery discard – burnt and unburnt (from Taylor, 1984)

As some of the discard particles are relatively small in size, the addition of water may prove effective in improving compaction performance.

Both burnt and unburnt colliery discard contain sulphates. Taylor (1984) collected the average sulphate contents for a large number of unburnt and burnt samples, summarized in Table 6.2 (ranges in brackets).

Table 6.1 Compaction test data for colliery discard, 2.5 kg rammer method (Taylor, 1984)

Material	Average water content (%)	Average optimum water content (%)	Average maximum dry density (Mg/m³)
Unburnt colliery discard	10.5	13	1.74
Burnt colliery discard	9.5	16.5	1.77

Table 6.2 Results of sulphate tests on colliery discard (Taylor, 1984)

Material	Sulphate (% by weight) acid soluble	Sulphate (% by weight) water soluble
Unburnt colliery discard	0.20 (0.04 to 3.20)	0.10 (0.01 to 0.96)
Burnt colliery discard	0.70 (0.02 to 4.00)	0.18 (0.01 to 1.02)

The substantially higher average sulphate contents of the burnt colliery discard should be noted and is probably due to the oxidation of pyrites to sulphates during firing. Further data on the sulphur contents of unburnt colliery discards are shown in Fig. 6.3; it will be seen that the maximum water soluble content (0.2 per cent) is substantially higher than that of the data provided by Taylor (1984). Scatter must be expected and each discard should be thoroughly tested.

6.2.2 Use of colliery discard as fill

Hird *et al.* (1998) describe the use of colliery discard as a landfill liner. They conclude that discard varies in suitability depending upon several factors and that each must be investigated in detail to ascertain a discard's suitability. They believe that for a permeability requirement of 10^{-9} m/s, it is unlikely that consistently satisfactory results would be obtained with less than 20 per cent fines, although given good mixing and compaction, a maximum particle size up to 50 mm would not have a significant affect on permeability. Compaction at, or slightly wet of, optimum water content, should be attempted and the influence of confining stress on permeability of discards is significant, as it is with clays. This should be recognized when specifying tests and interpreting test results.

There are frequently large quantities of colliery discard available in the former British coalfields and for this reason its use as bulk infills for derelict colliery shafts and similar has been investigated. Cole and Figg (1987) describe the use of a mixture of colliery discard, pulverized fuel ash, lime and water as an infill for limestone caverns in the English Midlands. The

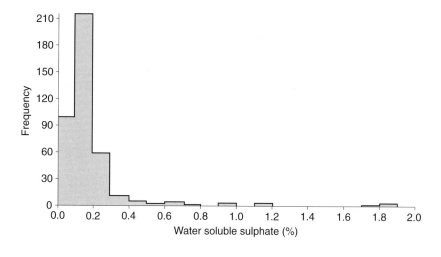

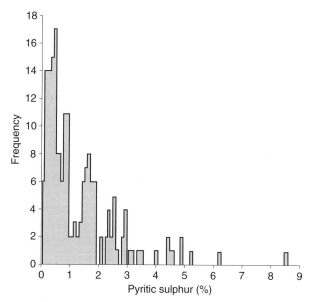

Fig. 6.3 Sulphur bearing mineral contents in unburnt colliery discard (from Sherwood, 1995)

strength of the resulting mixture increased with time and was reportedly due to the pozzolanic reaction of its constituents. The use of this kind of mixture for other bulk filling would seem appropriate, particularly in those areas close to large discard supplies. The performance of the mixture will depend in part on the grading of the discard as well as the properties of the pulverized fuel ash and pre-construction trials are essential.

Conversion of pyrites to gypsum is expansive and may be partly responsible for the breakdown of discards at shallow depth during weathering. Use of unburnt colliery discard as fill should be avoided beneath sensitive structures, particularly if a rise in temperature is likely (for example, beneath a base slab for a warehouse, boiler, industrial, commercial or residential property) because of the possibility of damage due to a potentially expansive reaction.

6.2.3 Frost-heave susceptibility and chemical attack of buried construction materials

Croney and Jacobs (1967) state that burnt colliery discard is very susceptible to frost-heave and therefore should not be used in the top 450 mm of road construction. Note also the requirements of the *Specification for Highway Works* (1998), and quoted in Section 3.5.2, regarding deposition of sulphur bearing fills adjoining buried construction materials.

6.3 Pulverized fuel ash
6.3.1 General

Modern coal burning power stations produce pulverized fuel ash which comprises fine grained well rounded and largely silt-size particles with various proportions of sand-size particles; sizes vary significantly from power station to power station, depending upon the nature of the coal burnt. In the UK, pulverized fuel ash consists typically of silica (50 per cent), aluminium oxide (30 per cent) and ferric oxide (10 per cent), together with smaller percentages of calcium, magnesium and potassium oxides, and other substances in trace quantities. Pulverized fuel ash is usually conditioned with water to improve its handling properties before delivery to site (termed 'selected fill') and some is pumped to storage in lagoons ('lagooned fill')

Another product of coal burning power stations is furnace bottom ash. It is the coarser residue which falls to the bottom of the furnace and may be stored with pulverized fuel ash in lagoons. For this reason, lagoon pulverized fuel ash from some power stations may be substantially more varied in its composition than from others. Furnace bottom ash may be considered as a fill in its own right although some of the coarser particles may break down on compaction.

Experience indicates substantial variation between the properties of pulverized fuel ash from different sources, and a significant variation in the engineering properties of a given pulverized fuel ash, when sampled at different times. Results of compaction tests made on pulverized fuel ash from Eggborough power station are illustrated in Fig. 6.4. There is considerable variation between the maximum dry density results, and the curves themselves are flat, exhibiting little 'peakiness'. Variations in properties may also arise depending upon whether identical material was employed for each point of a compaction test or whether fresh material was

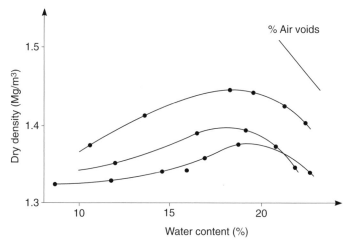

Fig. 6.4 Variation of dry density with water content for lagooned pulverised fuel ash, Eggborough power station (from Cabrera, Braim and Rawcliffe, 1984)

adopted throughout. Care is necessary in sampling and testing pulverized fuel ash if reliable and consistent results are to be obtained.

6.3.2 Use of pulverized fuel ash as fill

Two attractive features of pulverized fuel ash as engineered fill are its low weight (specific gravity typically from 1.9 to 2.4) and its self-hardening properties. Lightness has obvious advantages for filling over soft soils and it has been used as backfill behind bridge abutments for this reason. Weight reductions of up to 25 per cent have been claimed (see Section 12.6.3). Clarke and Coombes (1996) investigated the strength properties of pulverized fuel ash. Strength was found due partly to suction and partly to pozzalanic effects and, when the specimens were saturated to remove suctions, there was a substantial strength loss. There was also a significant hardening with age, together with an increasingly brittle response for the pulverized fuel ash tested, with some ashes reaching peak stress at less than 0.5 per cent strain. The authors considered that the *Specification for Highway Works* (1998) could be unsafe and that the recommendations given in BS 8004 (1994) for earth retaining structures could be too conservative, because strength was likely to increase with time. For full details see Clarke and Coombes (1996).

Substantial hardening of conditioned pulverized fuel ash may be expected when mixed with 10 per cent cement and 28 day strengths varying from 7.1 to 13.8 MN/m^2 have been reported (Sherwood, 1995). This property permits the use of cement stabilized conditioned pulverized fuel ash as a capping layer (*Specification for Highway Works*, 1998). Its use has also found favour as backfill for mine-workings. Grout mixtures comprising 1 part sulphate-resisting cement to 12 parts pulverized fuel ash have been employed (Robertson-Rogers, personal communication, 1997) with clean water added to produce a pumpable consistency (flowability between 300 and 600 mm in a concrete flowmeter). Sand may be used to replace the pulverized fuel ash (to a maximum of 50 per cent) if a limit to the spread of the grout from the target area is desired.

The particle size and shape of pulverized fuel ash mean that the upper layers can be difficult to spread and compact: it may become highly unstable and erosion-prone in wet weather and dust nuisance may be common when dry. Use of a starter layer is required, partly to provide a good working platform and partly to provide a capillary cut-off against upward migration of groundwater. Likewise a thickness of general fill (often about 600 mm) is recommended between pulverized fuel ash and the underside of the capping layer or sub-base. *The Highways Agency Advice Note* HA 30/87 reports that pulverized fuel ash backfill can be washed out by accidental flooding, forming voids. This is also commented upon by Head (1994). In this respect, pulverized fuel ash is similar to some natural uniformly graded fine granular soils (see Section 4.3.1). Comprehensive detailing of the drainage system is essential when pulverized fuel ash fill is to be employed.

Environmentally, there are good reasons for treating pulverized fuel ash with caution, if it is likely to come into contact with water sources. After initial placement, quantities of leachate with elevated levels of boron, sulphates and other salts may be released (Halcrow, 1994). This may be a function of conditioning, storing and stockpiling. The chemical content of the pulverized fuel ash should be carefully investigated before a decision to use it is made. If it is decided to use pulverized fuel ash on a project and sampling and testing have shown it to be satisfactory, then that particular pulverized fuel ash should be employed and no other, unless a correspondingly careful test programme has demonstrated its suitability.

6.3.3 Frost-heave susceptibility and chemical attack of buried construction materials

Croney and Jacobs (1967) state that coarse pulverized fuel ash (less than 40 per cent passing the 0.075 mm sieve) is unlikely to be frost-heave susceptible. Fine pulverised fuel ash may be susceptible 'probably dependent upon the coals from which they were derived' and should not be used within the top 450 mm of road construction unless frost-heave susceptibility tests indicate otherwise. The authors remark that the frost-heave susceptibility of fuel ashes can be reduced by cement stabilisation.

Note also the requirements of the Specification for Highway Works (quoted in Section 3.5.2) regarding deposition of sulphur bearing fills adjoining buried construction materials.

6.4 Other waste materials

6.4.1 General

The Department of the Environment, Transport and the Regions Survey of derilict land in England (1991) highlighted the existence and potential utility of many natural wastes and industrial by-products which could be used as engineered fill. Natural wastes include:

- slate quarry wastes
- china clay pit wastes
- fluorspar mine waste
- tin mine waste.

Industrial or man-made wastes include:

- steel and blastfurnace slags
- spent oil shale
- incinerator waste
- spent railway ballast
- road planings
- demolition waste.

The use of wastes in construction is considered in British Standard BS 6543 (1990), where some guidance is given on their chemical content in relation to their potential to attack building fabric. A flow-chart for determining the suitability of waste materials for engineered fill purposes is given in Fig. 6.5.

6.4.2 Slate waste

There are numerous waste tips in North Wales, some of which are in national parks, and comprise principally '500 mm down' material. The slate would be durable and is reportedly relatively chemically inert but, obviously enough, it has a very high Flakiness Index (Smith and Collis, 1993). It is also highly likely to break down to smaller (flaky) sizes on transport, placement and subsequent compaction. Nevertheless, it was employed as a dam fill at Dinorwic power station and its use as a granular sub-base has been reported (Sherwood, 1995); hence, it would appear suitable for bulk fill purposes. Its geographical location is such that transportation costs to most parts of the country would be expensive, which would have to be borne in mind when considering its use.

6.4.3 China clay pit waste

This waste is the result of extraction and production of china clay and comprises:

- overburden
- micaceous residue

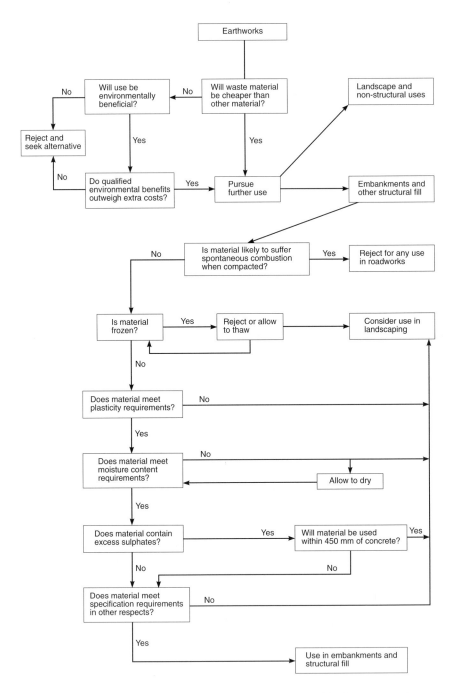

Fig. 6.5 Flow chart for determining suitability of waste materials for use as engineered fill (from BS 6543, 1990)

- sand-size granitic rock fragments
- coarser waste rock materials (stent).

The sand-size granitic rock fragments have been employed as fill, although their mica content may give rise to compaction problems.

When screened and crushed, stent has been used to produce aggregates for various uses. Again, the location of china clay wastes in the extreme south-west means that transportation costs to most other parts of the country would be prohibitive.

6.4.4 Flourspar and tin mine waste

Only a small amount of flourspar waste is produced annually and it appears to have a ready market outside the construction industry. There is a substantial amount of tin mine waste in spoil heaps and tips in Cornwall, but there are concerns over its durability and its chemistry may be adverse. Unless a substantial programme of investigation were to be put in hand to demonstrate its suitability, no further consideration of its use as engineered fill appears warranted. Use as fill in landscape areas might be considered although note should be taken of the possible contamination of aquifers and water courses. Its situation in the extreme south west of the country would make transportation to most other locations in the United Kingdom prohibitively expensive.

6.4.5 Steel and blast furnace slags

Steel slag is usually very heavy costing more to transport than most other fills. It can be chemically active having residual iron, free lime (CaO) or free Magnesia (MgO) and therefore has the potential to produce undesirable leachates and expansion. BS 6543 (1990) warns that it should be allowed to weather before being used as general fill in construction to allow opportunity for the free lime and magnesia to reduce by leaching. Some countries specify a maximum free lime content of 4.5 to 5.0 per cent (Smith and Collis, 1993). Steel slag should not be employed under buildings where groundwater is a possibility because of potentially expansive reactions following hydration of the free lime and magnesia it contains. Cracking in the lightly reinforced concrete floor slabs in council housing in the West Midlands of England was put down to heave of fresh steel slag (*New Civil Engineer*, 1984). Expansion of the free lime and magnesia was believed responsible.

Blast furnace slag is lighter though marketable and consequently likely to be more expensive than most industrial fills. Older stock-piled blast furnace slags may:

- contain undesirable chemicals
- contain steel slags
- may vary in quality from batch to batch.

For these reasons, each batch should always be tested for undesirable properties.

6.4.6 Spent oil shale

This material is located in one relatively small part of central Scotland. It is generally smaller than 50 mm but may break down to smaller sizes on handling and compaction. Although extensively used in Scotland in the past, this material may contain an appreciable sulphur content which may preclude its use within the built environment unless appropriate precautions are taken.

There are indications that the material may be frost susceptible.

6.4.7 Incinerator waste

This material has the appearance of ash but may sometimes be incompletely burnt. BS 6543 (1990) recognizes that it may have uses as fill. However, it should not be used beneath structures due to its high sulphur content and possible toxicity.

6.4.8 Spent railway ballast

Of large and relatively uniform size, this material would seem ideal for use as fill in some circumstances but unfortunately is frequently contaminated by oils, tars and coal. When cleaned, it is usually recycled within the railway industry and is seldom freely available for sale in any quantity.

6.4.9 Road planings

This material would also appear ideal at first sight because in some cases it may be produced local to construction, with consequent reduction in transport costs. However, there may be concern over its possible toxicity and appropriate chemical analyses are essential before any decision on its use as a fill are taken.

6.4.10 Demolition waste

As with other industrial wastes, the presence of undesirable contaminants is the main problem with demolition and other construction wastes. Usually, they take the form of timber fragments and sulphates (from plaster); unacceptable levels of sulphates may also be present in the bricks themselves. Waste from former industrial sites may also be contaminated with coal, tars, oils and a host of other substances. However, the market for environmentally sound products is increasing and the demolition of old buildings is becoming increasing intelligent as a consequence. Rock crushers are available to grade the material to the required sizes, depending upon the characteristics of the crusher and the strength of the material.

6.5 Compaction qualities of industrial fills

From the foregoing, it should be clear that the chemical properties of industrial fills may pose a threat to the built environment and that these properties are probably the biggest single factor controlling their use. However, there may also be good environmental reasons for employing such fills, particularly if areas blighted by unsightly spoil heaps and tips are made more attractive, thus increasing amenity. Assuming that the fill is within economic haul distance, their use should certainly be considered along with the possibility of the following:

- a temperature rise during the fill's operational life
- frost-heave
- that groundwater will become contaminated or an aquifer or water-course threatened, or that there is a threat to buried construction materials
- methane generation.

When compacted, colliery discard exhibits the characteristics of the siltstones, sandstones, shales and mudstones from which it was largely derived. Because its water content is normally below optimum, it may be compacted with a vibrating smooth-wheel roller, although a tamping roller may also be found effective. It is susceptible to collapse settlement (see Section 4.5.3). During compaction trials, wetting using the methods described in Section 10.5.3 could be tried thus reducing the potential for collapse settlement. Thin layers (say 150 mm or less) permitting more comprehensive wetting should assist, as should compaction to a higher compactive effort, otherwise collapse settlement may be expected where a rising groundwater table or inundation occurs.

The relation between dry density and water content is usually flat for pulverized fuel ash (see Section 6.3.1). The absence of a peaky compaction curve means some flexibility in selecting a placement water content, but if compacted too dry, dust may be a nuisance. Pulverized fuel ash is often used behind bridge abutments to reduce fill load on compressible foundations. In these circumstances, compaction using light vibrating equipment may be considered. Clarke and Coombes (1996) suggest placing pulverized fuel ash in 225 mm layers for compaction to 150 mm by using between four and eight passes of pneumatic tired or vibratory rollers.

For the other wastes previously described, attention should be paid to the fundamental earthworks tests such as initial water content, particle size distribution and the water content v dry density relationship, when deciding the compaction equipment to employ. The following notes may be of assistance:

- Quarry wastes will probably contain a large proportion of overburden materials (either soil or rock) which may dictate the plant to be used

- Trials with smooth-wheel, tamping roller, grid or vibrating roller should be considered. Provided that the material is essentially granular and/or any clay is dry of optimum, vibrating equipment will probably enhance compaction characteristics
- Slags may benefit from the high contact stresses provided by a smooth-wheel or grid roller; vibrating equipment will probably be most effective
- Demolition and incinerator wastes may contain low strength materials, such as plaster, bricks and weaker concretes. High contact stresses may not be desirable: the weaker materials could crush and powder, promoting a gap grading in the particle size distribution. Pneumatic tired equipment could be tried, varying tire pressures to determine optimum characteristics.

7. Note on earthworks specifications

7.1 Introduction

An earthworks specification must address:

- the provision of a well constructed excavation or placement site forming a reliable platform for the subsequent fill operations
- the provision of a sound and durable fill, capable of being handled, placed and compacted to a standard which is appropriate to the requirements of the structure as a whole
- provision of a means of compaction to enable the serviceability (and if necessary the ultimate) limit state criteria to be met.

There are many other factors: for example, the need to address questions of site safety (Chapter 14). However, this Chapter is limited to technical considerations and the reader is referred to the appropriate publications elsewhere for guidance on non-technical issues.

There are three fundamental types of earthwork specification:

- the method specification
- the end-product specification
- the end-performance specification

In addition, and as will be shown, there are numerous hybrid specifications, which contain elements of all three. A discussion of the various types of earthworks specification is given by Reichert (1980).

7.2 Method specification

This type of specification dictates all elements of the work to be done; for example, as far as compaction work is concerned, it directs the contractor to the layer thicknesses, the plant type and the number of passes for a given fill. Provided that the contractor can show that he has followed precisely the method dictated by the engineer or designer in the specification, the responsibility for any subsequent failure usually rests with the engineer. The *Specification for Highway Works* (1998) contains much method specification material.

Unless use is to be made of the *Specification for Highway Works* (1998), a method specification has to be designed in the first place and much effort is normally directed to formulating the method(s) to be used for the fill(s) under consideration. This work is normally done by the engineer or designer. Once designed, the contractor has to control the fill types, place and/or compact the fill as directed by the specification.

7.3   End product specification

For this type of specification the engineer or designer specifies the degree of compaction necessary for the given material to support the structure by reference to the criteria prescribed by the serviceability and/or ultimate limit states. The level of compaction is expressed in terms of one of several geotechnical properties, such as a percentage of the maximum dry density, an undrained shear strength or an MCV value (see Section 8.4). Control by on-site testing should be rigorous and is normally conducted by the contractor or a specialist sub-contractor under the supervision of the engineer or designer. The responsibility for any subsequent failure will normally rest with the contractor, unless it can be shown by reference to the records of control tests, that the specified level of compaction has been met throughout. Under these circumstances, responsibility for the failure is likely to rest with the engineer or designer for selecting an inappropriate end product for the particular fill concerned or an inappropriate method for its measurement during the design and control phases.

Although popular, the end-product specification refers only to the performance of the fill on completion of site work and not in the permanent works condition. As will be shown in Section 8.3.2, there are several factors which can affect the engineering integrity of a fill: for example, climatic or vegetation effects can produce volume changes, especially in cohesive fill. These factors can be mitigated by the appropriate specification design but they can never be completely removed; in circumstances such as these, the responsibility for permanent works failures using this type of specification can be difficult to resolve and the employer may be left with a large bill for failed works.

An example of an end-product specification for engineered fill supporting low rise structures is given in Appendix 1 (based on Trenter and Charles, 1996).

7.4   Performance specification

This form of specification seeks to resolve the issue of responsibility for permanent works failure by placing it mainly upon the contractor. The specification is usually written in terms of the required serviceability (or ultimate) limit state; for example, the maximum differential settlement in a stated length of embankment should not exceed 10 mm five years after construction, or the fill should support foundations designed to an allowable bearing pressure of 75 kN/m^2 with a settlement not exceeding 15 mm for the specified working life of the structure. This is obviously an onerous form of specification as far as the contractor is concerned, because it seeks to place the risk of failure on to the contractor for future events over which it may have no control. For example, vegetation planted by the employer could produce volume changes which would result in greater than the specified differential movement over part of the embankment length.

In the event, the performance specification has to be designed and controlled. These operations will probably follow the pattern set for the end-product form of specification although the contractor (or designer) will have to give much thought to protecting its position during the structure's working life. Realistically, this means a list of exclusions of items which could influence performance. Such items would include vegetation, drainage and changes in hydrogeological factors, such as those which influence groundwater level brought about, for example, by cessation of colliery pumping (see Section 10.6.5).

7.5   Hybrid types of specification

As already noted, there are numerous hybrid forms of earthworks specification. The most popular approach is to use the *Specification for Highway Works* (1998) as the basis, whilst instituting relatively small changes, affecting for example plant type, number of passes and layer thicknesses. These changes are often made from local knowledge of fill type and experience with particular equipment but introduction of these changes may complicate the issue of liability under the contract and this should be borne in mind.

8. Design, construction control and monitoring

8.1 Introduction

In no part of geotechnical engineering are design and construction and, in some instances, monitoring, more intimately linked than in earthworks. The control of fill placement may be considered an extension of design and is so treated here. The majority of earthworks (leaving aside cuts and the foundations for embankments and landfills) deals with remoulded or partly remoulded soils; hence the fill, when placed, has to be continuously checked to ensure that the remoulded properties selected for design such as density, air voids content, shear strength and MCV values, are being obtained in the field. Good earthworks design goes further, requiring performance monitoring in addition to construction control.

Engineered fill may be defined (Charles, 1993) as fill which is selected, placed and compacted to an appropriate specification so that it will exhibit the required engineering behaviour. For a given project, the designer must normally:

- consider the nature of the structure and the level of compaction required
- assess the factors affecting the serviceability limit state of the finished earthworks
- select suitable fill (to the extent that there is a choice available)
- select the initial water content for the level of compaction and the confining pressures concerned
- consider the use of treatment processes.

Preliminary design is done on the basis of site investigation information. However, the link between design and construction already mentioned means that information affecting design may be obtained from compaction trials and/or from the main works themselves. Therefore, earthworks design is often iterative, with the preliminary design altered as experience accumulates on site. This can have contractual consequences if the contractor is asked to undertake work for which it has not priced; this should always be borne in mind when preparing the contract documents.

8.2 Investigations for earthworks

In principle, a site investigation for any structure should provide:

- the information required by the engineer or designer to design the permanent works
- the information required by the contractor to design and programme all the various construction activities, including the temporary works.

Most structures involving earthworks, like roads, railways and airports, landfills, residential, commercial or industrial estates, require other features to be investigated. They include:

- cut formation level for pavement design and cut-slopes for stability
- landfill liner foundation level for settlement and possible heave
- embankment foundations for bearing capacity, settlement and stability
- strength and compressibility characteristics of the natural soils forming the foundations to the fill platform.

These features require the characterization of the soil and rock in their natural rather than in their remoulded condition. Earthworks are near surface structures: embankments, for example, are usually placed at as shallow a depth as the stability, bearing capacity and settlement properties of the underlying soils permit. Although deep cuts are the obvious exception, even they have shallow entry and exit points. For this reason, the natural ground at shallow depth is of great interest to the earthworks engineer, who concentrates on natural shallow depth features, such as solifluction deposits and/or glacial or periglacially induced soil fabric.

The fieldwork and testing phases of the site investigation for earthworks should investigate:

- potential fills over whatever depth is necessary to secure the required quantity. This may be limited to the extent of the cut depths, where balanced cut and fill is planned. Where this will only yield part of the total fill requirement, there should be investigations at other borrow locations
- the natural ground forming the cut slope and the cut formation, together with foundations for structures like embankments and landfill liners
- groundwater conditions for all structures, noting that artesian (or sub-artesian) pressures can be critical for landfill liners, because of the possibility of uplift pressures on an impermeable liner base
- the presence or otherwise of sulphur-bearing minerals in the proposed fill which could have deleterious consequences for buried concrete or for lime-stabilized work such as capping layers (see Section 3.5.2).

There are several useful texts on site investigations in general, e.g. Clayton *et al.* (1995) and *Site Investigation in Construction* (1993) published by The

Institution of Civil Engineers. Good descriptions of some new methods of investigation are given in the *Proceedings of the International Conference on Advances in Site Investigation Practice* (1995). Perry and West (1996) provide a helpful review of desk study sources.

For problems of foundations design (e.g. at bridge and viaduct sites), standard texts such as Tomlinson (1994) and Fleming *et al.* (1985) should be consulted.

8.3 Preliminary design considerations
8.3.1 Fill suitability

A fundamental part of the design process is fill selection. Fill may be regarded as both 'unsuitable' and 'suitable' and, within suitable fill itself, 'hierarchies' of suitability for various engineering purposes exist. Note that the *Specification for Highway Works* (1998) recognises 'acceptable' and 'unacceptable' fills, as defined in its Clause 601. These terms are not employed here, unless direct reference is being made to this specification. Instead, the terms 'suitable' and 'unsuitable' are adopted.

Unsuitable fill

A list of unsuitable materials, based on the *Specification for Highway Works* (1998) is as follows:

- clay soils having a liquid limit (BS 1377: 1990: Part 2: Test 4) in excess of 90 per cent and a plasticity index (BS 1377: 1990: Part 2: Test 5) in excess of 65 per cent. (Some engineers might find these figures rather high and would prefer to adopt lower limits, especially in wetter terrains, or to contemplate the use of lime stabilization procedures)
- any material containing topsoil, wood, peat or lignite or other organic substances
- any material containing potentially damaging sulphur-bearing minerals (see below)
- any material containing bio-degradeables
- any material containing scrap metal
- frozen or water-logged substances
- material susceptible to combustion, spontaneous or otherwise
- material from contaminated sites
- material which by virtue of its particle size, shape or hazardous chemical or physical nature cannot be properly handled and effectively compacted (e.g. hazardous wastes and some slate wastes).

The *Specification for Highways Works* (1998) distinguishes between unacceptable fill which can be treated and rendered acceptable for the permanent works and unacceptable fill which cannot. The latter includes fill having hazardous chemical or physical properties which require special measures for its handling and disposal.

International Union of Railways Design Code (1994) also specifies unsuitable materials. Its requirements are somewhat more stringent than those of the *Specification for Highway Works* (1998) echoing the more demanding needs of railway, as opposed to highway, fills. The maximum allowable contaminants in fill may be obtained from the Inter-Departmental Committee on the Redevelopment of Contaminated Land, ICRL 59/83 (2nd Edition) to which reference should be made.

Suitable fill

Deciding on suitable fill is one of the key operations in an earthworks project. In practice, fill selection is a matter of deciding what is unsuitable on a site and making the best of the materials remaining. Factors which may influence a designer's decision on suitability will include:

- the practicability or otherwise of conditioning to acceptable limits (see Section 10.5)
- haul distances and the ease of transport of alternatives
- the influence of construction traffic on the fill
- frost-heave susceptibility
- presence of deleterious substances such as sulphur-bearing minerals.

There are substantial environmental pressures to avoid importing large quantities of fill from off-site and, unless there is a shortfall in volume, the designer will be expected to persevere with conditioning on-site materials to the extent necessary to provide the required material.

Hierarchy of fills

Depending upon the engineering requirements, there is usually a hierarchy of suitable fills at a given site drawn up on the basis of their potential use. The following is one example which may be relevant to a larger fill operation:

- structural fill: for such uses as corrugated steel structure surround, reinforced earth and gabion infill
- capping and drainage: suitable to form capping or drainage layers in cuts or embankments
- bulk fill (1): best quality; suitable for use in embankments (particularly close to structures), and to support shallow foundations
- bulk fill (2): as above, but requiring conditioning prior to use
- bulk fill (3): suitable for mine-shaft, mine workings or other bulk infill. (May need some structural fill depending upon the nature of the workings)
- containment fill: suitable to form containment bunds in which

landscaping fill may be placed. Must be sufficient for compaction in thin layers to form satisfactorily stable side slopes

- landscaping fill: suitable fill which may be used to form landscape areas
- agricultural or horticultural fill: otherwise unacceptable fills but suitable for soiling or topsoiling landscape and other areas
- unsuitable fill: fill incapable of being processed to form material suitable for use in the works.

It will be evident that further hierarchies exist within the above classification. For example, the best containment fill would be used alongside public spaces or close to sensitive structures where stable side slopes were necessary, whilst less good material would be used in areas inaccessible to the public.

8.3.2 Factors affecting the serviceability limit state

Satisfying ultimate limit state is not normally a consideration with engineered fill and so only the serviceability limit state is dealt with here. This state requires consideration of several factors which include:

- *changes in effective stress*: due to variations in groundwater level within the fill or to changes in imposed loading for which the fill was not designed (especially relevant to cohesive fill)
- *changes in fill water content (a)*: due to inundation caused by a rising water table or by concentrated run-off into low-lying filled areas causing collapse settlement (especially relevant to cohesive fill and to some weak rocks), and
- *changes in fill water content (b)*: due to vegetation growth or by climatic variations; settlement due to desiccation together with heave due to water ingress can occur (especially relevant to cohesive fill)
- *chemical changes*: many chemical changes in potential fill (natural and industrial materials) are expansive and can cause heave of the fill and any overlying structures (Chapters 3 and 6)
- *changes due to decomposition of inorganic matter*: such changes cause volume reductions as well as gaseous omissions; fill containing organic matter should never be used
- *erosion potential*: although the engineering characteristics of granular fill, when placed and compacted to appropriate standards, are generally good, the erosion potential of silty soil and uniform fine and fine to medium sand is relatively high and special measures may be necessary (see Section 4.5.4).

The designer should consider each of the above factors in relation to the structure, identifying any which could impact upon the serviceability limit state and the appropriate precautions taken.

8.3.3 Nature of structure and compactive effort required

The nature of each structure should be carefully considered, particularly its sensitivity to settlement and differential settlement; guidance on the structural engineering aspects of low rise structures may be obtained from Tomlinson (1995), Tomlinson *et al.* (1978) and Atkinson (1993). Note that because of its more severe dynamic loading, fill supporting railway trackbeds is often designed to a more stringent specification than highway fill; guidance on the design of earthworks for railways may be obtained from the *International Union of Railways Design Code* (1994).

To determine the level of compactive effort for a given fill, the method illustrated in Fig. 8.1 may be followed. Fig. 8.1 illustrates two compaction curves corresponding to the 2.5 and 4.5 kg rammer methods, together with the zero, 5 and 10 per cent air voids content lines. The areas enclosed between the maximum dry densities for the 2.5 and 4.5 kg rammers; 95 per cent of the maximum dry densities for the 2.5 and 4.5 kg rammers; and the air voids content lines may be subdivided as shown.

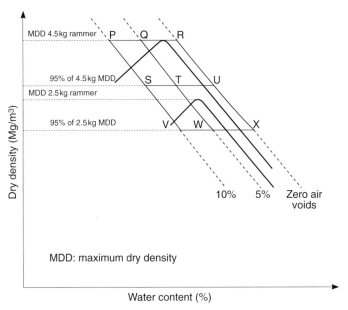

Fig. 8.1 Selection of compactive effort for engineered fill. For explanation see text (modified after Trenter and Charles, 1996)

Depending upon the nature of the problem in hand, the following levels of compactive effort may be used as a guide:

- *Area QRTU* (Air voids content 5 per cent or less): foundations for buildings (granular fill); capping layers (from selected granular fill); granular fill on the passive side of a gravity retaining structure

- *Area TUWX* (Air voids content 5 per cent or less): foundations for buildings (cohesive fill); capping layers (lime stabilized cohesive fill); general cohesive fill for 600 mm depth below a capping layer; granular fill for the active side of gravity retaining walls; cohesive fill for both sides of gravity retaining walls; fills liable to collapse settlement with sensitive overlying structures
- *Area STVW* (Air voids content between 5 and 10 per cent): mass fills for embankments (granular and cohesive), not liable to collapse settlement. Consider upgrading to area TUWX for mass fills for railway and airport runway embankments
- *Area below VW* (Air voids content between 5 and 10 per cent): non-structural fills for landscaping purposes.

The limits of the various areas, quoted above, may be altered to suit circumstances. For example, 90 per cent of the 2.5 kg rammer method may be substituted for 95 per cent, if conditions warrant.

Different recommendations are given for foundations on granular and on cohesive fills because the latter can prove troublesome when compacted to a high compactive effort, dry of optimum and in low confining stress circumstances (see Section 8.3.4). Even if cohesive fill is placed wet of optimum to avoid these difficulties, it can dry out due to climatic and other effects and heave can be a problem with erratic and unforeseen consequences. It may be better to accept a slightly lower level of compactive effort with the possibility of some settlement, provided that the criteria of Charles and Burland (1982) are met.

These authors suggest that for settlements corresponding to volumetric strains less than 0.5 per cent, fill should provide a good foundation for overlying structures, and that at less than 1 per cent problems are unlikely. At settlements corresponding to volumetric strains in the fill greater than 2 per cent, the authors suggest that there might be serious difficulties with overlying structures. Laboratory tests using the procedures outlined by Head (1994) should always be conducted to determine whether or not the given fill, compacted to the efforts described above and to the water contents outlined in Section 8.3.4, will meet these criteria. Note that BS 1377: 1990: Part 5: Test 4 also describes tests to measure swelling pressure and settlement on saturation.

The weight and vibration of construction traffic can be a problem when compacting hard up against a structure, whether existing or under construction: for this reason lower compactive efforts may be appropriate for fills of all types on the active side of such structures, including gravity retaining walls; for fills on the passive side, higher compactive efforts can be applied (strength of the structure permitting), but the possibility of heave occurring with low water content cohesive fills placed at high compactive effort should be borne in mind (see also Section 10.6.3). Depending upon construction sequence, propped retaining walls are likely to be less sensitive to compaction method.

8.3.4 Initial water content
General

Clay fill presents most problems because of the possibility of either collapse settlement or heave. Initial water content must be considered in the light of the compactive effort and the confining pressure. The relationship between these three factors was discussed in Section 3.5.1. Construction difficulties such as over-compaction, mattressing and formation of construction shear surface must also be avoided (see Section 3.4).

Confining pressure depends upon the overall design of the structure (e.g., the height of the embankment or the depth of the excavation to be backfilled) and is something over which the geotechnical engineer normally has little control. However, there may be some room for manoeuvre with compactive effort and initial water content because they can often be manipulated to give the best engineered fill for the purpose. An additional aid is the possibility of stabilization.

Collapse settlement

Collapse settlement may be a problem for cohesive fill (and some weak rocks) placed dry of optimum, which has been relatively lightly compacted and which exists under high confining pressures (Fig. 3.7(a)). For settlement sensitive structures and where there is a chance that cohesive fill will be inundated during operation, an initial water content slightly wet of optimum is suggested. Together with a relatively high compactive effort, collapse settlement should then be reduced or avoided. Situations in which this approach may be appropriate include those where relatively high confining pressures exist, such as:

- deep backfilled excavations in which a water table may rise-up into the base of the fill
- the basal layers of high embankments in low-lying terrains, where flooding is possible
- high embankments on side-long ground, where there is a possibility of inundation by ponding on the uphill side
- where failure of drainage installations could flood the fill.

Heave

Heave may occur with cohesive fill which has been heavily compacted dry of optimum and which exists at low confining pressures (Fig. 3.7(b)). If heave is to be reduced or avoided, an initial water content slightly wet of optimum is suggested but with only moderate compactive effort. Situations in which this approach could be adopted include those where relatively low confining pressures exist; they include:

- fill supporting porches, garages, extensions and other lightly loaded structures
- fill placed to support floating floor slabs

- fill placed around the outside of structures to form pathways
- top layers of fill behind pre-cast concrete elements, gabions or cribbed walling
- where failure of drainage installations could flood the top layers of the fill.

In all cases, collapse settlement and swell tests (BS 1377: 1990: Part 5: Test 4) should be conducted on representative samples.

8.3.5 Stabilization processes

Whether or not treatment is adopted depends upon how wet the initial water content is with respect to optimum, because it determines the strength and compressibility characteristics so important to the serviceability limit state. For particularly wet cohesive fills, addition of lime may be necessary to permit trafficking during construction and the avoidance of the pitfalls referred to in Section 3.4.

Comments on the lime stabilization process are given in Section 10.5.2.

8.4 Design and control testing

8.4.1 General

For a material of a given particle size, there are five principal test methods adopted in the design of engineered fills: the compaction test, the undrained shear strength or laboratory vane test, the Moisture Condition Value (MCV), the California Bearing Ratio (CBR) and the permeability test. Each method provides engineering properties which permit predictions of the likely engineering performance of the fill in the permanent works condition and may therefore be used for design. The tests can also be employed to set limits on the property or range of properties acceptable for the given fill and the engineering problem in hand.

Control testing is of equal importance. It requires that the fill, when placed, be tested *in situ* to check that the properties selected during design are being obtained on site. For all but the compaction test, control testing is performed using the same type of test as adopted during design; for the compaction test, control uses *in situ* dry density and water content determinations. For some projects, where heavy loads are expected, or where substantial vibrations may occur in-service, such as earthworks for high speed rail, design and construction control may be appropriate using the deformation modulus; this could apply both to the sub-grade or to the overlying formation. In such cases, construction control would be performed using *in situ* plate loading tests. See also the *International Union of Railways Design Code* (1994).

A description of design and control tests is given in Sections 8.4.3 to 8.4.8). The advantages and disadvantages of these tests are summarized in Table 8.1, where the BS 1377: 1990 Part and Test numbers are also given. A practical point often overlooked is the speed at which tests can be done and

Table 8.1 Advantages and disadvantages of various engineering properties for design, acceptability and control testing of fills. Figures in brackets refer to the Part and Test numbers of BS 1377: 1990 (adapted from Trenter, 1999), reproduced by kind permission from CIRIA

Property	Design and acceptability		Control	
	For	*Against*	*For*	*Against*
Particle size (2:9)	Governing factor in performance of fills		As *Design and acceptability*	Test lengthy to perform and equipment cumbersome
Water content with respect to plastic limit (2:3.2, 2:5.3)	Properties easily measured	Precision* of plastic limit test low	As *Design and acceptability*	As *Design and acceptability*
Optimum water content and maximum dry density (4:3.3 to 4:3.7)	Properties fundamental to engineering performance Particle size up to 20 mm tested**	Time taken for compaction test performance (usually much in excess of 24 hours)	Equipment for control tests accommodated in mobile site laboratory	Accuracy of density values from sand replacement tests questioned (Parsons, 1992)
Moisture Condition Value (4:5.4 to 4:5.6)	Particle size up to 20 mm tested	Not readily related to fundamental engineering properties	Equipment accommodated in mobile site laboratory; speed of use	As *Design and acceptability*
CBR value (4:7)	Property frequently used for pavement design Particle size up to 20 mm tested**	Not readily related to fundamental engineering properties apart from empirical correlations	As *Design and acceptability*	As *Design and acceptability*
Undrained triaxial shear strength (7:8)	Fundamental to trafficability and to bearing capacity of fills Water content and bulk density obtained from test specimen	Not readily related to OWC and MDD	As *Design and acceptability*	38 mm test specimens too small for many fills containing gravel; 100 mm test specimens require expensive equipment for testing and sample extraction
Unconfined compressive strength (7:7)	As for *Undrained triaxial shear strength*	As for *Undrained triaxial shear strength*	Much lighter and more portable than the undrained triaxial device	38 mm test specimen only: too small for many fills containing gravel
Hand vane (7:3) as an alternative undrained shear strength test (see text)	As for *Undrained triaxial shear strength*	As for *Undrained triaxial shear strength*	Light weight, small and easily transportable	Only for clay fill containing little or no coarse sand or gravel

Table 8.1 Continued

Permeability tests (5:5, 6:4, 6:6)	Fundamental to the design of landfill liners, dam cores and other impermeable earth structures; wide variety of test types available including some in situ (see text)	Wide range of application (See Table 8.3)	As *Design and acceptability*	Tests too complex and time consuming for routine site use; best to correlate with results of other test types at the design stage (see text)

* Precision is defined in ISO 5725 Part 1 (1994)
** Up to 37.5 mm particle size can be catered for in some circumstances (See Section 2.6.1)

NB: for water content and plastic limit determinations, measurements are made on the fraction of the sample finer than the 425 μm sieve and the results may not be representative of the whole sample.

the results reported. It is of major importance with control testing because results requiring more than 24 hours to obtain may not assist the control function. This should be borne in mind in selecting the test type and also the size of test laboratory, because they will both govern the throughput of results.

8.4.2 Setting design and control limits

Design and construction control limits have to be set for the various tests described. For example, if the compaction test is selected (see Section 8.4.3), limits are normally placed on the water content of the fill, especially cohesive fill. Likewise, if the shear strength approach is employed (see Section 8.4.4), shear strength values (usually a mean value together with a range about the mean) are quoted. In setting limits, the engineer must consider:

- the design requirements, as discussed in Section 8.3
- the relevant geotechnical properties of the fill at the cutting or borrow sites. There is no point in selecting design water contents if the potential fill cannot realistically be expected to provide them, even with extensive (and expensive) conditioning
- the likely weather conditions when the fill is to be placed, and construction aspects such as under- and over-compaction, mattressing and the like (see Section 3.4).

If the approach illustrated in Fig. 8.1 is employed, then the design requirement will have been set by reference to the properties defined by the area of the diagram selected. It is then necessary to check that fill having these properties is suitable for trafficking: this may be done by relationship testing (see Section 8.4.8).

For foundations, Simons and Menzies (1977) suggest that shear strength results should not deviate by more than 50 per cent from a conservatively assessed mean value over a depth equivalent to at least two thirds of the foundation width below the underside of the foundation. The mean shear strength will be determined during design; control testing should ensure that this mean is met over the above quoted depth, and that the control test results do not deviate by more than 50 per cent from this design mean value.

8.4.3 Compaction test

The traditional approach to the design of engineered fill is the compaction test, either the BS 2.5 or the 4.5 kg rammer method. It may be employed for all types of structure. For the given compactive effort and fill specific gravity, the test provides the following information:

- the air voids content of the compacted soil at any dry density or water content
- the variation of dry density with water content for the soil being tested.

Air voids

As noted elsewhere, a low air voids content (high degree of saturation) usually secures a stable fill. However, air voids content cannot be employed on its own for design and control purposes; a water content limit must also be specified, otherwise unsatisfactorily wet (or dry) fills could result.

When the design air voids content has been selected, it can be controlled during construction together with the water content range using dry densities and water contents measured *in situ*. A specific gravity of 2.7 can often be assumed for British conditions (but see below). In these circumstances, equation 2.5 given in Section 2.2, becomes:

$$A_v = \left(1 - \frac{\rho_d}{2.7}[1 + 2.7w]\right) \tag{8.1}$$

where ρ_d is the measured dry density (Mg/m^3) and w is the water content.

Air voids measured in this way can be used with the suggested levels of compactive effort illustrated in Fig. 8.1.

In practice, the air voids content can be a difficult property to measure because of the variation in specific gravity exhibited by some materials. As noted in Section 6.2, coal content can vary substantially in colliery discards, with a scatter of specific gravity results as a consequence; similar variations can also occur in chalk. Great care should be taken to obtain representative results. Tests on several specimens from each sample may be needed.

Dry density

An alternative to the design and control approach given in Section 8.3.3 is to express dry density as a percentage of the average maximum dry density measured at the investigation stage. Either the BS 2.5 or 4.5 kg rammer method is adopted, depending upon the nature of the problem. For example, if the average maximum dry density of a particular fill type has been established using the 2.5 kg rammer method, the control value will be quoted as say 95 per cent of this figure. This approach is often termed the 'relative dry density' or 'relative compaction density' to distinguish it from the 'relative density' used in another context (see Section 4.3.3).

The disadvantage of this approach is that by specifying a relative compaction density, the designer gives no indication of the air voids content: a figure of 95 per cent average maximum dry density can be obtained for fills compacted both dry and wet of optimum water content; for the former case, the air voids content could be unsatisfactorily high for the problem in hand, while for the latter, it could be unnecessarily low. Although a popular method, because of its simplicity, designing in terms of relative dry density has this distinct disadvantage which should be remembered.

Another disadvantage of the compaction test when used as a control is the time taken for its performance. Depending upon the resources of the testing laboratory, throughput can be slow. This may not be a problem during the design stage, but could be serious during construction. An example could be where the soil types at the borrow were variable, requiring back-up testing during fill placement or where conditions at the borrow proved to be significantly different from those expected on the basis of site investigation information. This should be taken into consideration when deciding upon the design and control approach.

Control requires use of *in situ* dry density methods, such as sand-replacement test for fine to medium grained soil (BS 1377: 1990: Part 9: Test 2.2); water replacement test suitable for coarse grained soil (BS 1377: 1990: Part 9: Test 2.3); or the core-cutter method for clay soil (BS 1377: 1990: Part 9: Test 2.4). An account of the various tests is given in *Soil Mechanics for Road Engineers* (1951). Note that tests conducted on the current layer may give unrepresentatively low results because of disturbance by the compaction equipment; for this reason, some engineers favour testing the previous layer which will have been recompacted during placing and compacting the current layer. For rapid *in situ* density control, use may be also made of a properly calibrated nuclear density gauge (BS 1377: 1990: Part 9: Test 2.5; Parsons, 1992; *The Highways Agency Advice Note* HA 70/94). If a nuclear density device is to be employed with colliery discard, the variation in coal content may affect its calibration (Hird *et al.*, 1998). Similar variations may be expected with chalk. Calibration checks seem essential before any earthworks contract where nuclear density gauges are to be adopted; they are best done during compaction trials (see Section 8.5).

In situ density tests also permit water content determinations on the material excavated in forming the test hole; consideration may be given to using a microwave oven for quick water content determinations, although calibration with properly conducted oven water content tests is essential.

8.4.4 Undrained shear strength test
Stability of embankment fill
Factors affecting the undrained shear strength of clay fill were described in Section 3.3.2. Use of the total stress approach (with undrained shear strengths) in embankment stability analysis is commented on in Section 12.4.

Placement control
Undrained shear strength may be employed to control fill placement. Control strengths selected for six embankment dams are given in Table 8.2, where other relevant information is also provided.

Table 8.2 Undrained triaxial strengths selected for fill control purposes

Embankment Dam (fill type)	Undrained shear strength range (kN/m²)	Other requirements
Cow Green (1) (clay till)	48–110	66 per cent of results to fall within stated strength range
Bewl Bridge (2) (Wadhurst clay)	55–110	80 per cent of results to fall within stated strength range (dry density > 95 per cent of MDD by BS 2.5 kg rammer method)
Ardingley (2) (Wadhurst clay)	60–100	70 per cent of results to fall within stated strength range (dry density > 98 per cent of MDD by BS 2.5 kg rammer method)
Cadney Carrs (2) (Oxford clay)	45–110	66 per cent of results obtained fell within the stated strength range (dry density > 97 per cent of MDD by BS 2.5 kg rammer method)
Kielder (3) (clay till core)	60–140	mean measured strength was 105 kN/m² and measured dry density was 100 per cent of MDD by BS 2.5 kg rammer method
Empingham (4) Upper Lias clay core	60–90	45 per cent of results obtained fell within the stated range; mean strength obtained was 75 kN/m²

(1) Vaughan *et al.* (1975); (2) Kennard *et al.* (1978); (3) Millmore and McNicol (1983); (4) Vaughan (1978b)

For the Bewl Bridge dam, the running mean was to fall within the range from 70 to $100 \, kN/m^2$ and for Ardingley, the running average of five consecutive tests was to lie within the range from 70 to $90 \, kN/m^2$. Triaxial testing at Kielder was supplemented by 250 mm diameter plate tests using plant as reaction; checks were also made using hand vane and pocket penetrometers, together with checks on rutting depths.

In all cases, use of the undrained triaxial test as a control was reported as being successful, with the stated strength ranges (and running averages where quoted) being met. It is interesting to note that for the materials tested, the strength ranges quoted corresponded to between 95 and 100 per cent of MDD (maximum dry density) as measured by the BS 2.5 kg rammer compaction test.

Clay fill foundations

A test measuring the fill's undrained shear strength appears an obvious choice when designing and controlling clay fill to support structures. A design shear strength is selected which is considered appropriate for the structure in question; for example, if a foundation is being designed to an allowable bearing pressure of $100 \, kN/m^2$, the required undrained shear strength may be calculated for the foundation depth and geometry. Laboratory tests on remoulded samples of the selected fill are conducted to determine the water content and density to which the fill should be placed to obtain the necessary shear strength.

In accordance with convention, bearing capacity failure is considered to occur undrained and so unconsolidated undrained shear strength tests are suggested. In British conditions, the fill will invariably become saturated over the long term so it may be wise to saturate and soften the specimen by circulating water through it prior to undrained shear, in the manner described by Bishop and Henkel (1962) for effective stress tests on compacted clay samples (see Section 12.3.2). This may lead to a more realistic long term measure of the undrained shear strength for design purposes. See also the discussion on selecting clay fill water contents in Section 12.3.2.

Methods of testing and sampling

Use of the undrained triaxial test machine requires access either to a commercial testing laboratory or to a reasonably sophisticated laboratory on site, equipped with electric power facilities. For clay fill containing little or no coarse sand or gravel, 38 mm diameter tube samples may be extracted using man-handled equipment. For clay fill with a significant granular content, including coarse gravel, a percussion boring rig capable of extracting 100 mm diameter tube samples will be necessary. All these factors increase expense. Some smaller sites may be controlled on the basis of the unconfined compression test machine (38 mm diameter test specimen), which is small, light and robust and which requires no electric power. However, it is less accurate than the undrained triaxial test and the other limitations still remain with respect to sampling the fill for control purposes.

Substantially quicker and cheaper than the undrained triaxial test is the laboratory vane. This test measures the undrained shear strength by means of a small (typically 12.7 by 12.7 mm) cruciform vane which is inserted into the remoulded test specimen. The equipment comprises a stout frame which supports the rod carrying the cruciform vane assembly, together with a base plate on to which the specimen container is fixed. Although commonly referred to as the 'laboratory' vane test, it is compact and reasonably light, is quick to perform, and may be used in the back of an all-terrain vehicle because no electric power is needed in its operation. From this point of view, it is a good control test, although less accurate than the undrained triaxial test. It can only be employed with clay fill, containing little or no coarse sand or any gravel.

Correlations between the results of laboratory vane and undrained triaxial tests may be necessary, because it is unlikely that there will be a one-to-one correspondence between the results of the two test types.

8.4.5 Moisture Condition Value test

The Moisture Condition Value test equipment (also known as the Moisture Condition Apparatus) is reasonably light and portable, requiring no electric power for its operation, and may be operated from the back of an all-terrain vehicle. Unlike the undrained shear strength test, which can be used on only a few cohesive fill types, the MCV can be performed on a wide range of materials illustrated in Fig. 8.2. This, together with its portability and speed of operation makes it a good test for control purposes.

There is no direct correlation between MCV value and the other commonly adopted engineering properties like dry density or shear strength. Such correlations may be made with the results of compaction, strength and CBR tests using relationship testing (see Section 8.4.8).

Cobbe and Threadgold (1988) noted that the MCV test was in effect a compaction test but, unlike the BS rammer versions already described, where maximum dry density is defined in terms of a certain level of compactive effort, the MCV is defined in terms of compaction to refusal. They suggested that the MCV could be employed as a rapid alternative to the compaction test (2.5 kg rammer method), with the drop height of the rammer increased to provide a wider range of water contents over which the test would be applicable. The advantage claimed was a speedy measure of the air voids content of the fill under test, thus permitting ready modification to plant operations. Further details are given in Cobbe and Threadgold (1988).

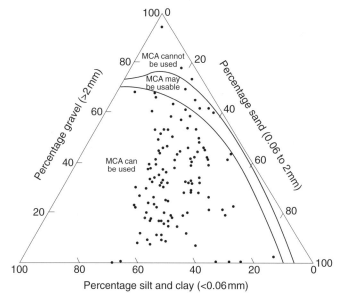

Fig. 8.2 Applicability of Moisture Condition Value (MCV) test (from Winter *et al.*, 1998)

8.4.6 *California Bearing Ratio test*

The CBR test has been widely used in the past and often forms the basis of pavement design. For this reason, it finds favour with some as a design and control method. Design testing is usually undertaken in the laboratory where the CBR can be measured for a variety of dry densities and also 'soaked' or 'unsoaked', corresponding to the groundwater or drainage conditions foreseen. Surcharges can be added to simulate the effect of construction thicknesses. Once a design CBR has been established, it can be controlled in the field either by sampling the placed fill and testing at the site laboratory using CBR equipment, or by adopting in situ CBR procedures. In the latter case, the absence of containment during testing can affect the outcome of tests on granular soils. A useful discussion on the CBR test (with respect to pavement design) is given in *The Highways Agency Advisory Note* HA 44/91.

Like the MCV, the CBR test is empirical but can roughly be related to undrained shear strength using (Black and Lister, 1978):

$$c_u = 23 \times \text{ CBR (kN/m}^2) \tag{8.2}$$

where c_u is the undrained shear strength and CBR is the CBR value. Direct relationships may be established with shear strength and dry density via relationship testing, should this be desired (see Section 8.4.8).

Some engineers believe that the CBR test is probably best used for pavement design and construction control rather than for general earthworks engineering.

8.4.7 Permeability test

Landfill liners should reduce the uncontrolled egress of leachate formed within the landfill to the smallest possible quantity. Flow of leachate through the liner is one of the predominant processes of transfer, so the design and construction control of clay liners using permeability criteria is an obvious choice. There are two principal approaches:

- use of *in situ* test methods such as shallow ponds and the sealed double ring infiltrometer (SDRI)
- use of laboratory test methods, including the permeameter, the triaxial cell, the oedometer and the hydraulic or Rowe cell.

Shallow ponds have been used for measuring the *in situ* permeability of clay liners (e.g. Elsbury *et al.*, 1990). The liner is constructed using methods appropriate to full-scale work and an area is bunded off where under-drains were installed prior to liner construction (the test pad). Water is introduced under controlled conditions, usually for a period of days or weeks depending upon clay liner permeability, and the permeability k(m/s) is calculated using the expression:

$$Q = kiA \ (\text{m}^3/\text{s}) \tag{8.3}$$

where Q is the total quantity of water passing through the liner per unit of time; i is the hydraulic gradient, and A (m^2) is the area of the test section. For low permeability materials, evapo-transpiration effects could be significant and suitable protection for the ponded area may have to be provided.

The sealed double ring infiltrometer is an American Society for Testing and Materials (ASTM) test (D5093-90: 1997) to which reference should be made for full details. Essentially, the infiltrometer comprises a sealed inner and an outer ring grouted into the material to be measured. Normally, this is part of the liner (the test pad) which has been placed and compacted to the intended specification. The sealed inner ring is connected to a flexible water bag which allows water to flow downwards into the test pad. The water bag is weighed before and after each test and the flow Q per unit time calculated. Permeability may then be determined using equation 8.3, where A is the area inside the inner ring. The sealed outer ring's function is to provide a reservoir of water to flow downwards into the test pad at the same time as that from the sealed inner ring, thus ensuring one-dimensional flow for the latter. According to the ASTM, the test is suitable for materials having infiltration rates in the range from 10^{-7} to 10^{-9} m/s.

The alternative approach to *in situ* test methods are the laboratory tests quoted above, of which the fixed wall permeameter (falling head) and the flexible wall triaxial cell (constant or falling head) are the most popular (Murray, 1998). The former equipment is cheap, relatively simple and should be suitable for testing remoulded samples at the design stage. However, there may be leakage of permeant around the sides of a test specimen extracted from the liner during construction control, with inaccurate results as a consequence. This problem is avoided in the flexible wall triaxial cell, where the test specimen is enclosed in a membrane, and the specimen may be consolidated to an effective stress appropriate to that in the field. If constant head procedures are employed, the test duration is far longer than for the fixed wall permeameter. It also requires much more sophisticated laboratory facilities which, although presenting no problems to most commercial laboratories for testing at the design stage, would seldom be found on the majority of construction sites.

The advantages and disadvantages of the commonly used permeability test methods are summarized in Table 8.3.

Table 8.3   Advantages and disadvantages of commonly used permeability tests (figures in brackets refer to the Part and Test numbers of BS 1377: 1990)

Type of test	Advantages	Disadvantages
Falling head fixed wall permeameter (*test specimens remoulded in the permeameter*) (5:5)	Equipment cheap and relatively easy to employ. Suitable for site test duration relatively short. Can be used as a constant head test although test duration lengthened	Test specimen cannot be consolidated to expected *in situ* effective stress
Falling head fixed wall permeameter (*test specimen cut from a tube sample or directly from the lining*) (5:5)	As above	As above. Also permeant may leak between the sides of the specimen and the sides of the permeameter
Constant head flexible wall (*undisturbed or remoulded test specimen*) (6:6)	Test specimen can be consolidated to expected *in-situ* effective stress. Test specimen may be back-pressured to induce saturation	Equipment expensive, complicated to set up and to use. Not suitable for most sites. Test duration long

An issue in permeability testing for landfill liners and other geotechnical structures, not yet resolved, is the question of hydraulic gradient. Often in laboratory tests it can be greater than 30 but in the field less than 2 (Edelmann *et al.*, 1999). The effect that this difference has on predictions of permeability and erosion made on the basis of laboratory tests is not clear but experience to-date suggests that it may not be critical. Nevertheless, it is a strong argument for the use of *in situ* test methods whenever possible.

An approach to the whole issue of design and control for landfill liners would be to employ the more complex test procedures (including field tests) during design and to correlate the results with simpler and more rapid test methods for construction control. Thus comprehensive laboratory studies, preferably using the flexible wall triaxial equipment, could be conducted on various remoulded samples to determine the water content and the dry density at which the desired permeability (usually less than 10^{-9} m/s in the UK) is obtained. These values would be plotted (area PQRS in Fig. 8.3). Dry density and water content determinations may then be employed as a control in the field, to show that the results fall within the desired area. This approach is similar in principle to the one given in Fig. 8.1.

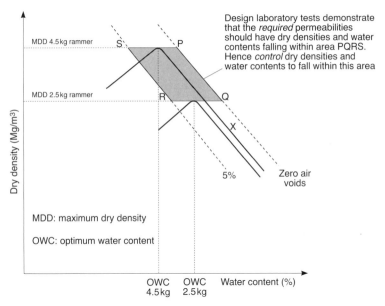

Fig. 8.3 Design and control approach for landfill liners

Note that the upper limit for the water content is likely to correspond to that controlling trafficability and, for sloping landfill liners, stability (see Sections 3.4 and 3.6).

A good discussion on testing for clay liners is given by Murray (1998).

8.4.8 *Relationship testing*

Relationship testing is the performance of several different tests on the same fill to measure several different engineering properties, with each test conducted at a number of different water contents. Using such a test programme, it is possible to correlate the results of the various different tests and to determine directly what, for example, a particular MCV value means in density, strength or CBR terms. It is particularly useful in determining how responsive a certain test type is for a given soil. For example, the MCV test is not generally used for granular soils (Fig. 8.2) and relationship testing may help to disclose the granular content at which the test loses efficacy.

This kind of testing is popular for new fills: compaction tests are performed to measure the variation of dry density with water content and the air voids relationships; undrained shear strength tests are made on the same fill to measure the variation of strength with water content; and MCV and CBR determinations may also be made on the same fill for varying water contents. The results, plotted on the same graph, permit the designer to correlate the various engineering properties and to select a design value. In selecting the test range, the engineer will be guided by the initial water content at the borrow and the likely site weather conditions. In upland areas, a concentration on soil wetter than initial water content would be reasonable. Testing should always explore the extremes: say between about 40 and 150 kN/m² in undrained shear strength terms. These strengths could constitute the approximate limits at which clay fill may be trafficked and compacted, respectively.

An example of this approach is given in Fig. 8.4. A useful discussion on relationship testing, including a sample test package, is given in *The Highways Agency, Advice Note* HA 44/91.

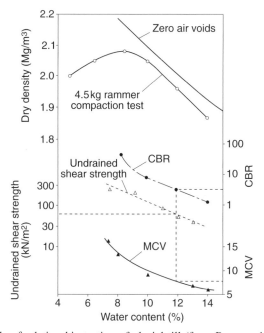

Fig. 8.4 Example of relationship testing of glacial till (from Parsons, 1992)

8.5 Compaction trials

8.5.1 General

Compaction trials are essential, particularly where sensitive or heavily loaded structures are to be placed on the fill or a landfill liner is to be constructed. They apply to all methods of design and control; indeed, they should be considered an extension to design in that they enable details of layer thickness, placement water content, plant type and number of passes to be finalized for the fill(s) under consideration. Compaction trials also provide information on the suitability of the testing procedures selected for the main works contract. For this reason, contract documents should be written to permit the compaction trials to proceed before main works fill operations, and to permit changes in procedure (if necessary) on the basis of the trial results.

It is often thought that compaction trials are designed to investigate the performance of compaction plant only, but the performance of the construction plant placing, spreading and dozing the fill can also be investigated. This is particularly important with weak rocks, such as mudstones, sandstones, the weaker limestones and chalks, and the stiffer overconsolidated clays. Compaction trials provide an opportunity to determine the extent to which different construction plant breaks down the fill to produce a well-graded material with good compaction properties.

Compaction trials also provide an excellent opportunity to test methods of conditioning soils and weak rocks (see Section 10.5). Chalk, for example, when placed wet, may require time to harden before compaction and before the next layer can be placed (see Section 5.3.3). This essential information can be established during the trials and under controlled conditions.

8.5.2 Method of approach

Two or more strips of ground should be cleared of topsoil which are wide enough to take the full width of the compaction plant and are sufficiently long to enable the plant to be manoeuvred into position and to reach its operating speed; a length of some 30 to 40 m is often found suitable, but the precise length selected will depend upon the size and speed of the plant and the space available. The width adopted should allow for the fact that during a comprehensive series of trials, at least 8 layers will have been placed raising the fill height to some one or 1.5 m above ground level; at a side slope of 1(vertical) in 1(horizontal); this would increase the width of the strip by at least one metre either side.

In some cases, the natural ground may be stiffer and more resilient than a large thickness of fill and a layer of fill placed and compacted directly upon it will yield higher density or strength values than if placed on fill alone. Consequently, where these conditions occur, at least three layers of fill should be placed and compacted before testing begins in order to obtain reasonably representative results. The first layer to be tested will usually be placed at the water content at the cutting or borrow pit from which the fill is to be sourced. The material should be compacted using the plant selected for the main works construction, placed in different layer thicknesses and control tested after various numbers of passes. At this stage, the results of the control tests could be reviewed and the optimum number of passes selected.

At the same time as these compaction trials are underway, trials could proceed on the other strip at an increased (or decreased) water content. The compaction trials should provide a good opportunity to determine the feasibility of conditioning by wetting (or drying): as noted elsewhere, adding water in such a way that the whole fill receives water in equal amounts can be difficult, if not impossible, for most stiff overconsolidated clays; likewise, conditioning by most of the methods, apart from the rotovator mentioned in Section 10.5, can be particularly weather dependent.

After three different layer thicknesses have been tested together with different placement water contents, the performance of the compaction plant can be reviewed and other equipment substituted. If two or more sources of fill are in contention, then more than two strips may be necessary, if the trials are to be completed in good time.

8.6 Control test frequency

A matter of importance to the successful outcome of a project is the frequency of control testing, i.e. the number of control test to be performed to ensure that the specification is being met. Control test frequency depends upon several factors:

- the volume of fill placed and the nature of the structure
- the uniformity of the fill, e.g. whether just one soil (or rock) type or several, and whether the material type(s) are uniform in themselves
- the outcome of the compaction trials, i.e. whether or not generally consistent control test results were achieved; the wider the spread of results during the trials, the more tests should be performed during main works construction
- the progress of the main works compaction itself.

Small volumes of fill often mean small sites, with much manoeuvring of the plant (which can disturb finished work) and difficulty in achieving a production line approach. Relatively more control tests than for large volumes are therefore warranted. Trenter and Charles (1996) suggested guidelines for the minimum control test frequency for fills supporting low rise housing, illustrated in Fig. 8.5: for larger sites of say $100\,000\,\mathrm{m}^3$ fill volume or above, control testing was suggested at the rate of about 2 per $1000\,\mathrm{m}^3$ of fill placed; for smaller volumes, the control testing rate was suggested at about 5 per $1000\,\mathrm{m}^3$.

The guidelines illustrated in Fig. 8.5 should be regarded as preliminary and much dependent upon the factors described above. Fill for a high speed

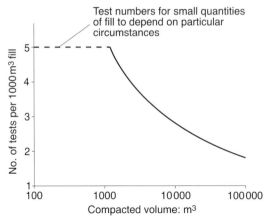

Fig. 8.5 Guidelines for minimum control test frequency (from Trenter and Charles, 1996). Proceedings of the Institution of Civil Engineers, Geotechnical Engineering, 119

railway embankment would demand more control than that for a corresponding road embankment and fill supporting residential buildings (typically with large fenestrated areas) might demand more than both. If a particularly heterogeneous fill were being produced at the cutting or at the borrow pit, the control test rate should be significantly increased, as it should if standards of workmanship on site were unimpressive. Likewise, for landfill sites, where maintaining strict permeability criteria were essential, a significantly enhanced control rate might also be necessary.

Suggested test frequencies for classification and acceptability testing for earthworks constructed under the *Specification for Highway Works* (1998) is given in Table 3.1 of *The Highways Agency Advice Note* HA 44/91. In this advice note, some tests are recommended on a daily or weekly basis (i.e. are independent of fill volume), whereas others are recommended per stated volume of fill.

8.7   Earthworks monitoring
8.7.1   General
Earthworks monitoring checks the performance of the fill during or post-filling, depending upon the design of the equipment. Normally, the engineering quantities measured are fill settlement or groundwater level, since both may have significant effects on performance. Thus if the specification required a certain maximum settlement after embankment construction, post-filling settlement monitoring would indicate whether or not settlement was within the stated limits. Hence monitoring is a control on the engineering performance of the fill platform.

Monitoring should be regarded as essential for sensitive structures and where groundwater rise within the fill is a possibility (see Sections 3.5.1 and 4.5.3). The techniques available include:

- surface levelling stations (monuments) to measure settlement of the fill surface (post-filling)
- settlement plates (rod extensometers) to measure the settlement of the fill thickness (during and post-filling)
- magnetic extensometers to measure the settlement at incremental depths of the fill (during and post-filling)
- USBR settlement gauges (during and post-filling)
- piezometers to measure the water level in the fill (post-filling).

Instrument readings should be made for as long as possible after construction, if necessary during commissioning the structure. In practice, except for large sites, it is difficult for continuous monitoring to extend beyond a year or so but, for sensitive structures, it is vitally important that measurements should be obtained during at least one wet season. If collapse settlement is occurring, due to inundation, some indication may be obtained during this period.

8.7.2   Surface levelling station (monument)

Such stations should be positioned as soon as an area of fill has been brought up to finished level. This will mean that the maximum time will be available for settlement readings, noting that, for obvious reasons, none can be made using this form of equipment during fill placement itself. Because of the heavy plant frequenting construction sites, a surface levelling station (illustrated in Fig. 8.6) should be robust, comprising a concrete block about 1 m³ in size, sunk about 300 mm into the fill surface; a metal stud should be cast into the top, from which optical levelling may be conducted. Readings will give the total settlement of the fill and that of the underlying soils, if they were not removed prior to filling.

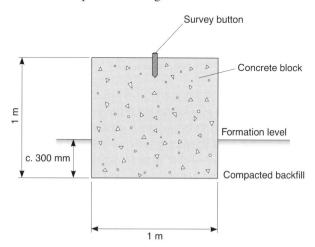

Fig. 8.6   Example of surface levelling station for measuring fill surface settlement

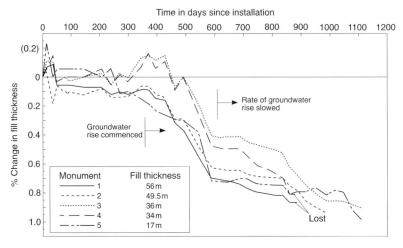

Fig. 8.7 Collapse settlement due to rising groundwater table in open-cast fill (from Trenter, 1993). Proceedings of the Conference on Engineered Fills

Fig. 8.7 illustrates settlement with time of open-cast fill, comprising Coal Measures mudstones, siltstones and subordinate sandstones at a site in the English Midlands (Trenter, 1993). Settlements obtained from readings of the various surface levelling stations are expressed as a percentage of the original fill thickness. Significant settlement commenced as the water table began to rise up in the fill, as evidenced by standpipe readings.

For more accurate measurements appropriate to sensitive structures, Hanna (1985) or Dunnicliff (1988) should be consulted.

8.7.3 Settlement plate (rod extensometer)

Unless the natural ground is stiff and will not deform significantly under fill (and structure) load, surface levelling stations measure settlement of the underlying soils as well as the settlement of the fill. This is a problem where the natural ground is soft and where the settlement of the soil beneath the fill could represent a significant proportion of the total settlement at the fill surface. In cases such as these, settlement plates (rod extensometers) may be employed. They monitor fill settlement continuously during and after placement and not from completion of filling only.

Settlement plates comprise a base plate, usually of the order of one metre diameter, on to which a suitable length of casing is welded. The base plate is placed on to the natural ground surface with the casing upstanding and fill carefully placed and compacted around it, during filling works. If it is necessary to extend the casing vertically upwards in order to cope with greater fill thicknesses, additional casing lengths may be welded or screwed on. From time to time, a rod of known length is introduced into the casing from the surface to the base plate and a reading of the settlement of the underlying natural ground is taken by levelling the top of the rod. The surface of the fill, say 2 m from the casing, is levelled at the same time at say four positions (N, S, E and W) and the results averaged. The difference between the settlement of the underlying natural ground and the fill surface is the settlement of the fill. Settlements may be measured at different times during and after filling and a graph plotted showing settlement against time.

Friction between the fill and the casing means that the fill can hang-up on the casing, so that the settlement at the surface close to the casing may be less than the true value. To avoid this undesirable feature, readings of the fill surface should not be taken too close to the casing. Care should also be taken to site the settlement plate on reasonably flat natural ground beneath the fill.

8.7.4 Magnetic extensometer

This equipment is often employed where, for example, the compressibility of one fill type is being compared with the compressibility of another, or where it is necessary to separate the settlement of the fill from that of the underlying soil upon which the fill is placed. Magnets are located in the fill about a central plastic tube grouted into a borehole sunk to hard ground beneath the fill. A probe lowered down the tube locates the magnets and measures their position with respect to the base of the borehole (presumed fixed). Results of the settlements recorded by a magnetic extensometer installed at the site referred to in Section 8.7.2 are illustrated in Fig. 8.8, where the settlements are recorded as percentage change in fill thickness.

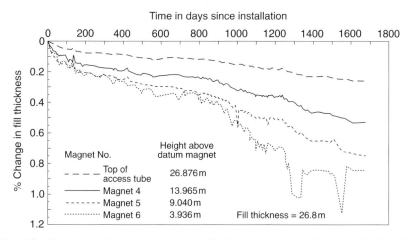

Fig. 8.8 Percentage change in open-cast fill thickness v. time for borehole installed magnetic extensometer (from Trenter, 1993). Proceedings of the Conference on Engineered Fills

A device which can be built up from the base of the fill, along the lines of the settlement plate and USBR gauge (described in the next section) is also available. It therefore has the distinct advantage over the surface levelling station in monitoring fill settlement continuously during and after placement and not from completion of filling only.

8.7.5   USBR settlement gauge

The USBR settlement gauge (United States Bureau of Reclamation Manual, 1974) comprises a series of cross-arms mounted on central steel-pipe sections, each cross-arm being separated by standard length spacers. The basal pipe section is grouted into hard ground beneath the fill (presumed fixed) and further sections added at a rate consistent with the rate of fill being deposited. Settlements of the various cross-arms are measured by a torpedo unit lowered down the central pipe sections. Unlike the settlement plate which provides the total fill settlement, the USBR gauge indicates the settlement of the fill at each cross-arm location. In this respect, the device compares with the magnetic extensometer.

Results obtained from a USBR gauge installed in 59 m of the open-cast fill referred to in Section 8.7.2 are given in Fig. 8.9. Settlements of each cross-arm (expressed as percentage change in fill thickness) are plotted against fill thickness to a log scale and an approximately linear relationship results. There is some scatter about the trend line but this should be expected given the variable nature of the open-cast fill concerned.

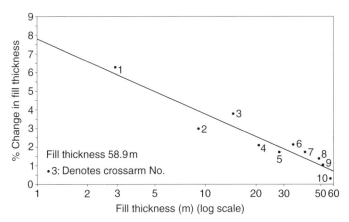

Fig. 8.9 Results of USBR settlement gauge: percentage change in open-cast fill thickness at cross-arm locations (from Trenter, 1993). Proceedings of the Conference on Engineered Fills

8.7.6   Piezometer

A piezometer (preferably a porous ceramic pot, equipped with granular surround) provides a direct indication of the water level at the location installed. Dipped at the same intervals at which settlement readings are recorded it provides direct evidence of any link between settlement and water rising in the fill (Fig. 8.7 is an example).

Because of the importance of establishing such a link, piezometers should be positioned as close as possible to the settlement measuring device: not only does this procedure provide maximum information at the position at which settlement readings are being taken but, by ring-fencing the top of the piezometer and the settlement device, allows better protection from construction plant.

Where pore pressure measurements are desired in clay fill, hydraulic ceramic piezometers are normally employed. They require a much more sophisticated level of monitoring, with each piezometer controlled via twin nylon tubes to a manometer in an adjoining gauge hut. Unlike the Casagrande piezometer which measures positive pore pressures only, such equipment can measure both positive and negative pore pressures. Further information may be had from Hanna (1985) or Dunnicliff (1988).

9. Excavation

9.1   Introduction

Excavation is the process by which soil or rock is removed in order to reach required line and level. Material resulting from such excavation is often employed as fill for embankment or for other construction purposes on the same project. Where the material is unsuitable or insufficient, suitable fill may be excavated from specially designated areas elsewhere, often termed 'borrow pits', and the unsuitable fill run to spoil.

The nature of the soil and rock to be excavated is normally determined during the site investigation and sections are prepared showing the ground and groundwater conditions in the area concerned. Locations at which excavation will be necessary below the groundwater table should be clearly identified on the sections, as should areas of unsuitable fill. Presumed excavation characteristics of the soils and rocks can be illustrated on these section drawings, together with information relating to fill placement, suitability and control.

9.2   Soil excavation

Most soil can be excavated readily in reasonable weather and the choice of plant is based upon achieving production targets, taking into account manoeuvrability and trafficability during placement. A brief description of some plant for excavation and haulage purposes is given in Appendix 2.

9.2.1   Impact of groundwater and weather

Water can have a controlling influence on the behaviour of some soils during excavation. Granular and clay soils of high plasticity are usually more tolerant of excess water than clay soils of low to intermediate plasticities. Particular care should be taken with low plasticity soils, such as tills when wet, because they can slurry-up and become virtually unworkable. Tills often contain water-bearing granular layers or lenses, which assist the slurrying process (see Section 5.2).

All earthworks should be undertaken with the possible presence of water in mind, either as run-off from rainfall or as groundwater, and steps taken to minimise its impact. Clause 602.15 of the *Specification for Highway Works*

(1998) requires that earthworks should be kept free of water including rainwater and water 'entering the earthworks from any source', which will of course include groundwater. The same clause requires that water should be lowered, by appropriate measures, sufficient to allow the permanent works to be constructed. Clause 602.16 list actions to be taken in carrying out the requirements of Clause 602.15, which are included in Section 10.3.

9.2.2   Misidentification of rockhead in glacial terrains

In glacial terrains (see Section 5.2), it may be difficult to assess rockhead depth accurately due to the presence of large cobbles or boulders in overlying tills. Disruption and delays may occur if what was considered to be a boulder at site investigation stage is shown to be rockhead during excavation for the main works. In such cases, excavation would have to continue in rock, although excavation in soil containing cobbles and boulders had been programmed. The opposite circumstance can be just as significant: where what was considered to be bedrock at the site investigation stage is found during construction to be a boulder. This can be of particular concern for foundations, because deeper penetration may be necessary in order to secure the required load carrying capacity. Again disruption and delays may occur.

Great care is necessary when undertaking site investigations in such conditions. A minimum penetration of 3 m below presumed rockhead and careful core logging are necessary to establish the true position. This requirement may be greater, depending upon the geological relationships identified during the preliminary site investigation. Further investigation during the main works contract may be necessary to clarify the position.

Confusion over rockhead level also arises because of buried channels: rockhead reliably established at one location may be encountered at a completely different elevation a short distance away because of channelling in glacial times. Geophysical methods have been found advantageous in locating rock head on many occasions, but borehole control is always necessary.

9.3   Definition of rock
9.3.1   General

In strength terms, rock can be classified as shown in Table 9.1. Seismic wave velocities are also shown.

According to Bell (1992), the very soft and soft rock categories correspond roughly to 'easy ripping' and 'hard ripping' respectively, and therefore correspond to 'weak rock' as defined in Section 4.1. Some engineers believe that seismic velocity (shown in Table 9.1) provides only a very rough indication of rock behaviour on excavation and consequently the data shown should be treated with caution.

Table 9.1 Rock strength classification (after Bell, 1992)

Rock hardness description	Identification criteria	Unconfined compressive strength (MN/m^2)	Seismic wave velocity (m/s)
Very soft rock	Material crumbles under firm blows with a geological pick; can be peeled with a knife; pieces up to 30 mm thick can be broken by finger pressure	1.7 to 3.0	450 to 1200
Soft rock	Can just be scraped with a knife; indentations one to 3 mm produced under firm blows with a geological pick; dull sound under the hammer	3.0 to 10	1200 to 1500
Hard rock	Cannot be scraped with a knife; hand specimen can be broken with a single firm blow of a geological pick; rings under the hammer	10 to 20	1500 to 1850
Very hard rock	Hand specimen breaks after several blows of a geological pick; rings under the hammer	20 to 70	1850 to 2150
Extremely hard rock	Hand specimen breaks after many blows of a geological pick; rings under the hammer	>70	>2150

9.3.2 'Rock' in contract documents

Although 'rock' can be readily identified by most engineers and engineering geologists, there can be difficulty in framing an adequate definition of rock for contract purposes. In many contracts in the UK, rock is expected in relatively small quantities and, if so entered in the bill of quantities, attracts high rates from tendering contractors. If the bill is subsequently proved wrong and much larger volumes of rock are encountered, the employer pays disproportionately. Another potential source of difficulty is that the rock is harder or stronger than could have been foreseen at the time of tender. A reasonably correct definition of 'rock' as opposed to 'soil', together with its hardness or strength is therefore important. It is normally defined in one of the following ways (some disadvantages of the definitions follow in brackets):

- by reference to a named geological stratum or well known rock type, e.g. Old Red Sandstone or Granite. (Relating 'rock' to a named stratum or rock type can lead to arguments over correct identification; in any case, boulders in surface drift deposits requiring excavation may be of a completely different kind from those of the underlying solid rock named in the contract; this is especially the case in glacial terrains, where erratics are common)
- by reference to strength characteristics, e.g. a minimum unconfined compressive strength or a strength range. (Relating rock to an unconfined compressive strength or strength range may also be flawed because discontinuities rather than the intact rock, upon which the unconfined compressive strength is measured, may be more important in excavation terms)
- by reference to a means of excavation, e.g. by blasting or use of certain tools. (Defining rock by the tools used for excavation removes from the contractor the responsibility for using his own skill and experience in selecting a means of excavation)
- by reference to its volume, e.g. rock fragments to be of a certain size. (Relying on volume, by reference to individual masses could lead to disputes over measurement)
- by reference to designated deposits on a site plan, identified by site investigation data. (Reliance on designated deposits on a site plan, based on interpretation of rock from borehole data can be unreliable, unless a thorough site investigation is performed).

The *Method of Measurement for Highway Works* (1991), does not refer to rock, but to hard material and uses the following methods to define it:

- Material which requires the use of blasting, breakers or splitters for its removal but excluding individual masses less than $0.20\,\text{m}^3$ (i.e. by reference to means of excavation and by volume)
- those strata or deposits so designated in the contract (i.e. by reference to a named stratum).

Of the various methods discussed, the one which relies upon close characterisation of the site investigation data may be the most satisfactory if it produces a reasonable picture of the conditions relating to excavation. Boreholes, trial pits and geophysical methods are adopted to locate and describe the rock and to provide a full description of rock discontinuities. A comprehensive suite of strength determinations (unconfined compressive and point load tests) is performed to characterize the intact rock strength. This information may be employed with excavatability schemes such as that proposed by Walton and Wang (1993) or Pettifer and Fookes (1994) and discussed further below. Core samples should be made available to tendering contractors, with the borehole records alongside, so that the approach adopted by the engineering geologist responsible for logging the core can be judged by the contractors' specialists. Photographs, when used on their own, often fail to provide the same level of information as cores themselves.

Another approach might be by reference to productivity (say in m³/hour), using soil excavatability as a comparator. Here, the engineer or designer would specify rock as being that material whose removal by soil excavation methods is not considered feasible, and which demanded the appropriate plant to maintain productivity at a certain figure (say 50 per cent) of that achieved during soil excavation. This method relates rock excavation to known productivities, rather than physical attributes such as volume, type or strength, and it provides an inducement to the contractor to use its skills and experience to devise appropriate excavation methods, without specifying the tools to be adopted. However, note should be made of the substantial differences in the nature of bucket excavation between soil and rock, and the effect it could have on the 'flowability' of the material into and out of the excavator bucket. The approach also recognizes that excavation is not only about the physical break-up of the rock but is also about loading and hauling, both important parts of the excavation cycle.

Excavatability trials are as important as compaction trials (see Section 8.5). Note that contract documents should be written in such a way as to permit changes in procedure on the basis of the trial results.

9.4   Rock excavation
9.4.1   General

Excavation in rock may be accomplished by:

- direct excavation
- pre-treatment to break-up or fragment the rock
- blasting.

Under favourable conditions, rock can be excavated directly by bulldozer, back-hoe or face shovel. This is especially the case at, or close to, rockhead, where it may be significantly weathered. With decreasing weathering and with increasing rock strengths and unfavourable discontinuity patterns, pre-treatment is necessary. Such pre-treatment usually comprises ripping, using a tine attached to the rear of the bulldozer. This may break up the rock sufficiently for its removal by bulldozer blade. In the case of strong unweathered rock with unfavourable discontinuity patterns, even ripping with powerful plant may prove inadequate as a pre-treatment and the rock may have to be loosened by blasting or ultimately fractured by blasting.

Blasting is a topic with substantial safety and environmental concerns. Specialist publications and/or organizations should be consulted if it is to be employed.

9.4.2 Use of excavation schemes

A chart relating the excavatability (diggability) of rocks to factors such as rock strength and discontinuity spacing was prepared by Franklin, Broch and Walton (1971) and is reproduced in Fig. 9.1(a). Excavatability was subdivided into dig, rip, blast to loosen and blast to fracture. Since that time, modern excavation equipment has changed considerably and an up-dated approach is given by Walton and Wang (1993), reproduced in Fig. 9.1(b). This relates

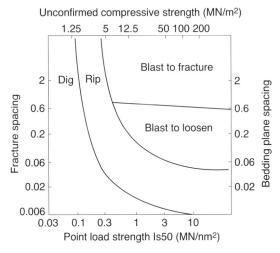

(a) Franklin, Broch and Walton (1971) original diggability chart

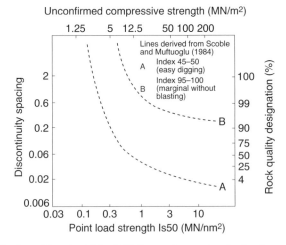

(b) Modification of the chart (Fig. 9.1(a)) covering modern hydraulic excavators

Fig. 9.1 Excavatability chart (from Walton and Wang, 1993)

excavatability to rock (point load) strength and to discontinuity spacing as before, but the frequently used Rock Quality Designation (RQD) has also been added. Also incorporated is the 'Diggability Index Rating' of Scoble and Muftuoglu (1984), given in Table 9.2, which takes into account rock weathering, strength, and discontinuity spacing.

Table 9.2 Diggability index rating (after Scoble and Muftuoglu, 1984)

Parameter	Ranking				
Weathering	Completely	Highly	Moderately	Slightly	Unweathered
Rating (W)	*< 0*	*5*	*15*	*20*	*25*
Strength (MN/m^2) (UCS)	< 20	20–40	40–60	60–100	> 100
Is (50) (MN/m^2)	< 0.5	0.5–15	1.5–2.0	2–3.5	> 3.5
Rating (S)	*0*	*10*	*15*	*20*	*25*
Joint spacing (m)	< 0.3	0.3–0.6	0.6–1.5	1.5–2	> 2
Rating (J)	*5*	*15*	*30*	*45*	*50*
Bedding spacing (m)	< 0.1	0.1–0.3	0.3–0.6	0.6–1.5	> 1.5
Rating (B)	*0*	*5*	*10*	*20*	*30*

This index rating may be used as the basis for a Diggability Classification for Excavators, presented in Table 9.3.

Table 9.3 Diggability classification for excavators (after Scoble and Muftuoglu, 1984)

Class	Ease of digging	Index $(W + S + J + B)$	Typical plant which may be used without blasting
I	Very easy	< 40	Hydraulic backhoe < 3 m^3 e.g. CAT 235D
II	Easy	40–50	Hydraulic shovel or backhoe < 3 m^3 e.g. CAT 235 FS or 235 ME
III	Moderately	50–60	Hydraulic shovel or backhoe > 3 m^3 e.g. CAT 245 FS or 245 ME
IV	Difficult	60–70	Hydraulic shovel or backhoe > 3 m^3 e.g. CAT 245 or O&K RH 40 (short boom if a backhoe)
V	Very difficult	70–95	Hydraulic shovel or backhoe > 4 m^3 e.g. Hitachi EX 1000
VI	Extremely difficult	95–100	Hydraulic shovels and backhoes > 7 m^3 e.g. Hitachi EX 1800 or O&K RH 75

Naturally, schemes and classifications such as these can only provide an impression of the actual conditions, as far as excavatability is concerned, but their use may be helpful at the preliminary stage and as a guide to setting up and carrying out excavatability trials.

The excavation scheme by Pettifer and Fookes (1994) may also be consulted.

9.4.3 Pre-treatment by ripping

Pre-treatment by ripping is controlled by a number of factors including:

- size and power of plant
- method of working
- nature and orientation of discontinuities
- strength of intact rock.

Size and power of plant

It is self-evident that the weight and power of plant will influence its ability to excavate rock, as will the bucket size and geometry which controls the ability of the fragmented rock to flow into and out of the bucket.

Method of working

If ripping is necessary, the direction of travel of the bulldozer and the spacing between runs will influence the outcome. The closer the spacing, the more intense the treatment but also the greater the cost and the time taken.

Run direction may be dictated by the size and the shape of the working area. It may not always be possible to select the run with respect to geological features such as dip and/or discontinuity spacing. In circumstances such as these, the combination of hydraulic breaker and light tractor plus ripper may be more productive than a much heavier bulldozer used on its own.

Assessing an appropriate method of working requires considerable planning, involving the plant engineer and his engineering geologist colleague. It should certainly not be dictated simply by what plant happens to be available at the time.

Nature and orientation of discontinuities

All rocks contain discontinuities. For a given intact rock strength, the closer the spacing between discontinuities, the easier excavation will be and the greater the productivity. This is demonstrated in the excavatability chart of Walton and Wang illustrated in Fig. 9.1(b). However, note must be taken of discontinuity orientation as well as spacing. Ripping is normally most favourable when the run is up-dip or at right angles to a major discontinuity set and where free faces (including previously excavated surfaces) are available.

Weathered discontinuities day-lighting into the working surface and those with large aperture (openness) are usually favourable because of the ease with which the tine can penetrate the opening and the blocks can be dislodged, especially if the discontinuities dip at roughly 45 degrees to the direction of the tines.

Strength of intact rock

The strength of the intact rock between the discontinuities is also an important determinant of rippability. It may be measured by using the unconfined compression test or the point load test conducted on rock cores. As would be expected, for a given discontinuity set, the higher the rock strength, the greater the resistance offered to ripping.

A good discussion of rock excavation by ripping is given by Pettifer and Fookes (1994).

9.5   Bulking and shrinkage

Bulking occurs when soil or rock is excavated: one cubic metre of soil or rock at the borrow does not translate into one cubic metre of fill in the lorry or when placed and compacted on site. A guide to bulking factors is given in Table 9.4.

Table 9.4   Guide to bulking factors for soils and rocks (from Horner, 1988)

Soil	'Bulking factor'	Rock	'Bulking factor'
Granular	10–15 (%)	Igneous	50–80 (%)
Cohesive	20–40 (%)	Metamorphic	30–65 (%)
Peat	25–45 (%)	Sedimentary	40–75 (%)
Topsoil	25–45 (%)	Chalk	30–40 (%)

The factors shown in Table 9.4 should be used when estimating transport haulage capacities, noting that the actual factor will depend upon local circumstances and could vary throughout the borrow pit or cutting.

For most soils and rocks, the result of excavation, transport, placement and compaction as fill is a net bulking: this amounts to between zero and 10 per cent for the majority of soils and weak rocks and to between 5 and 20 per cent for harder rocks. Some materials, particularly chalk and sand demonstrate a net shrinkage: for chalk, this amounts to between zero and 15 per cent and for sands to between zero and 10 per cent. Bulking can have a significant effect on the balance of cut and fill volumes and hence the cost of a scheme.

The above phenomena of bulking should not be confused with wastage, which inevitably occurs on most construction sites. Typical reasons for wastage are:

- construction and patching up of haul roads
- raising the formation levels of settling embankments (which can use significant quantities of fill where the embankment overlies soft compressible soils; the amount should always be calculated)
- overbuilding of embankments (see Section 12.7.2)
- removal of otherwise suitable fill rendered unacceptable by wetting up
- inaccuracies in the calculation of cut and fill volumes.

Some 5 per cent of fill volume is often allowed for wastage. Like bulking, wastage can also have a significant effect on haulage for a major project and should be allowed for when estimating transport costs.

Examples of planning and constructing earthworks are given in Appendix 3.

10. Placement and compaction of fill

10.1 Introduction

As with excavation (see Section 9.2.1), weather has a major influence on placement and compaction. In some wetter parts of Britain, earthwork sites can close down over the winter period whatever the fill employed. Note should be taken of the two *Specification for Highway Works* (1998) clauses on handling water at earthworks sites, mentioned in Section 9.2.1.

10.2 Preparation of site

The site should be cleared of all unsuitable materials including those listed in Section 8.3.1. Derelict foundations may have to be removed and, where excavations have to be made, due consideration given to the stability of adjoining structures and to Health and Safety requirements (Chapter 14). Drainage grips should be provided on the uphill side of excavations and the provision for sump-pumping made where this is considered necessary.

During site preparation, topsoil is usually stripped as one of the first actions to be taken. This is understandable if it is to be re-laid and is obviously necessary if the area concerned is to receive fill. But ground from which the topsoil has been stripped can immediately be turned into a quagmire by construction plant. For site areas providing access without the benefit of haul roads, and not themselves receiving fill, it may sometimes be better to leave the topsoil in position to provide a better trafficking surface.

Particular care should be paid to sites bordering existing properties, because vibration from plant particularly, but not limited to, vibrating compactors, could cause cracking. New (1986) reports that human perception of vibration is highly subjective and that some members of the public may be minded to complain as soon as vibrations from an outside (or unusual) source exceed human perception level. The situation is likely to worsen with duration of the vibration, particularly outside working hours. Photographic surveys of adjoining structures taken prior to the works are recommended in such circumstances, for use as comparisons in case of later claims.

A useful list of actions to be taken during planning earthworks construction is given in *Australian Standard* AS 3798 (1990).

10.3 Fill deposition

Wherever possible, fills of widely different types (e.g. clay and granular soils) should be segregated at the borrow or point of excavation and placed in separate and roughly horizontal layers across the whole width of the compacted area. Mixing suitable clay soils with suitable granular soils does not necessarily lead to a suitable fill (see Section 3.3.2). Random placement of fill types can produce unpredictable settlements at formation level. The final 600 mm or so of fill should be placed and compacted in one continuous operation across the whole fill area.

Steps should be taken to protect construction during adverse weather. Damage occurs not only because of infiltrating rain or uncontrolled groundwater flow but also because of traversing plant. The *Specification for Highway Works* (1998) requires that the upper 600 mm of clay fill (Classes 2 and 7) beneath formation level receives double the compactive effort it would receive at lower levels in order to increase strength and reduce permeability, and hence better to withstand the damaging effects of construction traffic. (However, note the remarks on heavy compaction made in Section 2.5).

Actions to be taken include:

- shaping the surface excavated (or filled) to falls and sealing with the appropriate number of passes of compaction plant
- excavating grips or drainage ditches to collect run-off and/or groundwater and pumping off-site if necessary (note the need to trap silt before discharging into permanent drainage systems)
- covering the surface excavated or filled
- further compaction of clay fill to increase its strength and imperviousness and hence its resistance to damage from traversing construction plant
- placing no fill before compaction plant is on site to work it
- leaving a protective thickness of material in place above formation level; the *Specification for Highway Works* (1998) requires 300 mm minimum be left as a protective thickness above formation level but this should be increased in the case of clay soils, since this material is more easily damaged.

It is just as important to protect the work during excavation if the resulting material is to be employed as fill. Failure to do so could mean that otherwise suitable fill is rendered unsuitable due to weather and construction traffic and has to be run to spoil.

10.4 Factors influencing compaction
10.4.1 General

Effective compaction is a function of both plant and fill type. Plant achieving specification and productivity targets for one fill may not do so for another. Thus the engineer and his plant specialist colleague must discuss and agree the approach, with the site investigation and other data to hand. Unfortunately, many decisions are taken on the basis of what is available in the yard. The engineer should realise that employing such equipment in the long term may be far more expensive than bringing in more suitable equipment from elsewhere, because the overall costs in terms of loss of productivity and effective compaction could be much higher.

As far as equipment is concerned, achieving adequate compaction depends upon:

- the compaction plant, its size, weight and operating speed
- fill layer thickness
- fill water content
- number of passes.

Compaction plant

The depth of spread of compactive effort is related to the mass per metre roll of the compaction plant. The heavier the plant, the deeper the spread of compactive effort into the fill layer. Likewise the slower the speed at which the equipment is operated the greater the compactive effort imparted. Note that the contact area between a roller and the underlying fill is restricted to a narrow strip foundation, the size of which depends upon the mass of the roller and the consistency of the fill. Its size becomes exceedingly small for a light roller on a dense fill.

Layer thickness

Thinner layers promote the uniform penetration of compactive effort. Large amounts are absorbed manoeuvring stones into position within the compacted layer and stone sizes in excess of about two thirds the layer thickness should not be used. Some modern compaction plant have meters which record and read-out the compacted layer depth and the density obtained. Much used on the continent they have not found favour in the UK, perhaps because of scepticism over their accuracy. On-site calibration during compaction trials could help to resolve doubts (see Section 8.5).

Water content

Achieving the required low air voids content is strongly dependent upon the water content of the fill: the higher the water content, the more rapidly the desired low air voids content is achieved; the lower the water content, the more energy will be needed, in terms of plant size and number of passes. There are construction difficulties in adopting too high a water content with cohesive fill and the discussion in Section 3.4 should be referred to.

Number of passes

For a given type of compaction plant, layer thickness and water content, increasing the number of passes increases the compactive effort transferred to the fill and results in lower voids. However, if the layer thickness is too large for the type of plant, additional passes will not succeed in compacting the base of the layer and the only result will be to compact the top of the layer to 'refusal', with the basal part of the layer remaining under-compacted.

10.4.2 Influence of fill type on choice of compaction plant

Fill type has a significant effect on the choice of compaction plant and details are given in Table 10.1 (from BS 6031: 1981). Further considerations include:

- Granular tills and other coarser granular soils are normally best compacted using smooth wheel or grid rollers to provide the high contact stresses necessary to break down and/or to manoeuvre the larger fragments into a denser packing. For coarse gravels heavy towed equipment should always be employed. A vibratory component almost invariably produces better compaction with granular soils.

   Uniform fine sands are probably best compacted using a single vibrating roller, preferably watering the fill as required. These fills usually need some confinement and it may be found that the current layer may not be achieving specification, although the previous (underlying) layer does.

   Smooth wheel and grid rollers may also be considered for compacting some industrial fills and demolition wastes, and vibrating rollers have been found to perform well with burnt and unburnt colliery discard (Chapter 6). Weaker components in demolition rubble (bricks, mortar, plaster and weaker concrete fragments) may crush into fine particles or powder under the high contact pressures from this equipment. Pneumatic rollers may have advantages in such cases (see below).

   Smooth wheel compaction plant is particularly useful for sealing and shaping fill surfaces to prevent infiltration between lifts, but scarification is frequently necessary to help bond the next layers, especially where more plastic clay fill is employed.
- For clays and finer grained soils, dry of optimum, the sheepsfoot roller may be employed. Because of its action, lumps and chunks are broken up and the top of the previous compacted layer is left rough, offering good bonding with the fill of the current layer. It is reportedly successful in the USA with clay soils used for landfill liners. For maximum effect, the layer thickness should be about equal to the length of the feet, plus 50 mm, according to Privett *et al.* (1996). Based on work in the USA, these authors recommend long thin feet to assist

Table 10.1 Typical compaction characteristics for natural soils, rocks and artificial materials used in earthwork construction (from BS 6031: 1981, Table 4)

Material	Major divisions	Subgroups	Suitable type of compaction plant	Minimum number of passes for satisfactory compaction	Maximum thickness of compacted layer (mm)	Remarks
Rock-like materials	Natural rocks	All rock fill (except chalk)	Heavy vibratory roller not less 180 kg per 100 mm of roll Grid roller not less than 800 kg per 100 mm of roll Self-propelled tamping rollers	4 to 12	500 to 1500 depending on plant used	If well graded or easily broken down then this can be classified as a coarse-grained soil for the purpose of compaction. The maximum diameter of the rock fragments should not exceed two-thirds of the layer thickness
		Chalk	See remarks	3	500	This material can be very sensitive to weight and operation of compacting and spreading plant. Less compactive effort is needed than with other rocks
Artificial	Waste material	Burnt and unburnt colliery shale	Vibratory roller Smooth wheeled roller Self-propelled tamping roller	4 to 12 depending on weight of plant	300	
		Pulverized fuel ash	Vibratory roller Self-propelled tamping roller Smooth wheeled roller Pneumatic tired roller			Includes lagoon and furnace bottom ash
		Broken concrete, bricks, steelworks slag, etc.	Heavy vibratory roller Self-propelled tamping roller Smooth wheeled roller			Non-processed sulphide brick slag should be used with caution

Table 10.1 Continued

Material	Major divisions	Subgroups	Suitable type of compaction plant	Minimum number of passes for satisfactory compaction	Maximum thickness of compacted layer (mm)	Remarks
Coarse soils	Gravel sand gravelly soils	Well graded gravel and gravel/sand mixtures; little or no fines Well graded gravel/sand mixtures with excellent clay binder Uniform gravel; little or no fines Poorly graded gravel and gravel/sand mixtures; little or no fines Gravel with excess fines, silty gravel, clayey gravel, poorly graded gravel/sand/clay mixtures	Grid roller over 540 kg per 100 mm of roll Pneumatic tired over 2000 kg per wheel Vibratory plate compactor over 1100 kg/m² of baseplate Smooth wheeled roller Vibratory roller Vibro-rammer Self-propelled tamping roller	3 to 12 depending on type of plant	75 to 275 depending on type of plant	
	Sands and sandy soils	Well graded sands and gravelly sands; little or no fines Well graded sands with excellent clay binder				
	Uniform sands and gravels	Uniform gravels; little or no fines Uniform sands; little or no fines Poorly graded sands; little or no fines Sands with fines, silty sands, clayey sands, poorly granded sand/clay mixtures	Smooth wheeled roller below 500 kg per 100 mm of roll Grid roller below 540 kg per 100 mm of roll Pneumatic tired roller below 1500 kg per wheel Vibratory roller Vibrating plate compactor Vibro-tamper	3 to 16 depending on type of plant	75 to 300 depending on type of plant	

			Type of compaction plant	Number of passes	Layer thickness (mm)	Remarks
Fine soils	Soils having low plasticity	Silts (inorganic) and very fine sands, rock flour silty or clayey fine sands with slight plasticity; Clayey silts (inorganic); Organic silts of low plasticity	Sheepsfoot roller; Smooth wheeled roller; Pneumatic tired roller; Vibratory roller over 70 kg per 100 mm of roll; Vibratory plate compactor over 1400 kg/m² of base plate; Vibro-tamper; Power rammer	4 to 8 depending on type of plant	100 to 450 depending on type of plant	If water content is low it may be preferable to use a vibratory roller. Sheepsfoot rollers are best suited to soils at water contents below their plastic limit
	Soils having medium plasticity	Silty and sandy clays (inorganic) of medium plasticity; Clays (inorganic) of medium plasticity				
		Organic clays of medium plasticity				Generally unsuitable for earthworks
	Soils having high plasticity	Micaceous or diatomaceous fine sandy and silty soils, plastic silts; Clay (inorganic) of high plasticity, 'fat' clays				Should only be used when circumstances are favourable
		Organic clays of high plasticity				Should not be used for earthworks

The information in this table should be taken only as a general guide. When the material performance cannot be predicted, it may be established by earthworks trials. This table is applicable only to fill placed and compacted in layers. It is not applicable to deep compaction of materials in situ.

N.B. If earthworks trials are carried out, the number of field density tests on the compacted material should be related to the variability of the soils and the standard deviation of the results obtained. Compaction of mixed soils should be based on that subgroup requiring most compactive effort.

remoulding soil clods and to bond with the previously compacted layer beneath.

The number of passes of a sheepsfoot roller is related to the foot area covering the drum. If the foot area is 20 per cent of the drum area, then a minimum of five passes would be necessary. In practice, the sheepsfoot begins 'walking out' when maximum compaction has been reached. Sheepsfoot rollers are not recommended for granular soils or for clay soils wet of optimum. The tamping roller is a popular variant in Britain. Having larger feet, the contact stresses are lower which means that it can better operate in the wetter conditions frequently encountered. One version of this equipment has a dozer blade which makes for versatility.

- Hard clays, shales, mudstones, sitstones, sandstones and other weak rocks may benefit from some form of heavy vibratory roller. With these materials, vibratory techniques often lead to better performance in dry density terms than do static techniques, although vibratory compactors can dig themselves in if the initial layer thickness is too large. Tamping rollers are also useful in such fills.

Heavy towed vibrating rollers usually operate at lower frequencies than do the lighter variants, adding an element of impact loading which is reportedly advantageous for cohesive fill (Parsons, 1987). The effect of vibratory equipment on adjoining structures should be remembered (see Section 10.2).

- Pneumatic rollers have the advantage of adjustment, not only to weight by adding ballast, but also to tire width by varying tire pressures. It is possible to adjust in two ways: (a) increase the tire pressure at constant wheel load which reduces the contact area at the surface and increases contact pressure, or (b) increase the wheel load at constant tire pressure which increases the contact area at the layer surface. These properties make the pneumatic roller a good piece of plant to experiment with difficult materials.

Sands, clayey sands and sandy clays are probably most usefully compacted by pneumatic equipment. It is frequently employed with pulverised fuel ash and its possible use with some other types of industrial fill has already been noted.

Parsons (1992) gives information on the characteristics of several soils compacted by various pieces of equipment. In Figure 10.1, the performance is illustrated for three soil types typical of British conditions, 'sandy clay', 'well graded sand' and 'gravel-sand-clay'. Direct comparison is difficult because of the difference between layer thickness and water content and because different sizes of plant were frequently used. Nevertheless, good performance of the vibrating equipment is evident, even though it was substantially lighter than the other plant investigated. Satisfactory

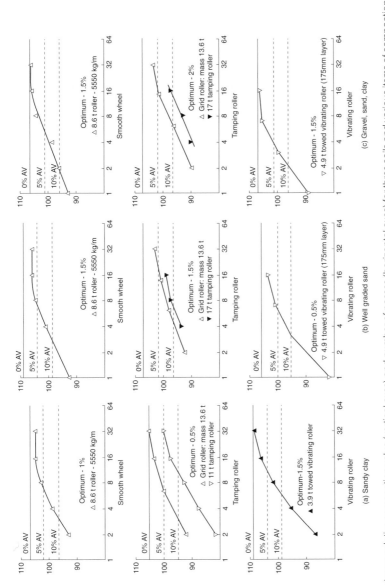

Relationship between relative compaction value (vertical axes) and number of passes (horizontal axes) for three soils and various items of compaction equipment. Relative compaction expressed as percentage of maximum dry density achieved by BS 2.5 kg rammer method (from Parsons, 1992). All layer thicknesses 150 mm unless otherwise stated.

Fig. 10.1 Performance of compaction plant on different soil types (from Parsons, 1992 with adaptations from Trenter, 1999), reproduced by kind permission from CIRIA

performance is observed for the smooth wheel roller which has always been popular in Britain.

10.5 Fill conditioning
10.5.1 General

When the fill has too low or too high a water content, either because of the weather during excavation or because the fill was excavated from below the groundwater table, it may need wetting or drying before or during placement. The same applies to some clay or weak rock fills, excavated in chunks and which cannot be properly compacted. This process is frequently referred to as fill 'conditioning' and may take the following forms:

10.5.2 Lime stabilization

Quicklime (CaO) is a common conditioning medium for wetter fill but hydrated (slaked) lime may be used for drier material. Special measures are necessary for investigating the suitability of the fill to be treated. The following should be identified:

- the presence of sulphur bearing minerals (sulphates and sulphides)
- the presence of soils of adequate plasticity (minimum plasticity index 10 per cent)
- the presence of any organic material
- groundwater and its chemical content.

Lime stabilization has two stages: the first known as 'lime modification' and the second as 'lime stabilisation'. Lime modification occurs with all clays and is accompanied by a reduction in their water content and plasticity; lime stabilization occurs when the lime reacts to produce a cementitious product which stabilizes the clay over the long term. Lime modification appears always to work with British soils but failures with stabilization have been reported with some, perhaps because of their particular clay mineral content.

Rogers *et al.* (1997) state that, in addition to an immediate drying of wet clay soil (with accompanying strength increase), the following changes occur:

- reduction in clay mineral electrical double layer thickness (the adsorbed water layer)
- flocculation of clay particles
- increased shear resistance between particle agglomerates and greater strength of the agglomerates themselves
- reduction in plasticity index due to an increase in the plastic limit and a decrease in the liquid limit.

As pointed out in Section 3.5.2, the concentration of sulphur-bearing minerals is likely to be least at shallow depth; furthermore, the most highly weathered (and hence the most plastic) soils also usually occur at shallow depth. Consequently, fill from the top 2 or 3 m of the cut excavation is often the most suitable for lime stabilization purposes. Should this material prove inadequate, investigation should focus upon zones elsewhere within the cut depth or upon other borrow pits which demonstrate adequate plasticity, low organic matter and the least sulphur-bearing mineral content. Perry *et al.* (1995) recommend the procedure given in Fig. 10.2 for assessing the suitability of soils for lime treatment purposes. Information on site investigations for lime stabilization is also given in *The Highways Agency, Advisory Note* HA 74/95, where information on chemical testing procedures is also given.

Softening following wetting has been recorded and may be due to patches of untreated or only partly lime treated fill in the midst of areas treated to specification. Good compaction and drainage, both during construction and in-service, appear essential; Perry *et al.* (1995) also report that well compacted lime stabilised soils with an air voids content less than 5 per cent should help guard against sulphate induced heave.

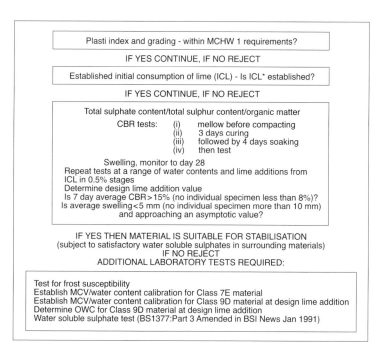

* Initial consumption of lime: BS 1924: 1990: Part 2

Fig. 10.2 Flow chart for assessing soil suitability for lime stabilization purposes (from Perry *et al.*, 1995)

10.5.3 Mechanical conditioning

As noted elsewhere, overconsolidated clay and some weak rocks such as shale and mudstone can be difficult to compact, particularly at water contents below their plastic limit. Uniform compaction is then difficult, if not impossible. With these materials, and when compaction to high standards is necessary, a mechanical conditioner (in practice probably a rotovator) which both breaks down the chunks and which can add water should be considered. The disadvantage of this technique, apart from the expense of having more equipment on the site, is that the filling process is geared to the rate at which the equipment can deliver the conditioned fill. More than one processor on site may be necessary.

For major earthworks such as embankment dams, the alternatives reported for conditioning large volumes of overconsolidated clays (Kennard *et al.*, 1978) include:

- hosing directly on to the clay during spreading, including hosing directly on to the bulldozer blade
- hosing into scrapers as they discharge
- piped spray irrigation systems
- sluicing the clay at the borrow pit
- spraying from a specially fabricated water tank mounted on a converted motor scraper, combined with disc harrowing to reduce material to specified size.

Of the various methods, the last reported appears to have been most successful. However, there is a question as to how useful these techniques are in achieving uniform wetting throughout the fill. Often a layer only a few millimetres thick at the surface is thoroughly wetted and most of the succeeding layer and the one beneath are not affected at all. Some engineers think that over the long term, the water from the wetter layers drains, making for a more homogeneous whole. Vaughan *et al.* (1978) produce evidence to the effect that this does not occur and that the wet layer remains wet and the adjoining dry layers remain dry, even when the quantity of dry material is substantially in excess of the wet.

The expense of having several rotovators on site may therefore be justified by a better conditioned and more uniform fill.

10.5.4 Stockpiling

This approach requires the fill to be placed in conveniently sized heaps, on a granular base, which is itself laid to falls so that the drained off water can be removed. It is limited to free-draining materials, such as granular soils. Expert advice is needed to decide whether the grain size is such as to allow free drainage: a small amount of fines in an otherwise sandy soil could drastically lengthen the time necessary for drying, and the process might not be viable as a consequence.

10.5.5 Aeration

With this technique, the fill is spread in thin layers over as wide an area as possible and dried to the desired placement water contents using discing or harrowing. Charles (1978) states that the change in water content required to produce a given change in undrained shear strength is a linear function of fill plasticity index and quotes the expression:

$$\Delta \text{ water content } = \frac{PI \times \Delta c_u}{5.8 \times c_u} \tag{10.1}$$

where *PI* denotes the plasticity index and c_u the undrained shear strength. The expression is reportedly valid for the undrained strength range $20 < c_u < 100 \,\text{kN/m}^2$.

As with stockpiling, aeration means that the fill must be placed in the open where, in the British climate, it can just as well receive rainfall as sunshine; the technique is consequently best suited to those locations having plenty of space together with a recognisably dry season, otherwise the whole filling process becomes more than usually weather dependent.

10.5.6 Consolidation by drainage

This technique is most often employed for major projects such as embankment dams where a clay fill is particularly wet, and significant pore pressures could be set up during construction. Its use in large road embankments has also been reported. Bishop and Vaughan (1962) showed that the pore pressure parameter r_u was highly sensitive to water content varying from about zero at OWC -1 per cent to 0.6 at OWC $+ 1$ per cent for the sandy clay Selset fill. They report that a side slope of about 1 (vertical) in 5 (horizontal) would have been necessary for a factor of safety of 1.5, had not horizontal drains been adopted.

Horizontal drainage layers are laid at vertical intervals which depend upon the vertical coefficient of consolidation c_v of the compacted fill and hence control the rate at which pore pressures dissipate. The drainage layers are themselves laid to falls sufficient to drain the water from the consolidating fill. The disadvantage of this method is that the drainage layers require material meeting the usual filter rules, if clogging is to be avoided, which may be expensive and may not always be easily available.

Gibson and Shefford (1968) investigated the efficiency of horizontal drainage blankets with respect to surrounding clay fill. They found that a drainage blanket only 10^3 times more permeable than the fill was 'likely to be useless'. An acceptable efficiency was achieved by using a drainage blanket 3×10^4 times more permeable than the fill.

Grace and Green (1978) provide a graph showing the relationship between permeability of fill and distance between drainage layers for 90 per cent consolidation.

10.6   Special problems
10.6.1   Load bearing fill

There can be unacceptable differential settlements if the nature of the fill and its thickness vary substantially. Rogers (1992) recommends that variations in fill depth under a building should not exceed 15 per cent of the average fill thickness, in order to reduce the possibility of deleterious differential settlement.

Feather edges (one part of the structure resting on natural ground and the other upon fill) should be avoided. Where possible, the site should be worked with structures built either upon natural ground or upon fill of roughly uniform thickness. In practice, some stepping of the natural ground may be necessary (Fig. 10.3). Vertical step height should be small in comparison to step length to minimize vertical discontinuities. Checks for settlement and differential settlement should be made.

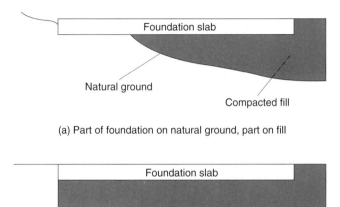

(a) Part of foundation on natural ground, part on fill

(b) Foundation placed entirely on fill

Fig. 10.3   Stepping natural ground to achieve more uniform foundation conditions

Particular care is needed where structures are to be placed over or near the high wall of a former quarry or open-cast mine. This problem was investigated by Skinner and Charles (1999) who distinguished between:

- quarries backfilled to the top of the former quarry walls and
- quarries completely buried by backfilling operations.

For the first case, they found that with very steep-angled high walls (usually the situation with former rock quarries or open-cast mines), even small fill settlements produced potentially damaging ground movements at the fill surface where it adjoined the high wall. For the second case, the geometry of the former quarry high wall was less important than the ratio of the depth of superimposed fill to depth of the former quarry; the larger this ratio became, the smaller the settlement, although its effects occurred over a much wider area.

For full details, Skinner and Charles (1999) should be consulted but it is clear that high walls can threaten the stability of structures built on fill. Figure 10.4 offers suggestions as to how treatment may proceed.

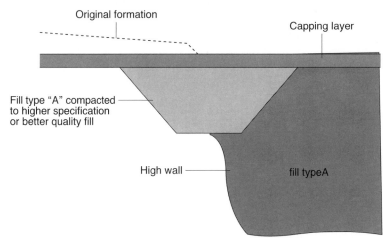

Fig. 10.4 Nature of measures required to reduce settlement adjoining a quarry or open-cast high wall

10.6.2 Fill at multi-purpose sites

A multi-purpose filled site could comprise load bearing and non-load bearing (landscaped) areas. Different levels of compaction may be selected for each purpose and, if available, different fills. Should it be decided that a lower level of compaction is warranted for the landscaped area, a transition zone around the load bearing area should be provided. In Fig. 10.5, a transition zone width of half the fill thickness or 5 m, whichever is the greater, is suggested for preliminary purposes. The final dimensions to be adopted will depend upon the fill types and the degrees of compaction selected.

There may be large boulders at some sites which could be impossible to incorporate into compacted fill in the usual way. Their removal off site could be expensive. Assuming that the fill were deep enough in relation to the boulder sizes, a practical way of coping would be to place them at the bottom of the excavation, sufficiently far enough apart to enable placement and compaction of fill to proceed around them.

The discussion on hierarchy of fills (see Section 8.3.1) should be referred to for further details.

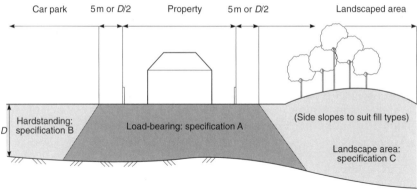

D denotes fill thickness at the location concerned

Fig. 10.5   Typical compaction scheme beneath mixed-use area

10.6.3   Stresses from compacted fill on retaining walls

Solutions are available for estimating stresses acting on the back of retaining walls due to compacted fill. Ingold (1979) presents a solution for free draining (granular) soils and Clayton *et al.* (1991) for clay soils.

Granular fill

Assuming that the granular fill is placed and compacted in thin layers behind the retaining wall, the horizontal pressures will vary, from residual passive to active. Starting at the base (Fig. 10.6(a)), the stress acting will be the residual passive which can be shown to be (Ingold, 1979):

$$\sigma_{hp} = \sqrt{(2q\gamma/\pi)} \tag{10.2}$$

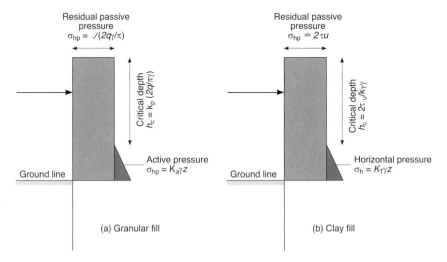

Fig. 10.6   Stresses from compacted fill on the back of retaining walls

where q is the line load due to the compaction equipment and γ is the unit weight of the fill. (Note that the fill's angle of shearing resisitance ϕ is not involved). Given uniform fill thickness and line load, σ_{hp} will be constant.

However, as the compacted fill ascends higher and higher behind the wall, there comes a depth h_c below the top of the wall where the active pressure σ_{ha} will begin to exceed the residual passive pressure σ_{hp}, where:

$$h_c = K_p \sqrt{(2q/\pi\gamma)} \qquad (10.3)$$

and

$$\sigma_{ha} = K_a \gamma z \qquad (10.4)$$

The terms K_a and K_p are the active and passive earth pressure coefficients, respectively, and z is the distance from the top of the wall. Note that in Fig. 10.6(a) at the very top of the wall, passive conditions will not develop. As this distance is small, it may be neglected for most practical purposes.

The above described approach is highly idealized. It assumes that all the movements necessary to assure active and passive conditions will occur which, depending upon wall design and construction, may not be the case. Moreover, it assumes that the residual passive stress is controlled by the line load q and not by the compactive effort; in other words, the residual passive pressure would be developed whether one or any number of passes of the roller were in contention.

Clay fill

Stresses behind the back of a retaining wall are more difficult to estimate for clay soils because of the possibility of swelling (see below). A solution, illustrated in Fig. 10.6(b), is similar in principle to that for granular soils. Again, starting at the base, the residual passive pressure $(\sigma_{hp} \approx 2\tau_u)$ exists behind the wall until, at a critical depth h_c below the top of the wall, the horizontal stress σ_{ha} begins to exceed the residual passive pressure σ_{hp}, where:

$$h_c = 2\tau_u/K_T\gamma \qquad (10.5)$$

In this expression, τ_u is the undrained shear strength of the fill, K_T is the ratio of total stresses (σ_h/σ_v) and γ is the fill unit weight. Below h_c, the horizontal stress becomes:

$$\sigma_{ha} = K_T\gamma z \qquad (10.6)$$

The problem in adopting this solution lies in estimating K_T. As noted, clay fill may swell, particularly if formed from overconsolidated clay excavated from depth. Therefore K_T at the end of construction may be much smaller than K_T in service. Furthermore, the size of K_T will itself depend upon wall construction, particularly whether or not movement is permitted which would reduce the stresses on the back of the wall. Estimation of τ_u also presents problems, if formed from overconsolidated clay, because of the difficulties in compacting to produce an homogeneous whole. In practice, the best approach for such soils, and one likely to produce reasonably consistent results, is to employ a mechanical rotovator (see Section 10.5.3) to reduce the clay to chunks of relatively small size (much smaller than layer thickness) and of reasonably uniform water content.

10.6.4 Deep hydraulic fill

Large areas of deep hydraulically placed fills, such as are laid down for reclamation purposes, bring their own problems for design and construction. They are seldom, if ever, laid in thin layers and in any case layer thickness can be difficult to control to the extent normal for land-based operations. Control tests are usually performed when the fill has been brought up to final level and some form of densification such as vibroflotation is employed to produce the required degree of compaction. Static cone penetration tests made *in situ* (BS 1377: 1990: Part 9: Test 3) are a preferred method for control purposes because the technique is rapid and relatively economic; the equipment when properly calibrated and maintained is accurate.

Initially, the relative density D_r is set for the particular engineering requirements of the site and the static cone penetration test is employed to control the value selected. However, there may be difficulty in relating reliably the cone resistance q_c to the relative density D_r. Although correlations exist between q_c and D_r (Meigh, 1987, Lunne *et al.*, 1997), there is significant scatter in the results of the relatively few sand samples tested, and the engineer has to decide whether the granular fill concerned is of low, medium or high compressibility, an unenviable task unless significant additional testing is performed. The matter is discussed in detail by Lunne *et al.* (1997), including an approach to deciding compressibility. Note the importance of selecting the correct cone sensitivity for the fill type and depths employed.

Other methods of control include the standard penetration test and the dynamic cone penetration test (Tests 3.3 and 3.2, respectively, of the above quoted BS 1377: 1990).

10.6.5 Investigations at former quarry and open-cast sites

Former quarry sites or other large open excavations can act as major sinks, affecting the groundwater table for large distances. Boreholes sunk close to an open excavation when determining the feasibility of backfilling may consequently show a depressed groundwater level. This may lead the engineer to believe that the water table will be at a lower elevation, when the excavation is backfilled, than in fact will be the case. This is illustrated in Fig. 10.7. Since the amount of collapse settlement is proportional to the saturated fill thickness (see Sections 3.5.1 and 4.5.3), a false impression of the amount of collapse settlement will be obtained.

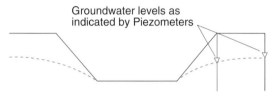

Groundwater levels as
indicated by Piezometers

(a) Former quarry (open-cast) excavation showing
    position of groundwater table at the time of the site
    investigation

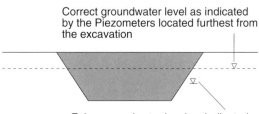

Correct groundwater level as indicated
by the Piezometers located furthest from
the excavation

False groundwater level as indicated
by Piezometers too close to excavation

(b) Backfilled excavation showing final groundwater
    level in fill

Fig. 10.7 Right and wrong ways of estimating groundwater levels in backfilled
excavations

Most open-cast sites are backfilled at the same time as excavation
progresses, so the engineer and the engineering geologist have to investigate
groundwater conditions before work commences. This is normally done by
sinking boreholes and installing standpipes or piezometers before open-
casting begins. The groundwater table measured at this stage is usually a
guide to what can be expected on completion of excavation and subsequent
backfilling, allowing for the normal seasonal influences.

The hydrogeology of open-cast sites can be particularly complicated with
flooded worked-out seams day-lighting into the excavation, which may
require special pumping measures as excavation proceeds. The worked-out
seams should always be blocked-off during backfilling but water-tightness
cannot be guaranteed; the water level in the fill could rise up to, or higher
than, the elevation of the seam. In the past, long term water levels in the
mines were stabilized by deep pumping and, if still in operation, this could
affect the water level in neighbouring open-cast sites. Where open-cast
workings are planned, it is essential to check whether such pumping is, or
has recently been, in operation and, if so, what are the long term plans for its
continuation.

When backfilling a major excavation or open-cast site is under
consideration, a thorough hydrogeological study should be undertaken, with

expert advice, so that there can be few doubts as to the extent of the groundwater rise and the extent of possible collapse settlement.

10.6.6 Investigations of solution features

Much of England which is underlain by chalk may exhibit these features, even where there is a cover of younger Tertiary or superficial materials in excess of 10 m or more. Over geological time, acid rainwater and run-off finds its way into the body of the chalk through fissures and joints, dissolving and enlarging them until, in many cases, major voids are formed. At some stage, the roof of the void collapses into the space beneath, a process which can continue upwards to the ground surface. Granular soil cover usually provides most solution features, in part because of the permeability to rainfall and run-off; clay cover provides the least.

The collapsed material which fills the void reflects the nature of the overlying strata but it is often weak and compressible in comparison with the host chalk. The engineer should be concerned by solution features for the following reasons:

- voids filled with weak compressible infill may exist close to the underside of foundations
- weak compressible infill may promote instability in slopes in otherwise good chalk requiring remedial measures or, at least locally, consideration of slacker side slopes than otherwise
- weak compressible infill may appear in the formation, requiring special measures for pavement design, including for example, removal and replacement, or capping layers where none would otherwise be necessary.

Mathews *et al.* (2000) provide a summary of methods for locating solution features, reproduced in part in Table 10.2.

Apart from drilling, where the cores or samples allow a visual record which should be reasonably reliable, the success of the other methods depends in part on the contrast afforded between the chalk and the infill contained within it. Clear distinctions may be drawn between say the penetration resistance within or outside a void if the chalk forming the void surface is hard and unweathered, and the infill weak and compressible. If these conditions do not apply, there may be doubts. For this reason, it is best to persevere with several methods, using borehole control wherever economic circumstances permit. Certainly, remote-sensing records should be the first to be examined, along with detailed geological records and the results of a walk-over survey.

Judgement and expertise in allocating the various resources economically and effectively are necessary in locating solution features. For further details, Mathews *et al.* (2000) should be consulted. Information on the locations of dissolution features in the U.K. is provided by Edmonds and Kirkwood (1990).

Table 10.2 Summary of methods for locating solution features (adapted from Mathews *et al.*, 2000)

Method	Dependent property	Type of data	Comments
Direct methods			
drilling	visual/index properties	vertical profiling	expensive and time consuming; numerous boreholes required*
static and dynamic cone testing	penetration resistance	vertical profiling	cheaper than drilling but numerous tests necessary
trenching	visual	sectioning	limited depth of investigation
Geophysical methods			
magnetic	magnetic susceptibility	lateral variation	rapid coverage of large areas; has been used successfully**
resistivity	resistivity	vertical profiling/ sectioning/ lateral variation	reasonably rapid coverage; has been used successfully**
conductivity	conductance, inductance	lateral variation	rapid coverage; has been used successfully**
Remote sensing	reflected EM radiation	lateral variation	cheap; provides rapid coverage but not all solution features have surface expression

* drilling can take several forms: e.g cable percussion; cable percussion with tube sampling (continuous or otherwise); rotary drilling with air or fluid flushes; rotary core drilling also with various flushes
** refers to use of the method in locating solution features

11. Cuts: some design and construction considerations

11.1 Introduction
Cuts are excavations made into the natural ground in order to achieve a design formation level. Unlike embankments (Chapter 12), design is concerned solely with the properties of the *in situ* soils and rocks, which are usually undisturbed, except insofar as the excavation process itself may introduce disturbance. This may be important with rock slopes where blasting, if used, could fracture and weaken the host rock.

11.2 Cuts in soil: method of approach
The following concentrates on geotechnical aspects of cutting design and construction. More general advice is given in *The Highways Agency Advice Note* HA 44/91 and a list of limit states appropriate to cut design is quoted in *Eurocode 7* (1995).

For a given geometry (i.e. depth and side-slope), cut-slope stability in soil depends upon:

- strength and density properties of the natural ground, allowing for its soil fabric or structure
- groundwater and/or pore pressure conditions, including pore pressure redistribution over time
- presence of features such as weak layers, unfavourably located bedrock or ancient failure surfaces.

The analysis of cut-slope stability may proceed as follows:

- The deepest parts of the cut are identified and section drawings prepared based on site investigation information; worst case conditions are usually assumed unless there is borehole or trial pit information to the contrary
- shear strength and density properties are assigned to the soil(s) and groundwater or pore pressure conditions are assessed: soil structure or fabric, weak layers, ancient failure surfaces or unfavourably located bedrock are taken into account

- preliminary stability analyses are made with simple cut-slope geometries and uniform successions, using charts or tables such as those developed by Chandler and Peiris (1989), given in Appendix 4, elaborated by hand stability methods; the influence of soil strength properties, groundwater and pore pressure conditions on factors of safety for given slopes are assessed
- stability is investigated using effective stress methods and relevant strength, groundwater (or pore pressure) data to provide the factor of safety for the long term or permanent works condition. Drainage or other measures may be introduced if the desired factor of safety is not achieved. If an estimate of the stability for the short term or temporary works condition is necessary, total stress methods and the relevant strength data may be adopted. The calculated factor of safety may be compared with the minimum values quoted in Table 13.3 (Chapter 13).

The procedure outlined above is repeated at structure and other significant locations, and at intermediate depths, using appropriate site investigation information.

It is easy for the less experienced engineer to concentrate on what is often a relatively small length of cut slope, as shown on the drawings, and to lose sight of the 'big picture' when it comes to stability analysis. It should be remembered that the area containing the proposed cut may be part of a much larger pattern of unstable ground, requiring wider reconnaissance than simply boreholes and trial pits at the cut slope location. For this reason, expert engineering geological (and geomorphological) appreciation may be necessary at an early stage in the site investigation, employing the appropriate remote-sensing aids. This also applies to embankment stability analysis (Chapter 12).

Thus stability analysis is a complicated procedure which requires more than routine allocation of soil properties and pore water pressure conditions to a proprietary computer programme; it should be under the control of a suitably qualified and experienced geotechnical specialist at all times.

11.3 Stability analysis: long term condition
11.3.1 General

Cut slopes with a life of decades are normally designed in terms of effective stress. This implies that, were failure to occur, it would take place so slowly that no excess pore pressures would be set up in the failing soil. For this design approach, and with slow draining clay, shear strength properties are measured in the laboratory on undisturbed specimens in consolidated drained shear (BS 1377: 1990: Part 8: Test 8). Alternatively, consolidated undrained tests with pore pressure measurements may be made (BS 1377: 1990: Part 8: Test 7).

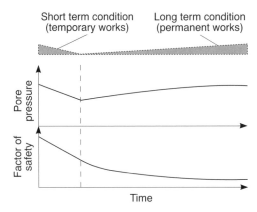

Fig. 11.1 Variation of pore pressure and factor of safety with time for a cut slope (adapted from Bromhead, 1992)

Figure 11.1 illustrates pore pressure and factor of safety changes with time, following cut formation. After the cut is made, the pore pressure decreases initially to a minimum at the end of construction (the short term condition) and then increases slowly over the long term. The corresponding factor of safety decreases rapidly with cut formation and then declines more slowly as the pore pressure increases with time. Bromhead (1992) states that post-cut pore pressures are unlikely to return to their pre-cut values. Applying the factor of safety to a design incorporating the initial pre-cut pore pressure should therefore ensure that the most severe pore pressure condition has been met. (This procedure would be over-conservative if the design included allowance for drainage).

As noted in Section 3.1, in British conditions there are normally consolidated and overconsolidated soils, with the latter ranging from lightly to heavily overconsolidated, depending upon the overconsolidation ratio. However, it is unlikely that many terrestrial deposits are truly normally consolidated in Britain, if only due to the changes in groundwater level which occurred in post-glacial times, and most softer deposits are lightly overconsolidated to some degree. Whether or not a soil is overconsolidated (and its overconsolidation ratio), has a major impact upon its behaviour in cut slope stability; likewise its behaviour as an embankment foundation (Chapter 12).

11.3.2 Strength properties (effective stress)
Peak strength

Triaxial test results are interpreted using conventional Mohr's circle analysis and so-called best-fit tangents to produce the peak shear strength; this comprises the peak effective cohesion c' and the peak effective angle of shearing resistance ϕ'.

A c' value is usually observed with overconsolidated clays but its magnitude can be complicated by sampling or test procedures. Working with failed cut slopes in brown fissured London Clay, Skempton (1977) showed that specimen size strongly influenced the peak c' (Fig. 11.2(a)). Values of c' for 38 mm diameter test specimens were much larger than those for 250 mm specimens, although the peak ϕ' values were identical in both cases. This was considered to be the influence of the fissures present in most overconsolidated clays, with larger specimens containing a more representative collection and hence lower c' values.

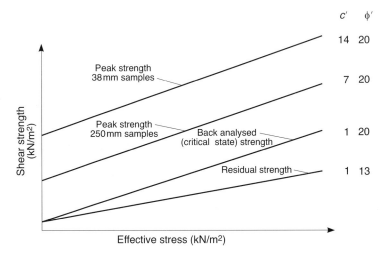

(a) Mohr's envelopes of stress for overconsolidated clay
(after Skempton, 1977)

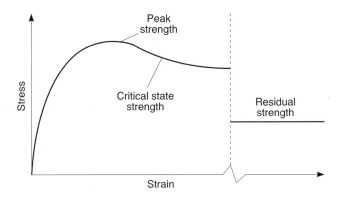

(b) Stress v strain curve for overconsolidated clay

Fig. 11.2   Mohr's envelope and stress v strain curve for overconsolidated clay

With normally or only lightly overconsolidated clays, the peak cohesion intercept c' is usually zero.

Because they are free draining, no excess pore pressures are set up when a granular soil fails, even if failure occurs relatively rapidly. Design values of ϕ, the angle of shearing resistance, may be obtained from the results of triaxial tests or from shear box tests (BS 1377: 1990: Part 7: Test 4 or 5). Static cone penetration tests made at the cut location and to the expected cut depths may be made, employing correlations such as the one given in Fig. 4.4 (Chapter 4). There are also well established correlations between the results of Standard Penetration Tests (SPTs) in granular soils and ϕ. Note that even a small quantity of fines (silt and clay) can reduce the free draining qualities of granular soils; in many cases, fines appear within well defined layers or lenses rather than evenly distributed throughout the granular soil, and this can alter drainage characteristics. (See also discussion in Section 11.3.3). Trial pits and/or samples should be inspected carefully to determine the disposition of any fines.

Critical state strength

Experience shows that cut slopes in overconsolidated clays containing fissures fail at lower shear strengths than the use of peak values would imply, even allowing for full dissipation of negative pore pressures (see Section 11.3.3). Investigations indicate that, as strain increases around the shear surface, progressive failure reduces the shear strength from the peak to the critical state strength, at which shearing continues under the given stress regime without any change in volume. Dilatancy in the failure zone, accompanied by water content increase is probably responsible for the strength reduction; fissures or other fabric features are probably central to the process. Muir Wood (1990) refers to the soil in these circumstances as being continuously remoulded and churned up, with random structure. A typical stress v strain curve for an overconsolidated fissured clay is illustrated in Fig. 11.2(b), where the peak, critical state (and residual) strengths are also shown.

Reference was made above to Skempton's work (1977) and the dependence of peak c' on sample size. Skempton also back analysed cut slopes in brown fissured London Clay which had failed over several decades: it was found that they yielded even lower c' values, only slightly in excess of unity (Fig. 11.2(a)); ϕ' again remaining the same. Skempton termed the back analysed strengths the fully softened strength, which is regarded as being identical to the critical state strength, mentioned above.

The very small c' values for overconsolidated fissured clay suggest that they could be ignored in any cut slope stability analysis in this material. However, Chandler and Skempton (1974) rejected this approach as being unnecessarily conservative and recommended use of small effective cohesion intercepts between 1.5 and $2 \, \text{kN/m}^2$. They also noted that the assumption of zero cohesion would lead to the conclusion that the limiting slope was, contrary to experience, independent of depth. Chandler and Skempton also believed that the application of zero or very small c' values would be incorrect for overconsolidated intact clay, like some glacial till, and pointed to the results of Skempton and Brown (1961), where a cohesion intercept of $9\,kN/m^2$ was measured for an overconsolidated but intact clay till. They also mentioned that the use of a zero or very small effective cohesion intercept would be quite inappropriate for shale or other materials where diagenetic bonding could lead to significant cohesion values.

Residual strength

When strain continues in overconsolidated clay, the clay platelets begin to orientate about a failure surface and, with continuing strain, they become polished and slickensided. In this respect, the clay micro-structure is quite unlike that at the critical state strength (Muir Wood, 1990); the strength along these failure surfaces is much lower than the critical state strength, with which it should not be confused (Fig. 11.2(a) and (b)). Such failure surfaces are common in British overconsolidated fissured clays and are termed 'ancient failure surfaces' in this book. They are a frequent cause of failure of both cuts and embankments and site investigations should be directed towards their discovery.

Estimates of the residual shear strength likely to exist on ancient failure surfaces in clay soils may be obtained from extended strain shear box tests on undisturbed samples (BS 1377: 1990: Part 7: Tests 4 and 5) or from ring shear tests (BS 1377: 1990: Part 7: Test 6; and Bromhead, 1992). The residual cohesion value c'_r is often ignored in stability analyses involving ancient failure surfaces and the assessed value of the residual angle of shearing resistance ϕ'_r only is adopted; correlations between ϕ'_r and plasticity index, and also ϕ'_r and clay fraction are available (Fig. 11.3).

Residual ϕ'_r values measured by the ring shear device may be less than the back-analysed values by between 1 and 3 degrees, assuming c'_r to be zero (e.g. Trenter and Warren, 1996).

Selection of design strength

There is a bewildering array of possible approaches to parameter selection for cut slope stability analysis. The following are offered as suggestions for first time failures in clay soil:

- for fissured or otherwise structured overconsolidated clay, adopt a critical state strength with a zero cohesion intercept c'_{cs}, if a zero intercept is measured in the laboratory. If a positive intercept is obtained, reduce it, if necessary, to a maximum of $2\,kN/m^2$. In either case, adopt the angle of shearing resistance ϕ' recorded in the tests

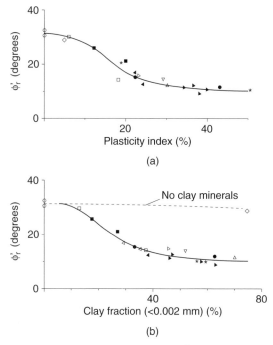

Fig. 11.3 Residual angle of shearing resistance ϕ'_r v plasticity index (a) and v clay fraction (b) (Skempton, *et al.*, 1989)

- for intact (non-structured) overconsolidated clay, use the measured c' to a maximum of say $10\,kN/m^2$, again keeping the ϕ' value as recorded in the tests. The fresher and more unweathered the soil, the higher the cohesion intercept, to the limiting value quoted.
- for normally or lightly overconsolidated clay, use peak strengths, putting the cohesion intercept c' equal to zero if necessary (often zero cohesion will be measured).

For failures involving the reactivation of ancient failure surfaces:

- adopt the measured residual angle of shearing resistance ϕ'_r, with c'_r put to zero. As noted, if measured using the ring shear apparatus, ϕ'_r may be slightly conservative and this should be remembered when assessing the factor of safety (Chapter 13).

11.3.3   Groundwater and pore pressures
General

As part of the stability analysis, the existing (pre-cut slope) groundwater table should be established. This may be done by installing Casagrande piezometers on the line of greatest slope of the proposed cut, typically at the head of the slope, the toe of the slope and, for larger cuts, roughly at the midpoint. More than one line of piezometers may be necessary, depending upon cut size and length. The depths to which the piezometers are installed will depend upon the groundwater table and the strata succession, particularly upon special features such as ancient failure surfaces discussed in Section 11.5. Selecting a design water table demands much experience. Ideally, piezometric and rainfall data extending over many years should be collected in order to determine the highest possible groundwater table. This is seldom practicable and for many projects resources are such that piezometer readings are only collected for a period of months; fortunately, rainfall data for extended periods are available from the relevant authorities.

Most British sites show a rise in groundwater table in the period October/November to January/February, thereafter declining over the spring and summer, probably reaching their lowest levels in August/September time. Readings taken in the late autumn/early winter period are likely to encounter the highest groundwater tables and everything possible should be done to ensure that piezometer data are collected over that period. Even so, the groundwater table established may not necessarily be the highest on record; that would depend on antecedent rainfall at the site in question, going back many months or possibly years. For this reason, even if groundwater table readings are available for the late autumn/early winter period, they should be interpreted conservatively.

In addition to the seasonally affected groundwater table, allowance should also be made for storm effects. Skempton *et al.* (1989) investigated the storm response of the groundwater table at five sites having different ground conditions and slopes (and hence run-off characteristics). They found a definite relationship between rise in groundwater table ΔH and the storm rainfall R for each site. They suggested that, as a first approximation, the ratio $\Delta H / R$ could be taken as 4 and could be employed as a characteristic parameter for any particular site. This suggests a method for allowing for the effects of a winter storm on the design groundwater table. Rainfall records for (or adjoining) the site in question may be consulted for the worst winter storm and ΔH calculated using the above ratio. This figure may then be added to the elevation of the measured highest winter groundwater table to give the design groundwater level, i.e.:

Design groundwater table elevation $= \Delta H +$

highest measured winter groundwater table elevation

For the reasons already given, this may not be the highest possible groundwater level, but provided a conservative asessment is made of the available winter seasons' piezometer readings, the error may not be excessive. For further details, Skempton *et al.* (1989) should be consulted.

Attention should be paid to the possible presence of aquicludes which could support perched groundwater tables. Identification of impermeable layers, which may be very thin, can be difficult during the site investigation, especially if the work is done during a dry spell, when tell-tale seepages in boreholes and trial pits may be absent. The presence of aquicludes should always be expected in glacial soils, as should water-bearing layers or lenses of granular material.

The groundwater table selected for cut-slope design purposes will also depend upon the nature and the extent of the permanent drainage measures proposed. Guidance on the reduction in the groundwater level due to various drainage configurations can be obtained from Bromhead (1992).

Special problems with clay soil

Unlike free draining granular soils or rocks, where water flows through the inter-particle spaces or through cracks, fissures or joints, the permeability of clay soil is too low for 'flow' in engineering terms. Thus a cut made in clay reveals no free flowing water (except from granular pockets or weepages from fissures). The low permeability of clay soils means that the 'response time' of Casagrande piezometers is such that they will only record the groundwater table response to rainfall events of long duration and will show little if any response to a few hours rainfall. It is the same for the engineering operations of cutting (unloading) and filling (loading). These operations when lasting only hours or a few days will not be reflected in full groundwater table changes in Casagrande piezometers installed in clay soils. However, the pore pressure changes induced by these activities can be measured, provided that appropriate instrumentation such as hydraulic or pneumatic piezometers are employed.

The magnitude of the pore pressure change within the clay body on excavation depends on the soil's consolidation history, i.e. whether normally or overconsolidated and, for these latter soils, the overconsolidation ratio. After a cut has been made, the original pore pressures existing in the clay mass will reduce, even becoming negative for some heavily overconsolidated materials. Thereafter, the pore pressures will begin slowly to increase taking up a distribution appropriate to the new stress and drainage conditions imposed by cut formation.

The rate at which pore pressure redistribution (sometimes termed equilibriation or equalization) occurs depends upon several factors including the magnitude and nature of the stress changes, as well as the coefficient of swelling of the clay itself. For heavily overconsolidated clays like the London, Gault and Lias, redistribution can take decades. Quite often cuts which have remained stable for years fail because pore pressures rise to a value sufficient to promote instability. Skempton (1977) and Chandler (1984) found that redistribution could take 40 years or more, as evidenced by the failures of cut slopes in brown fissured London Clay.

11.3.4 Analysis
General
Detailed stability analysis is normally conducted using proprietary computer programs of which there are a number. The majority are based on a relatively few methods of analysis, a summary of which is given in Table 11.1.

Where no features exist to constrain the location of the potential slip surface, methods of analysis include:

- infinite slope
- circular arc.

Where such features exist, potential failure surfaces must cater for them; methods include:

- non-circular
- wedge (and sliding block) analysis.

A detailed discussion of the various methods will be found in Bromhead (1992). Slip surfaces corresponding to some of the above are illustrated in Fig. 11.4.

Infinite slope
The majority of failure surfaces in cuts (and embankment fills) are at shallow depth (e.g. Crabb and Atkinson, 1991). For a slope whose length is long in comparison to the depth to a potential failure surface, an infinite slope stability approach may be adopted; the failure surface is assumed to be a plane parallel with the embankment surface. The factor of safety for this condition (Skempton and De Lory, 1952) is:

$$F = \frac{c' + \gamma z(1 - r_u \sec^2 \beta) \cos^2 \beta \tan \phi'}{\gamma z \sin \beta \cos \beta} \tag{11.1}$$

where β is the cut (or embankment) slope angle to the horizontal, c' is the effective cohesion, ϕ' is the effective angle of shearing resistance and r_u is the pore pressure coefficient, defined as the ratio pore pressure on the failure surface u to the vertical total stress from the overlying fill σ_v (i.e. $r_u = u/\sigma_v$). The top of the flow line is assumed parallel with the slope. Note that unless the pore pressures are artesian with respect to the slope surface, the maximum value that r_u can take is about 0.5, corresponding to the top flow line being congruent with the slope surface (and assuming that the weight of water is about half that of the soil). An r_u value of zero corresponds to the flow line congruent with the failure plane.

For the case when $c' = 0$ (critical state strength), we have:

$$F = \frac{\tan\phi'}{\tan\beta}(1 - r_u \sec^2 \beta) \tag{11.2}$$

Table 11.1 Summary of some stability analysis methods (adapted from Geotechnical Engineering Office, Hong Kong, 1984)

Reference	Assumptions	Advantages	Disadvantages	Recommendations
Bishop (1955) *circular*	Considers force and moment equilibrium for each slice. Rigorous method assumes values for the vertical forces on the sides of each slice until all equations are satisfied. Simplified method assumes the resultant of the vertical forces is zero for each slice	Simplified method compares well with finite element deformation methods (average F within 8 per cent); computer programs readily available	Circular arcs do not always fit the failure surface (in the case of failed slopes) or the likely constraints of topography and features such as hard strata (in the case of potential failure surfaces)	Useful where circular failure surfaces can realistically be assumed
Janbu (1972) *non-circular*	Generalized procedure considers force and moment equilibrium for each slice. Assumptions on line of action of inter-slice forces must be made. Vertical inter-slice forces not included in routine procedure and calculated F is then corrected to allow for vertical forces	Realistic failure or potential failure surfaces can be adopted. Routine analysis can be easily handled by a programmable calculator or by hand	Published correction factors are for homogeneous materials and use of routine procedures can produce large errors in slopes composed of more than one material. Factor of safety is usually underestimated in these cases. Generalized method does not have the same limitations	Very useful where there are topographic and other constraints on geometry of the failure surface. Limitations of the routine method must be considered. Routine method not suitable for embankments where the potential failure surface extends deep into underlying foundation soil
Morgenstern and Price (1965) *non-circular*	Considers forces and moments for each slice; similar to Janbu procedure	Considered more accurate than Janbu; computer programs readily available	No routine (or simplified) method. Computer solution essential and often very time consuming	Very useful where there are topographic and other constraints on the geometry of the failure surface. Most useful for back-analysis of existing landslides
Sarma (1979) *non-circular*	A modification of Morgenstern and Price method which reduces the number of iterations necessary by the application of earthquake forces	Considerable reduction in computing time without loss of accuracy	Computer and programmable calculator solutions available	As for Morgenstern and Price

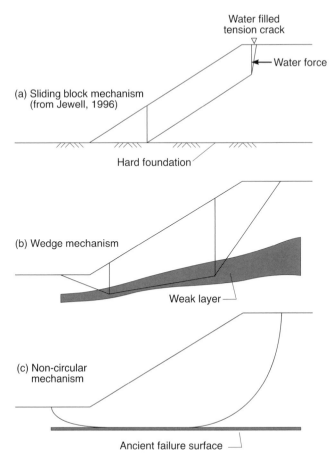

Fig. 11.4 Slip surfaces for use with cut (and embankment) slope stability analysis

Circular arc

Using this method, sufficient slip surfaces are analysed to permit the grid of circle centres to be contoured. Experience shows (Spencer, 1967; Chandler and Peiris, 1989) that the minimum factor of safety is most likely to be found when contouring a series of ellipses whose major axis is at right angles to the slope and slightly up-slope of its mid point. Trial circle centres should be adopted with this in mind.

Non-circular

Note the remarks made in Table 11.1 concerning the limitations of the Janbu (1972) method. If a computer program based on this method is being employed, it would be wise to determine whether or not it uses the routine or 'generalized' procedure.

Wedge analysis

The wedge analysis is a force equilibrium method and results cannot be directly compared with Morgenstern and Price and Janbu which utilise a combination of force and moment equilibrium. The difference between these methods increases as the factor of safety increases. The Geotechnical Engineering Office (1984) points out that the factor of safety obtained from a wedge mechanism is sensitive to the inclination to the horizontal of the inter-block forces and the inclination of the surfaces between the blocks. An analysis to determine the sensitivity of these factors for a given problem would appear appropriate, especially for larger banks and/or where the consequences of failure could be more than usually severe (Chapter 13).

Greenwood (1985) believes that in conditions where the earth pressure at rest value *Ko* is high (such as in heavily overconsolidated clay at shallow depth), the wedge analysis will provide a lower factor of safety than the circular arc.

Jewell (1996) put forward an alternative to the infinite slope comprising two sliding blocks, with a water filled tension crack at the top, which is really a special case of the wedge analysis. Unlike the infinite slope approach, it applies where the ratio length of side slope to depth to potential slip surface is relatively small. The depth of tension crack used in this method may be calculated from the expression:

$$z_o = \frac{2c'}{\gamma}\tan(45 + \phi'/2) \tag{11.3}$$

Peak strengths may be adopted when using equation 11.3, because tension cracks form at an early stage in the cut (or embankment) slope and they are unconnected with the critical state or residual strength processes.

The factors of safety computed using the above procedures may be compared with the minimum values suggested in Table 13.3 of Chapter 13.

11.3.5 Some results based on British motorway experience

In a valuable contribution, Perry (1989) collected data on the performance of embankments and cuts for a number of English and Welsh motorways. Information was provided for various height ranges, geological ages, drainage conditions, side slopes and other factors, with stability for the particular material under examination being expressed as a percentage of the failed length of slope to the total length of slope surveyed. Of the 570 km of earthworks involved, failure affected some 4 per cent; failure for both cuts and embankments usually comprised a combination of translational (slab) and rotational movements, only exceeding 1. 5 m depth in 5 per cent of the slopes investigated. The greatest incidence of failure occurred with overconsolidated clay of Tertiary age and older.

A selection of results for cut slopes is given below. Clay soils (particularly overconsolidated) were chosen because of their greater incidence of failure.

Table 11.2 Performance of British motorway cut slopes from 2.5 to 5 m high (from Perry, 1989)

Geological stratum	Age of construction (yr)	Length surveyed (m)	Slope angle (v:h)	Percentage failure
Glacial till	3 to18	4142	1:2.5	0
	22	204	1:2.5	20.5
	7 to 17	3291	1:2	0
	18	1750	1:2	1
	22	2319	1:2	3.7
	25	463	1:2	5.8
London Clay	6	533	1:3	1.9
	10	543	1:3	3.2
Gault Clay	10	353	1:2.5	3.8
	22	299	1:2.5	4.4
Lower Lias	4.5	529	1:2	0
	25	894	1:2	1.4

A height range from 2.5 to 5 m was adopted because Perry reported that 76 per cent of the cuts surveyed were lower than 5 m high.

Generally, failure rates are seen to be reasonably low, usually less than 5 per cent; the exception is a section of 22 year-old glacial till cut, where a failure rate of 20.5 per cent was recorded. The small length surveyed (204 m) suggests special factors operating. Understandably, without borehole information, Perry was unable to draw attention to such matters as ancient failure surfaces which could be present at some of the failed sections.

The incidence of failure increases with age of the earthwork, thus demonstrating the importance of age in stability assessments, together with a clear idea of the degree of maintenance work acceptable. In this respect, Perry (loc. cit.) suggests that for long term stability (corresponding to less than a one percent failure in 25 years), side slopes of 1 in 5 would be necessary in Gault and Lias Clays, both for cuts and embankments in excess of 5 m high. Such slopes are substantially slacker than the vast majority recorded during Perry's survey and would have a major impact on first time project costs.

11.4 Stability analysis: short term condition
11.4.1 General

The total stress approach to stability analysis assumes that cut slope formation takes place so rapidly that there will be no change in the water content of the soil; literally, the soil remains 'undrained' despite the engineering operations. It is assumed that the results of undrained shear strength measurements made on samples taken from the cut area before construction commences (typically at the site investigation stage) will be representative of the strength of the soil during the main works. Note that the undrained strength of a clay soil is critically dependent upon its water content: a relatively small change creates a corresponding large change in undrained shear strength, which is why the assumption of the undrained condition is so critical.

Experience shows that provided the drainage paths in the cut slope are not too short (which would enable rapid drainage), or that the construction period is not too long, the total stress approach may be adopted for cuts in clay soils over the short term. But the above two caveats are important: the engineer must be convinced by the site investigation that there are no significant drainage paths in the cut slope soil. Such features could include abundant fissures or foliations in overconsolidated clays, granular layers in an otherwise clay till or light cementing which could sustain open fissures. Moreover, it must be demonstrated that any significant delays to construction programme are unlikely to affect the short term condition.

The doubts surrounding the practicability of applying the total stress analysis together with the difficulty in selecting parameters in total stress terms (see below) are reasons why some engineers are reluctant to adopt this approach, preferring to analyse in effective stress terms, making the best estimate possible of pore pressure conditions after cut formation.

11.4.2 Strength properties (total stress)

A major disadvantage with the total stress approach is the scatter of results normally obtained from undrained triaxial tests made on conventional driven tube samples and the difficulty of deciding on suitable design shear strength values as a consequence. The presence of fissures and foliations in the clay is an obvious cause of scatter resulting from testing, but sample disturbance may also lead to inaccuracies. Vaughan *et al.* (1993) made a major contribution to the study of sample disturbance in clay soil and part of their results are summarized in Table 11.3.

Table 11.3 Effect of sample disturbance on undrained strength (from Vaughan *et al.*, 1993)

Material type	Effect on undrained shear strength
Soft clay:	
low plasticity	very large decrease
high plasticity	large decrease
Stiff clay:	
low plasticity	negligible
high plasticity	large increase

An approach to determining the undrained (total stress) shear strengths for stability analysis purposes could be as follows:

- For soft (normally or lightly overconsolidated) clay: sample disturbance will result in a reduction in shear strength, the amount depending upon the soil's plasticity (Table 11.3). A mean of the available test data is suggested; the lower the plasticity, the less conservative the mean. It may be preferable to use the results of *in situ* vane tests (BS 1377: 1990: Part 9: Test 4.4) rather than the results of conventional undrained triaxial tests made on samples.
- For stiff (overconsolidated) clay: as indicated in Table 11.3, sampling effects are negligible for low plasticity material, and a conservative assessment of the mean is suggested. For high plasticity clay, sampling may result in an unrepresentatively high shear strength, and a lower bound assessment may be considered
- For granular soils, employ a correlation such as the one shown in Figure 4.4 (Chapter 4).

11.4.3   Analysis of cut slopes

All the methods proposed in Section 11.3.4 are applicable to the total stress analysis; most proprietary computer programs have an effective stress and a total stress option. Note that the expression for the factor of safety for the infinite slope condition in total stress terms (Atkinson, 1981) is:

$$F = \frac{c_u}{\gamma H \sin \beta \cos \beta} \tag{11.4}$$

where c_u is the undrained shear strength, γ is the unit weight, H is the depth to the failure surface and β is the inclination of the slope to the horizontal.

Factors of safety obtained my be compared with the minimum values proposed in Table 13.3 (Chapter 13).

11.5   Effect of shallow depth features on stability
11.5.1   General

Although deep cuts and excavations are the obvious exceptions, earthworks are usually near surface structures. Consequently, when considering the design and construction of cuts (and embankment foundations), investigation must take into account shallow depth features, such as glacially-induced soil fabric and solifluction deposits, and their influence on stability. Such features were generated during the Pleistocene glaciations which affected most of Britain (Jones and Keen, 1993; Trenter, 1999). As its name suggests, glacially-induced soil fabric is a product of glacier or ice sheets; solifluction deposits occurred in the frozen periglacial lands beyond the glacier or ice sheet front.

There is an extensive literature dealing with the whole subject of shallow depth features and their engineering significance, of which those mentioned here are a small sample. A full discussion is given in Hutchinson (1991).

11.5.2 Glacially induced soil fabric

Fabric denotes the directional properties of a soil and rock, including solids and voids. It contains such features as layers, lenses, laminations, fissures, cracks and joints. The latter three items are often referred to as discontinuities and have a substantial influence on stability.

Few if any discontinuities, including shear surfaces, are recorded in granular till; clay tills, especially the more plastic variety, are most likely to contain them and to provide a rich source of potential stability problems for both cuttings and embankment foundations. More details of glacially-induced soil fabric are provided by Trenter (1999).

A classic case of glacially-induced soil fabric controlling the stability of cut slopes was described by McGown *et al.* (1974). Fissures in clay till striking parallel with and dipping towards a 14 m deep cut at Hurlford, Ayrshire, caused failure of the cut slope within weeks of construction; no problems occurred on the other side of the cut where the fissures dipped into the cut slope.

11.5.3 Solifluction deposits and shear surfaces

Solifluction deposits were formed in a periglacial environment as a consequence of the high pore-pressures set up during thawing of surface soils and, as such, may mantle very gentle slopes having gradients of only a few degrees. Lithologically, the deposits reflect the materials up-slope from which they were derived and they may attain thicknesses from a few tens of millimetres to several metres in accumulation zones down-slope.

Provided that they are uncemented or that that they have not been overconsolidated by dessication, solifluction deposits are normally softer than the deposits from which they were derived. This is immediately apparent to the experienced geotechnical engineer or engineering geologist making a trial pit survey. Less easily observed are slip surfaces which are found in the more clayey solifluction deposits, which include those formed from the overconsolidated clays such as the British Gault, Weald and Lias. Figure 11.5 illustrates the variety of slip or shear surfaces common in clayey solifluction deposits; shears in four directions are illustrated. Also shown are the basal, thermokarstic and underthaw shears occurring in the soils beneath. For full details, Hutchinson (1991) should be consulted. An account of solifluction deposits in southern England, with their associated ancient shear surfaces, is also given by Weeks (1969) and Skempton (1976).

The effect of soil structure on shear strengths obtained using total stress testing methods was mentioned in Section 11.4.2.

11.5.4 Other shallow depth features

In glacial successions, laminated silty clays of glaciolacustrine origin (see Section 5.2) are notorious for promoting failures, not only of cut slopes but of landslides as well (e.g. Trenter, 1999). Intra-formational shears (very thin

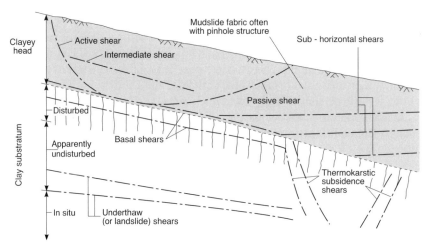

Fig. 11.5 Main types of shear surface in solifluction deposit and underlying stiff clay strata (from Hutchinson, 1991). Quaternary Engineering Geology, Special Publication No 7, The Geology Society

low strength clay seams, often continuous over a wide area) have been reported in clay shales and mudstones (Rogers, 1985), and may have markedly lower shear strengths than the adjoining soils or rocks. Rogers notes that they most often occur when sandstones and limestones are interbedded with the argillaceous sediments.

Where cuts are to be formed in clay soils or weak rocks containing ancient failure surfaces, note that 'residual shear strengths' may operate along the slip surfaces themselves (see Section 11.3.2). If undetected during the site investigation and not taken into account in design, ancient failure surfaces may cause major failures, even with relatively flat cut slopes. Unfavourably located bedrock can also contribute towards instability of overlying soil masses when cut slopes are made.

11.6 Drainage
11.6.1 General
Details of drainage design will be found in the appropriate texts but, in general, permanent works drainage includes:

- cut-off drains
- surface water interceptor drains
- counterfort and slope drains
- herringbone drains.

11.6.2 Cut-off drains
These drains are installed through a pervious stratum such as a water-bearing sand or gravel layer into underlying impermeable clay or bedrock.

They comprise a granular filled trench, usually with a geotextile surround between the granular fill and the host stratum, and with a perforated pipe at the base, designed to take the discharge. Normal filter rules apply with respect to the granular fill. Proper connections should be made between the cut-off and any field drains up-slope. The disadvantage with cut-off drains is that they may not always reach the impermeable material, so that the drain empties its contents into the pervious stratum producing the contrary to the desired result. Furthermore, if falls are insufficient, water may drain out of the pipe through any discontinuities in the underlying impermeable stratum causing its softening. Care should be taken to see that water from the drain is channelled away from the toe of the cutting.

11.6.3   Surface water interceptor drains

Unlike cut-off drains which are designed to cope with groundwater, surface water interceptors are designed to collect run-off which would otherwise alight on the cut slope. They are therefore installed on the uphill side of cuts excavated in side-long ground. They may consist of open channels, often concrete lined, or granular filled trenches similar to cut-off drains. The former are not recommended because open channels easily block; moreover, an improperly designed concrete lining could crack permitting ready access for water to the underlying soil. As with cut-off drains, water must be channelled away from the cutting toe.

11.6.4   Counterfort and slope drains

Counterfort drains are deep granular filled trenches excavated into the slope, at centre to centre spacings dependent upon the permeability of the host soils; methods for calculating drain size and spacing are given by Bromhead (1992). Much more expensive than cut-off drains, because of the quantity of excavation and granular fill needed per linear length of cut, they are also much more effective: first, because they can pick up irregular or inconsistent layers and lenses of permeable material and are therefore ideal for glacial terrains; second, because they give strength and stiffness to cuts in otherwise weak ground. For this reason, they are often employed for reinforcing cuts in water bearing material containing ancient failure surfaces. Note that the flows discharging into the toe drain linking the counterforts can be large and the toe drain itself requires careful design; inadequate capacity would mean that water backed up in the counterforts, keeping water pressures high and possibly promoting water 'break-outs' part way up the slope.

Slope drains are similar in principle to counterforts except that they are much shallower, only extending one or two metres below the slope surface. Consequently they are unable to pick up the same amount of groundwater flow. However, given that most instability is at shallow depth, it may be that they fulfil a useful function in lowering the groundwater table near the slope surface, with beneficial results. Because of their smaller size, they will not have the same stiffening effect on slopes as the much larger counterforts and may not be successful in stabilising slopes containing ancient failure surfaces.

11.6.5 Herringbone drains

As noted in Section 11.6.6, flatter slopes are not always more stable than steeper slopes. Drains, comprising shallow granular filled trenches excavated into the slope in a herringbone pattern, would appear useful in such circumstances. They can also pick up layers and lenses of permeable material which would otherwise discharge water at the slope face, perhaps producing dangerous back-sapping.

A good discussion of geological problems attendant upon some forms of drainage is given by Barton and Thomson (1986)

11.6.6 Some experience in British conditions

Permanent drainage of cut-slopes is critical to their long term stability. In a survey of cuts in England and Wales, Perry (1989) reported that the greatest percentage of failures occurred where no drainage had been provided. In an experiment in overconsolidated fissured Gault clay, a 9 m high by 25 m wide slope constructed at 1 (horizontal) in 2 (vertical) was brought to failure by the controlled addition of water, thus conclusively demonstrating, if such demonstration were needed, that a rising groundwater table can cause slope failures (Petley *et al.*, 1991). Farrar (1985) describes how the installation of slope (counterfort) drains at 5 m centres stabilized an existing cutting in the brown London Clay of the A12 Trunk Road. Failure first occurred some 35 years after construction, after which the slope was cut back to between 10 and 13 degrees, and instability continued until the drains were installed.

In overconsolidated soils, flatter slopes are not always more stable than steeper slopes, according to a study by Parsons and Perry (1985). It was conjectured that rainwater run-off was less easily shed from flat slopes. Potentially deleterious infiltration into the body of the clay slope occurred through features such as desiccation cracks and fissures more readily with flatter than with steeper slopes, producing a build-up in pore pressures at shallow depth. Drainage should not be neglected simply because shallow side slopes have been selected. Herringbone drains, discussed in Section 11.6.5, would appear useful in such cases.

If, as is usually the case with cut-slopes excavated below the general groundwater table, permanent drainage measures are to be installed, their construction may be married with the temporary works drainage to improve efficiency and reduce cost. Filters for permanent drains may become clogged during construction at particularly muddy sites and this should be kept in mind.

11.7 Cuts in rock: method of approach

11.7.1 General

Cut slope stability problems normally arise in rocks because of the discontinuities they contain and their degree of weathering, rather than the weakness of the intact material. Discontinuities may be bedding, joint, cleavage or fault planes created by the geological evolution of the rock mass itself, or they may be fissures or fractures caused by civil work, such as blasting. However caused, discontinuities and the rock's degree of weathering are fundamental to stability and to the design of cut slopes in rock.

Design rests on a thorough analysis of all available discontinuity data, because in many cases they control the location of potential failure surfaces or of groundwater seepage or flow. Indeed, a failure surface may occur along or through a major discontinuity set. Different circumstances may operate for weathered rocks whose behaviour in stability terms may be more akin to soil than to rock, depending upon the degree of weathering. Instability is liable at the junction between the highly weathered and the less weathered materials. Because the intact strength of weathered rocks is relatively low (compared with that of fresh unweathered rock), water pressure can have a major influence on stability in weathered terrains.

Some weak rocks are relatively uniform and lacking in significant structural features; in such cases, the difference between them and most overconsolidated (stiff fissured) clays lies in their natural water content which is normally substantially lower than their plastic limit. For such materials, the slopes at which cuts can be engineered depend upon shear strength and not discontinuities. Nevertheless, the shear strength for such materials can be substantially higher than for overconsolidated clays. By reference to Mercia Mudstone cliffs at Sidmouth, Devon, up to 100 m high, Chandler (1984) demonstrated a high effective cohesion value c' of $40\,\text{kN/m}^2$ and an angle of shearing resistance ϕ' of 34 degrees; similar high effective strengths were described for chalk cliffs. Lower effective strengths, although still considerably above those of overconsolidated clays, were noted for higher plasticity weak rocks, where progressive failure might be anticipated. For further details, Chandler (1984) should be consulted.

11.7.2 Stereonets and classifications

Stereonets

An indication of the stability of rock slopes can be obtained by plotting the discontinuity data on a stereonet and comparing their orientation with that of the proposed cut slope. Fig. 11.6 demonstrates such plots for three typical types of rock failure: plane, wedge and toppling. In assessing the likelihood of failure, account has to be taken of the angle of shearing resistance ϕ acting along the potential failure surface (see below). The stereonet approach is a specialist operation, requiring input from a suitably

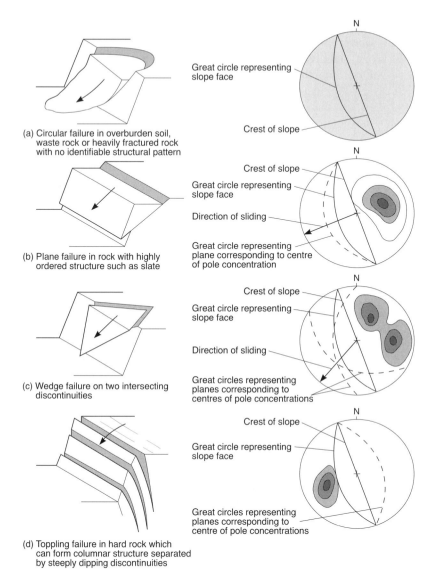

(a) Circular failure in overburden soil, waste rock or heavily fractured rock with no identifiable structural pattern

Great circle representing slope face

Crest of slope

(b) Plane failure in rock with highly ordered structure such as slate

Crest of slope

Great circle representing slope face

Direction of sliding

Great circle representing plane corresponding to centre of pole concentration

(c) Wedge failure on two intersecting discontinuities

Crest of slope

Great circle representing slope face

Direction of sliding

Great circles representing planes corresponding to centres of pole concentrations

(d) Toppling failure in hard rock which can form columnar structure separated by steeply dipping discontinuities

Crest of slope

Great circle representing slope face

Great circles representing planes corresponding to centre of pole concentrations

Fig. 11.6 Main types of failure in rocks and stereoplots of the discontinuity conditions likely to cause them (from Hoek and Bray, 1997)

qualified and experienced rock mechanics engineer or engineering geologist and permits ready visualization of the discontinuity pattern and its relation to cut slope geometry. It should always be attempted before more complicated analytical techniques are adopted. For full details, Hoek and Bray (1997) should be referred to.

Classifications

Preliminary indications of cut slope stability in rock can be obtained using rock classification schemes. Bieniawski (1989) listed various attributes of such schemes. They include the ability to:

- identify the most significant parameters influencing rock mass behaviour
- identify and group rock masses having similar engineering characteristics
- provide a basis for communication between site and design office and the various disciplines working on the project.

A well known classification scheme for tunnels in rock was proposed by Bieniawski (1979,1989). This scheme was modified for rock slopes by Romana (1985) and is presented in Fig. 11.7. The information required includes that obtainable from both rotary core drilling (specifically the Rock Quality Designation (RQD)) and from logging exposed rock faces (the Joint Adjustment Rating). It also takes into account the method of slope formation (the Adjustment Rating for Methods of Excavation). The strength of the rock mass classification approach lies not so much in the answer it provides but in the opportunity it affords systematically to register various relevant data. Like the stereonet, which also registers physical data in a highly systematic way, it is a good accompaniment to the more analytical approaches available.

Measuring discontinuity data

Fundamental to both the stereonet and the classification approaches are reliable discontinuity data. They are best obtained from existing cuts or from natural rock exposures using the line-sampling or scan-line technique. This requires a line (scan-line) to be run out and discontinuity data (e.g. dip, strike, openness, roughness, in-filling, as required by Anon, 1977) recorded, together with the distance between each discontinuity. The data are then plotted to scale. Other lines are run out at regular intervals, both parallel to the original and at right angles, to the extent that access and the degree of exposure make possible. Once collected, the data may be presented in both stereonet and classification formats.

Where no existing cuttings or natural exposures are available, the engineering geologist normally has to fall back on the discontinuity data obtained from rock cores. A high standard of logging is required, using the methods presented by Anon (1970). It is not as reliable as line sampling for the following reasons:

- unless special measures are taken (see below), the true dip direction of the discontinuities is usually unknown

Parameter		Bieniawski (1979) ratings for RMR (Ranges of values)						
1	Point load strength	>10	4–10	2–4	1–2			
	UCS strength (MN/m^2)	>250	100–250	50–100	25–50	5–25	1–5	<1
	Rating	*15*	*12*	*7*	*4*	*2*	*1*	*0*
2	RQD (%)	90–100	75–90	50–75	25–50		<25	
	Rating	*20*	*17*	*13*	*8*		*3*	
3	Discontinuity spacing	>2 m	0.6–2 m	200–600 mm	60–200 mm		<60 mm	
	Rating	*20*	*15*	*10*	*8*		*5*	
4	Condition of discontinuities	Very rough surfaces. Not continuous. No separation. Unweathered wall rock	Slightly rough surfaces. Separation <1 mm. Slightly weathered walls	Slightly rough surfaces. Separation <1 mm. Highly weathered walls		Slickensided surfaces. Or gouge <5 mm thick. Or separation 1–5 mm Continuous		Soft gouge >5 mm or Separation >5 mm Continuou-s
	Rating	*30*	*25*	*20*		*10*		*0*
5	Ground-water in joint	Completely dry	Damp	Wet		Dripping		Flowing
	Rating	*15*	*10*	*7*		*4*		*0*

Rating refers to the Rock Mass Rating (RMR) of Bieniawski

Adjustment rating for joints

Case		Very favourable	Favourable	Fair	Unfavourable	Very unfavourable
P	$[\alpha_j - \alpha_s]$	>30°	30–20°	20–10°	10–5°	<5°
T	$[\alpha_j - \alpha_s - 180°]$					
P/T	F_1	0.15	0.40	0.70	0.85	1.00
P	$[\beta_j]$	<20°	20–30°	30–35°	35–45°	>45°
P	F_2	0.15	0.40	0.70	0.85	1.00
T	F_2	1	1	1	1	1
P	$\beta_j - \beta_s$	>10°	10–0°	0°	0–(−10°)	<−10°
T	$\beta_j + \beta_s$	<110°	110–120°	>120°		
P/T	F_3	0	−6	−25	−50	−60

P denotes plane failure; T denotes toppling failure; [ ] denotes numerical value only.
α_s denotes slope dip direction; α_j denotes joint dip direction. β_s denotes slope dip; β_j joint dip

Adjustment rating for methods of excavation of slopes

Method	Natural slope	Pre-splitting	Smooth blasting	Regular blasting	Deficient blasting
F_4	15	10	8	0	−8

Tentative description of Slope Mass Rating (SMR) classes

$$\{\text{SMR} = \text{RMR}(rating) - (F_1 \times F_2 \times F_3) + F_4\}$$

Class number	V	IV	III	II	I
SMR	0–20	21–40	41–60	61–80	81–100
Description	Very poor	Poor	Fair	Good	Very good
Stability	Very unstable	Unstable	Partially stable	Stable	Fully stable
Failures	Large planar or soil-like	Planar or large wedges	Some joints or many wedges	Some blocks	None
Support	Re-excavation	Extensive corrective	Systematic	Occasional	None

Fig. 11.7 Modification of the geomechanics classification for rock slopes by Romana (1985) (from Bieniawski, 1989)

- it can be difficult to differentiate between drilling-induced cracks on the one hand and geologically formed discontinuities on the other
- the degree of openness of the discontinuities cannot reliably be inferred because of the process of core extraction.

The first of the above mentioned difficulties can be overcome, in some cases, by directional drilling, or by employing special equipment. A useful discussion of a number of techniques for this purpose is given by Hoek and Bray (1997). The performance of three different techniques of assessing true dip direction in Middle Coal Measure sandstones is given by Webber and Gowan (1995). The use of Closed Circuit TV for down-the-hole surveys is reported by McMillan *et al.* (1995). A discussion on the methods of investigating discontinuities in rock cuttings is also given by Matheson (1985).

11.7.3 Drainage aspects

As already noted, water pressures acting on the surface of any discontinuities can substantially reduce the stability of cut-slopes in rock. The amount of reduction and hence the need for drainage can be gauged during design but is likely to be greatest in intensely fissured and fractured rocks, and/or those which are highly weathered.

Because weathering of rocks can be so variable, both in depth of penetration and horizontal extent, borehole and trial pit information may mislead. A flexible approach should be adopted during construction in those cut areas believed to be both weathered and below the groundwater table; more elaborate drainage measures may be necessary than are proposed for the unweathered rocks along the route. Such an approach will require the input of a suitably experienced engineering geologist and drainage engineer during the construction stage. As far as possible, standard drainage details should be employed for various weathering regimes to reduce the delays due to re-design at this stage.

11.7.4 Cuts in weathered or fissured rock

If not foreseen during design, weaker weathered or intensely fissured and jointed rocks in the cut slopes can result in delays and cost overruns. The same applies to rock at formation level. Both the side slopes and the formation should be inspected at an early stage during construction. This should permit decisions to be made on site as to the nature of any side slope support necessary for the permanent works and the thickness of the pavement construction.

Hencher and McNichol (1995) describe how rock destined for cut slope formation was found on excavation to be substantially more weathered than expected on the basis of site investigation information. Complete re-evaluation of slope stability was necessary, including installation of support measures (see below) and the purchase of additional land to permit slacker slopes. The weathering of seat-earths in Coal Measures rocks can provoke difficulties and the same authors describe temporary stabilizing works for sections of a trunk road through these conditions, designed on a modular basis, 15 m in length.

In difficult terrains, a variety of designs for both cut slopes and pavements should be prepared, in advance of the main works, graded in accordance with the degree of weathering and/or fissuring. Construction may then proceed if these conditions are discovered, with the minimum of delay.

11.8 Stabilization of cut slopes
11.8.1 General

Cut slopes may require stabilization for the following reasons:

- failure of the slope as originally designed
- strictly limited land-take, requiring steeper slopes than the ground would safely provide unaided. This is common in an urban or sub-urban environment
- ground conditions at the time of construction are found to be less favourable than those foreseen at time of the site investigation. As a consequence, either slacker slopes have to be adopted (resulting in

increased land-take) or the originally planned side slopes are maintained but a form of stabilisation has to be adopted
• road widening is necessary.

For these conditions, stabilization may be achieved by soil nails, anchors or reticulated mini-piles (Fig. 11.8). Other methods of stabilization include drainage and embedded, gravity, gabion or crib walls. An excellent account of the various methods available for slope stabilization, together with comprehensive references and case studies is given by Hutchinson (1977).

11.8.2 Soil nails, anchors and mini-piles

Soil nails provide a method of increasing cut slope stability in appropriate soils and weak rocks (Fig. 11.8(a)). Typically they comprise linear steel members driven, or drilled and grouted, into the cut sides at centre to centre spacings typically from one to 2 m. Soil nails are installed top-down by successive small cuts, usually of the order of 2 m or such depths as are

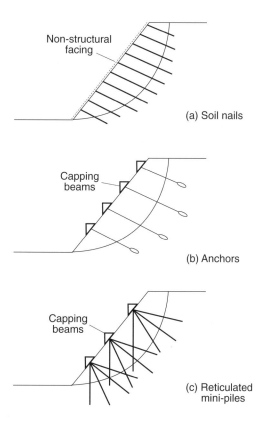

(a) Soil nails

(b) Anchors

(c) Reticulated mini-piles

Fig. 11.8 Approaches to stabilizing cut slopes

necessary to maintain stability. Construction employs the following sequence: excavation, nail installation, face construction and (where necessary) drainage. Unlike anchors (discussed below), there is usually no need to provide a structural retaining face since no significant compressive stress is introduced into the soil (except to ensure that the facing is pressed hard against the natural ground). All that is normally necessary is a light construction such as shotcrete or fabric seeded with vegetation to prevent soil ravelling about the face plates.

Nails are likely to be most successful in overconsolidated clays, shales, mudstones and other weak or weathered rocks. Their use with normally consolidated clays or loose granular soils would require careful consideration. Although functioning at low stress levels, an environment not normally favourable for corrosion, it is usual in Britain to provide some form of corrosion protection, such as plastic sheathing to the steel and at the connections to the facing, when used in permanent as opposed to temporary works. A useful account of soil nailing is presented by Ortigao *et al.* (1995) and in the discussion on this paper by Barley (1996) and by Bridle and Davies (1996).

Anchors (Fig. 11.8(b)) comprise corrosion-protected steel cables drilled and grouted into the ground, each comprising a bonded (or grouted) length, a free tendon length and an anchor head. They are stressed and consequently introduce significant compressive forces which have to be reacted against; this is normally done by a capping beam or beams located at the cut face. Installation is by the same top-down procedure as soil nails, although given the time taken in stressing the cables and forming the capping beams, progress may be slower. Anchors are applicable to a similar range of soil and weak or weathered rock types as soil nails. The principal difficulty with anchors is estimating the bond between the grouted length of anchor and the surrounding soil; each anchor has to be comprehensively tested on installation by applying 150 per cent of design load for permanent and 125 per cent for temporary installations, with displacements monitored (BS 8081: 1989).

Mini-piles (*pali radice*) are most often employed for underpinning foundations but their use for stabilizing slopes has also been reported (e.g. Lizzi, 1984; Ellis, 1985). Pile diameters vary typically up to 300 mm for foundations but those reported by Ellis for stabilization purposes were 100 mm diameter drilled and grouted with a single 25 mm reinforcing bar. Mini-piles are normally reticulated (Fig. 11.8(c)) and equipped with capping beams to cater for bending and tension. In this they differ from soil nails which are installed without capping beams and which rely on the soil-structure interaction of the large number of nails to reinforce the potential failure zone.

11.8.3 Reinforced earth applications

There are several reinforced earth applications for failed slopes and the technique is also frequently adopted for road widening purposes. Reinforced earth is bottom up construction and cannot be used for the stabilization purposes already described. However, it has wide application in both cut slope stability repair and in highway widening (Fig. 11.9).

The nature of the fill is a major consideration because it directly affects the cost of the scheme. Jones (1996) reports that well graded granular soil makes the best reinforced earth fill and that effective stress transfer is poor with clay fill; this means that reinforcement resistance cannot be so rapidly generated and that construction rates may be slowed. BS 8006: 1995 states that the best fills are those it terms 'frictional' and 'cohesive frictional' and comprise fill types 6I, 6J, 7C and 7D of the *Specification for Highway Works* (1998). These fills can be employed for any structural category (e.g. retaining walls, embankments and bridge abutments). Cohesive fills and soft chalk (saturation water content greater than 29 per cent) should only be employed for slopes of retained height 1.5 m or less and where failure would result in minimal damage and loss of access. See Tables 2 and 3 of BS 8006: 1995.

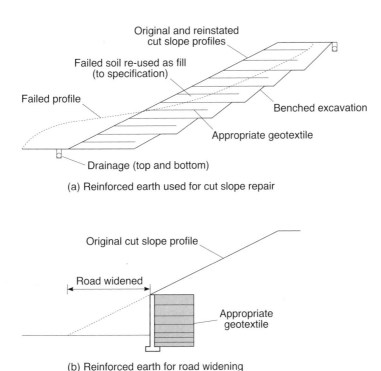

Fig. 11.9 Reinforced earth applications for cut slope repair and widening

For further details Jewell (1996), Jones (1996) and BS8006:1995 may be consulted. Calculation methods for reinforced soil and soil nails are set out in *The Highway Agency Advice Note* HA 68/94. The *Specification for Highway Works* (1998) also provides requirements for the method of compaction of reinforced earth structures. General advice on the geotechnical aspects of highway widening may be obtained from *The Highways Agency Advice Note* HA 43/91.

12. Embankments: some design and construction considerations

12.1 Introduction

Embankments are raised on natural ground in order to achieve a design formation level. They are more complicated structures than cuts because their design and construction require consideration not only of the embankments themselves (the fill), but of the engineering performance of the natural ground upon which they are built; moreover, embankments are usually constructed from remoulded materials whose engineering properties may be more difficult to predict than those of the undisturbed natural ground.

Design of embankment slopes cannot be seen in isolation from the strength and settlement characteristics of the foundation: a granular fill which would perform safely at say 1 (vertical) in 1.5 (horizontal) on a hard foundation could not be placed at this slope on soft clay without the risk of excessive settlement and/or bearing capacity failure. Therefore, for this particular type of fill, it may be necessary to slacken the embankment side slopes and/or to strengthen the foundation to withstand the embankment load.

A list of limit states applicable to embankment design is given in *Eurocode 7* (1995).

12.2 Method of approach

Steps to be taken by the designer include:

- an assessment of all geotechnical information from site investigation reports, in conjunction with design requirements such as embankment height and width at formation level, presence of structures and services, considerations of land-take and access
- the highest parts of the embankment are identified and section drawings prepared: the worst case foundation conditions are usually assumed where the embankment is highest, unless there is reliable investigatory evidence to the contrary. Other critical locations are selected, for example at structures, and section drawings produced
- the nature of the fill at the various borrow areas is assessed; where fill types vary (common over long lengths of embankment) appropriate fill disposition is studied

- hand and/or chart methods are employed for preliminary stability analysis; the tables of Chandler and Peiris (1989) useful for cut slope stability cannot be employed for embankments where deep failure surfaces are under investigation and where the shear strengths of the embankment fill and the underlying foundation differ. Charts due to Pilot and Moreau (1973) may be used in these circumstances, but note that pore pressures are not taken into account in their solutions
- long term stability is investigated using effective stress methods and relevant strength, groundwater (or pore pressure) data. This provides the factor of safety for the permanent works condition and the calculated value may be compared with the minimum value quoted in Table 13.4 (Chapter 13). Provision may be made for drainage or other measures if the desired factor of safety is not achieved
- short term stability is investigated using total stress methods and relevant strength properties. (An alternative effective stress approach is discussed below). This provides the factor of safety for the temporary works condition and the calculated value may also be compared with Table 13.4 (Chapter 13)
- with the embankment geometry established, the settlement of the embankment is calculated. This is usually done as a profile along the longitudinal axis. For major embankments, such as dams, motorways and railways, and where foundation conditions can vary significantly in a lateral direction, more than one profile should be calculated, say along the centre-line of each carriageway and at each shoulder for a road embankment. Calculations are particularly appropriate at structure locations and beneath drains to determine the possibility or otherwise of reversal of drainage direction, as a consequence of settlement.

12.3   Stability analysis: long term condition
12.3.1   General

Figure 12.1 illustrates the way pore pressure and factor of safety vary with time, both for the embankment fill and the underlying foundation soil. Depending upon its overconsolidation ratio and the depth at the borrow from which it was taken, pore pressures may be low or even negative in the fill when placed on the embankment (Chandler, 1978). Over time, the pore pressures will gradually increase to come into equilibrium with the climatic and other factors operating (Fig. 12.1(a)). Therefore, the factor of safety of the fill, which began at a relatively high level, reduces to a minimum, possibly decades after construction. In this respect, embankment fill behaves in a similar fashion to a cut slope. However, because pore pressure distribution is probably more complicated in embankments (given the different materials often employed as fill), pore pressure response may be less predictable.

Pore pressure behaviour differs completely in the underlying foundation soil. It begins to increase after the fill is first placed and reaches a maximum

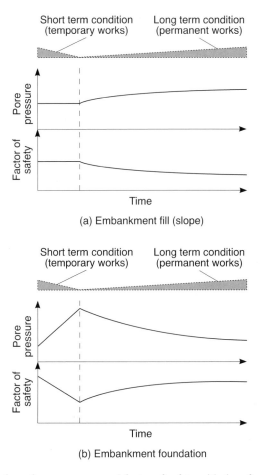

Fig. 12.1 Variation of pore pressure and factor of safety with time for embankment fill and foundation (adapted from Bromhead, 1992)

usually at, or shortly after embankment construction; it then declines slowly to approximate its pre-construction value. The corresponding factor of safety decreases after the foundation is loaded to reach a minimum at, or shortly after, completion of construction and then increases slowly as pore pressure decreases (Fig. 12.1(b)). Therefore, in stability terms, the embankment fill and the embankment foundation behave quite differently, reaching their minimum factors of safety at quite different times, i.e. in the short term for the foundation and over the long term for the fill.

The following sets out the approach to determining the essential properties of strength, groundwater (or pore pressure) and the method of analysis which may be adopted for analysing the long term condition.

12.3.2 Strength properties
Embankment fill

Clay fill: Consolidated drained or consolidated undrained triaxial tests with pore pressure measurements may be made on clay fill samples, tested against a back pressure to ensure that any air present in the fill remains dissolved in the pore water. The water contents selected for the tests will normally correspond to the engineer's best estimate of the fill's water content in the permanent works condition. This could be the water content of the fill as received from the borrow, or the OWC if the fill is to be conditioned to this or to a related value (such as OWC plus or minus 1 per cent). Bishop and Henkel (1962) showed that c' for compacted clay fill reduced rapidly as the initial sample water content increased, ϕ' being relatively little affected; low c' values may therefore be expected for clay fill placed wet of optimum water content.

Note that clay fill placed relatively dry may 'wet-up' and soften over long periods. Monitoring a 7 m high embankment formed from Gault Clay, Crabb and West (1986) found that the sides had wetted up (from rainfall) as had the foundation (from the underlying groundwater table). They also observed that the toe of the embankment was wettest and considered that failures might well commence there. These observations were made only some fifteen months after construction and demonstrate how rapidly clay fill softening can occur. Bishop and Henkel describe the results of strength tests on compacted clay in which water was allowed to circulate in the sample to investigate softening effects. The authors drew attention to the substantial reduction in c' for the softened sample (about 50 per cent of the 'unsoftened' value), although ϕ' remained virtually the same in both cases. This argues strongly for suitably low c' values for design, whenever a significant increase in fill water content is anticipated.

Given the above factors, it is difficult to offer any but the most general suggestions on strength property selection for clay fill. Fully softened or critical state strengths ($c' = 0$) may apply at the low effective stresses operating on the shallow depth failure surfaces typical of many embankments (e.g. Crabb and Atkinson, 1991) but for deeper failure surfaces, use of a c' value seems appropriate, its size depending upon the results of tests made at the expected long term water contents. Nevertheless, Skempton and Coats (1985a and b) and Penman (1995) also adopted critical state strengths for deep failure surfaces in fill, when analysing the Carsington embankment dam failure.

A relationship between peak angle of shearing resistance ϕ' and plasticity index is given in Fig. 12.2. Critical state and peak angles of shearing resistance are normally similar (although the cohesion intercept is zero for the critical state strength). Hence, and as a first approximation, ϕ' values obtained from the Figure may provide some information on critical state angles of shearing resistance ϕ'_{cs}.

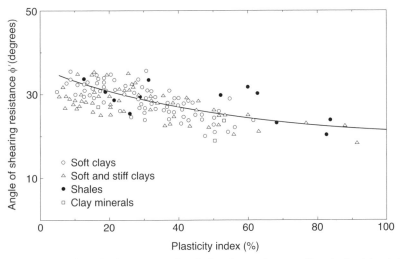

Fig. 12.2 Relationship between angle of shearing resistance ϕ' and plasticity index (from Terzaghi, Peck and Mesri, 1996)

Granular fill: The strength properties of granular fill may be determined using the procedures suggested in Section 4.3.3. Because granular fill is usually free draining, methods of test involving pore pressure measurements are unnecessary. However, only a relatively small proportion of fines (silts and clays) is required substantially to reduce a granular fill's permeability to the point that pore pressures are set up at failure. Penman (1971) and Penman and Charles (1976) suggested that soil or fill with permeabilities greater than about 10^{-5} m/s would not exhibit excess pore pressures: this suggests in turn that permeability tests on samples compacted to expected water content and density should be employed to determine whether or not the assumption of free draining fill is justified.

Multiple fills: Here the designer is faced with the difficulty of deciding which fill, or combination, will govern the shear strength of a given section of the embankment. The following design approaches are suggested:

- design on the basis of the parameters of the weakest and most compressible fill available. This is normally a sensible alternative when say 80 per cent or more of the total fill comprises one type only; minor fill constituents can be placed in the core of the embankment and near the top, where they would usually have least effect on stability or settlement
- where several fill types are in contention, each having a good chance of being employed at any given chainage, use the parameters appropriate to the weakest and most compressible. This is clearly conservative but the alternative sometimes adopted which is to attempt to mix fills is unsound: first, because it is often very difficult to mix fills *in situ* with a bulldozer blade, nor is it often desirable (see Section 3.3.2); second,

the proportions used in the mixtures made up in the laboratory for shear strength and other tests to support this method are often no more than guesswork, as far as the actual conditions on site are concerned

- another option where several fill types are in contention is to design on the basis of the weighted average shear strength (and other relevant engineering properties such as unit weight). Suppose, as an example, ϕ'_1 to ϕ'_4 were the angles of shearing resistance of four fills having volumes V_1 to V_4, the design weighted average angle of shearing resistance would be:

$$\phi' = \frac{\phi'_1 V_1 + \phi'_2 V_2 + \phi'_3 V_3 + \phi'_4 V_4}{V_1 + V_2 + V_3 + V_4} \tag{12.1}$$

A similar procedure could be adopted for estimating a design cohesion intercept value, c', assuming one were to be employed, or an undrained shear strength. Note that it is only the fill placed in the potential slip zone which has a bearing on stability and which should be used in calculating the weighted design value; it would be pointless taking into account fill placed well away from any potential failure surfaces

- where a significant amount of wet clay fill is to be employed, the designer may specify the chainages between which it should be placed. He may then be free to adopt whatever parameters or indeed conditioning he thinks fit over the specified length. However, this approach may produce difficulties for the programme if the contractor is constrained to place one particular fill at one particular location.

The above procedures may be adopted with fill(s) tested both in effective or total stress terms.

Foundation

The effective shear strength of clay foundation soil may also be measured using consolidated drained or consolidated undrained triaxial test with pore pressure measurements, on representative samples extracted from the natural ground.

There is a major difference between the behaviour of overconsolidated clay after cut formation and during embankment loading. Cut formation unloads the soil, opening any fissures and other discontinuities present, while raising an embankment loads the foundation soil. Fissures are closed, thus reducing permeability. A reduction in shear strength to the fully softened or critical state value is unlikely. Selection of shear strengths for an embankment in overconsolidated clay consequently differs from a cut formed in the same material. The following are offered as suggestions for strength parameter selection for first time failures involving the foundation soil:

- for overconsolidated clay, use a conservative assessment of the data.
- for normally or lightly overconsolidated clay, adopt a zero effective cohesion c' together with a conservative assessment of the data.

For failures involving reactivation of ancient failure surfaces in foundation soil:

- adopt the measured residual angle of shearing resistance ϕ_r' with a c_r' of zero. Note that if measured using the ring shear apparatus, ϕ_r' may be slightly conservative (see Section 11.3.2) which should be born in mind when assessing the factor of safety

Relationships between the residual angle of shearing resistance (ϕ_r'), the plasticity index and clay fraction are shown in Fig. 11.3 (Chapter 11).

Mobilization of fill and foundation strengths

A matter requiring judgement is the extent to which the maximum shear strengths of the embankment fill and the underlying foundation can be considered to act at the same time, should failure affect both the bank and the underlying foundation. Remembering that the embankment fill is remoulded, it is likely that during first time failure, the maximum shear strength will be mobilized at a quite different strain from that of the underlying natural soil foundation. For this reason, some engineers prefer to ignore the shear strength component offered by the embankment fill when designing for first time failure. This procedure is conservative but it may not be unduly so if a deep tension crack forms in the fill. Furthermore, if applied, it permits a lower factor of safety to be employed than would otherwise be the case (Chapter 13).

If this approach is considered too conservative, some estimate of the maximum shear strength mobilized by the embankment fill and the underlying foundation can be made, assuming that the majority of the failure surface is in the foundation. This is done by comparing the proportion of maximum fill strength mobilized when the foundation soil is at its peak strength. The shear strength operating along the presumed slip surface in the fill can be adjusted accordingly (Fig. 12.3). Where ancient failure surfaces

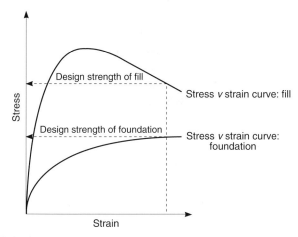

Fig. 12.3   Selection of design strengths for embankment fill and foundation soil

are present in the foundation, many designers would employ peak shear strength for the fill because the residual shear strength acting along the ancient failure surface would be mobilized rapidly and is unlikely to vary significantly with strain.

12.3.3   Groundwater and pore pressure conditions

Pore pressure in embankment fill

Pore pressure behaviour in embankment fill and the corresponding changes in factors of safety were outlined in Section 12.3.1. Superimposed upon the relatively simple model of gradually increasing pore pressures with time, measurements have indicated rapid fluctuations in pore pressure to depths of about 2 m (Vaughan *et al.*, 1978); below this depth, and to about 5 m, they were considered to be seasonal and measurable by conventional Casagrande piezometers. Perry (1991) noted that whilst fluctuating positive pore pressures could be generated at shallow depth, high suctions (negative pore pressures) existed at the embankment core. This suggests that at least for the higher and larger banks, neutralization of the suctions could take decades, as found for cuts by Skempton (1977), Chandler (1984) and discussed in Section 11.3.3. Crabb and West (1986) found that whilst the side slopes wetted up as did the base, the pore pressures in the core of their 7 m high embankment were far from equilibrium in the period monitored (about fifteen months). See also the discussion in Section 12.3.2 (clay fill).

Tension cracks are a frequently observed feature of clay fill and work by Anderson *et al.* (1982) on an embankment formed from overconsolidated Oxford Clay, demonstrated that once formed they served to channel water into the embankment, effectively increasing the permeability of the clay fill. Anderson *et al.* (1982) suggest that tension cracks could have two effects: first, by increasing permeability they could help trigger slides (albeit of shallow depth) following periods of heavy rain; second, the enhanced permeability could increase the rate of pore pressure redistribution, leading to more rapid softening and achievement of critical state strength (see Section 11.3.2). Interestingly, the authors found that the location of the tension cracks depended upon topsoil depth and vegetation cover, being least frequent when both topsoil and vegetation were thickest. This suggests that such means as top soiling and planting not only increase amenity but also assist in reducing shrinkage cracking, thereby reducing the possibility of shallow depth slides. The expression for depth of tension crack is given in equation 11.3, Chapter 11.

A method of approach to pore pressure distribution in embankment clay fill was advanced by Jewell (1996). An increase in positive pore pressure was suggested to about 1.5 m depth below embankment side slope, below which the pore pressure reduced to zero at about 2.5 m depth, as illustrated in Fig. 12.4. (Note, as pointed out by Jewell, the depths in Vaughan *et al.* (1978) are somewhat different, possibly because these authors were considering flatter

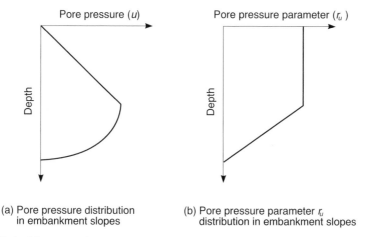

Fig. 12.4 Diagrammatic representation of pore pressure distribution for embankment slope (from Jewell, 1996), reproduced by kind permission from CIRIA

sided embankment dam slopes rather than steeper highway embankments). Drawing upon data by Atkinson and Farrar (1985) and Anderson and Kneale (1980), Jewell (1996) recommends using an r_u value of 0.20 to 1.5 m depth and a value varying linearly to zero from 1.5 to 2.5 m.

Pore pressure or groundwater in foundation

Some estimate has to be made of the groundwater or pore pressure conditions in the embankment foundation. Normally it is assumed that the pore pressure or groundwater changes caused during the construction of the bank will revert to pre-construction levels, over the long term, permitting the use of site investigation data. However, it should be remembered that construction of the embankment may itself cause changes in the groundwater table; flooding on the upstream side of an embankment built on side-long ground is a possibility. For this reason, most designers take a conservative view of site investigation piezometer information, particularly if they are limited to no more than a wet season's data.

There are some occasions when foundation pore pressures need to be measured during embankment construction. A case in point is when the embankment is being raised on compressible clay, and stability monitored in term of effective stress. More details are given in Section 12.4.4.

12.3.4 Analysis
Embankment fill

Where no features likely to constrain a failure surface are present in fill, an infinite slope, wedge analysis (sliding block) or Bishop circular arc method will normally be appropriate. Experience indicates that the majority of failure surfaces which affect embankment and cut slopes are shallow, so shallow depth potential failure surfaces should be investigated in any embankment slope stability analysis. However, note that compaction induced shear surfaces could align failure surfaces (see Section 3.4.5).

Embankment fill and foundation

Assuming that there are no features in the foundation soil, the circular arc method may be employed, extending through the embankment into the underlying foundation. If such features exist, a wedge analysis or a non-circular failure surface should be adopted, extending through the fill, with part of the surface constrained to align with the feature (Fig. 11.4, Chapter 11).

Resulting factors of safety (including those from the calculations made for the embankment fill) may be compared with those quoted as minimum values in Table 13.4 (Chapter 13).

12.3.5 Some results based on British motorway experience

The work of Perry (1989) concerning earthworks for English and Welsh motorways was introduced in Section 11.3.5, where the performance of some cut slopes was examined. Information on a number of embankments taken from his report is given below; a height range from 2.5 to 5 m was selected because embankments less than 5 m high provided some 81 per cent of the sample; clays particularly the overconsolidated variety provided most problems and are included.

It is immediately evident that the embankment side slopes are relatively steep with 1 in 2 being selected for all but the glacial till. It is therefore no surprise that the incidence of failure is relatively high for the

Table 12.1 Performance of British motorway embankments from 2.5 to 5 m high (from Perry, 1989)

Geological stratum	Age of construction (yr)	Length surveyed (m)	Slope angle (v:h)	Percentage failure
Glacial till	7	1307	1:2.5	0
	16	392	1:2.5	0
	22	311	1:2.5	1.5
London Clay	5,6	625	1:2	14.6
	10	9499	1:2	6.2
Oxford Clay	10	1191	1:2	23
	22	1500	1:2	7.1
Lower Lias	13	2402	1:2	1.7
	25	694	1:2	12.6

overconsolidated clays (London, Oxford and Lias), with percentage failure varying up to 23 per cent. But it is, at first sight, puzzling that for the London and Oxford Clays the percentage failure is higher for the younger than for the older banks. This is quite unlike the situation existing for the cut slopes discussed in Section 11.3.5, where not only was the incidence of failure far lower (usually below 5 per cent) but the younger cuts displayed a lower incidence of failure than the older, as would be expected. It suggests that in the case of the younger embankments reported by Perry, the negative pore pressures (suctions) existing in the fill at placement rapidly dissipated as water entered the banks and c' quickly reduced towards the fully softened or critical state value. The embankments failed as a consequence.

It is of interest to estimate the r_u value existing at failure for these younger embankment slopes. Perry confirms that the failure surfaces were of shallow depth (see Section 11.3.5) and consequently were unlikely to have penetrated the foundation soil; therefore, the method of Chandler and Pieris (1989), given in Appendix 4, may be employed in the calculation. Assuming an average embankment height of 3.75 m and that the cohesion has softened to 3.5 kN/m^2, we have a $c'/\gamma H$ ratio of 0.05 for a unit weight of 18 kN/m^2. If an angle of shearing resistance ϕ' of say 22.5 degrees is assumed for the fills, this calculation yields an r_u value of 0.42 at failure. Thus for the younger embankment examples concerned, r_u may have increased from a possibly negative value at the time of construction (depending upon the overconsolidation ratio of the clay fill and its depth at the borrow pit) to the relatively high value of 0.42 in a period between 5 and 10 years.

Adopting a zero effective cohesion intercept when analysing Perry's data results in an r_u value of -0.16. This value would not appear to accord with experience in most British conditions and suggests that the critical state approach ($c' = 0$) may not always apply, even when the failure surface is at shallow depth, as it was for the majority of the failures reported by Perry.

Matters concerning construction and drainage are further discussed in Sections 12.7 and 12.8.

12.4 Stability analysis: short term condition
12.4.1 General

It was demonstrated in Section 12.3.1, that for the foundation soil beneath the embankment, the factor of safety was minimum at or shortly after the end of construction (the 'short term condition'). As embankment raising normally lasts only weeks or months, the assumption is made that the foundation soil remains undrained over this period, i.e. there is no change in water content between commencement and end of embankment construction. This is the assumption behind the undrained or total stress method of analysis for the short term condition.

12.4.2 Strength properties

Embankment fill

As discussed in Section 3.3.2, Vaughan (1978a) and Vaughan *et al.* (1978) recognize clay of high plasticity (liquid limit in excess of 50 per cent) and of low plasticity (liquid limit less than 50 per cent), both materials exhibiting substantially different properties in undrained shear.

High plasticity clay fill should be tested slowly to allow pore pressures to redistribute; Vaughan *et al.* (1978) mention a rate of strain for the slow tests of 0.05 per cent/hour. When tested in this way, an undrained shear strength some 20 per cent less than the strength measured in conventional undrained tests results. The method of sample preparation is also critical for high plasticity clay. The authors consider the best method would be to extract samples from a trial embankment, rather than by testing specimens dynamically compacted in the laboratory using BS rammer procedures, because of the completely different (and unrepresentative) compacted structure that results. However, the sampling and testing procedures above described would put severe constraints on many design programmes and it might be worthwhile considering testing samples statically compacted in the laboratory, testing in the conventional manner, and decreasing the measured strength by a factor of 0.8 to account for the 20 per cent reduction referred to.

Vaughan *et al.* (1978) believe that the compacted structure of a low plasticity clay fill has negligible effect on the undrained strength and that the conventional undrained triaxial test provides a reliable indication of shear strength for design purposes.

In Section 12.3.2 there is a discussion on the ways of selecting strength properties for design purposes when several fills are involved.

Foundation

See the discussion in Section 11.4.2.

Note that when used in connection with embankments on soft (normally or lightly overconsolidated) clay, the results of *in situ* vane test may be used with correction factors (Bjerrum, 1972); these factors were based on the actual behaviour of embankments on these materials and are therefore likely to be of special relevance.

12.4.3 Analysis

Embankment fill

As with the analysis for the effective stress approach (Section 12.3.4), an infinite slope, wedge analysis (sliding block) or Bishop circular arc method will normally be adopted for embankment fill.

Embankment fill and foundation

Assuming that there are no features in the foundation soil, the circular arc method may be employed, extending through the embankment into the underlying foundation. If such features exist, a wedge analysis or non-circular failure surface should be adopted extending through the fill, with part of the surface constrained to align with the feature (Fig. 11.4, Chapter 11).

Resulting factors of safety (including those from the calculations made for the embankment fill) may be compared with those quoted as minimum values in Table 13.4 (Chapter 13).

12.4.4 The short term condition in terms of effective stress

It is possible to conduct an analysis of the short term condition in terms of effective rather than total stress, should this be desired. The principal problem with this method is estimating the magnitude of the pore pressure in a clay foundation soil as the embankment is raised. A guide may be obtained by undertaking laboratory pore pressure dissipation tests (details from Head, 1994) which will indicate the magnitude of the pore pressure rise for each increment in vertical effective stress, as the bank is constructed. Stability analyses may then be made, in effective stress terms, and the factors of safety calculated for the predicted foundation pore pressures. If it is found that the predicted pore pressure rise is such that the factor of safety would fall to an unacceptably low level (Table 13.4, Chapter 13), then construction would have to be slowed or halted until pore pressures have dissipated sufficiently to permit construction safely to proceed.

However, it would be most unwise to accept these predictions at face value and construction should only take place with comprehensive monitoring of the foundation pore pressures. Casagrande piezometers are unsuitable in low permeability clay soils (see Section 11.3.3) and hydraulic or pneumatic piezometers should be installed for pore pressure measurement. To avoid damage during embankment construction, the piezometer leads will have to be buried in trenches exiting to appropriately sited gauge houses, away from the filled area. Monitoring of displacements is also highly recommended because it provides further information on embankment stability. Using this information, the accuracy or otherwise of the laboratory test based pore pressure predictions can then be monitored and the rate of construction adjusted to ensure that factors of safety are always sufficiently high. Many engineers prefer this approach to the total stress method because of the opportunity it gives to monitor progress. It is of course possible to undertake a parallel total stress analysis, if resources permit.

Unacceptably high pore pressures can also be set up in embankment fill, particularly those constructed from low plasticity clay (Vaughan *et al.*, 1978). The same instrumented approach can be adopted in these cases, although note that pneumatic piezometers are not recommended for partly saturated soil (as often encountered with fills) or with gas generating organic materials (such as might be encountered in some soft compressible soils).

See also Section 13.3 for a discussion on the use of the Observational Method.

12.5 Settlement

12.5.1 General

Settlement estimates are particularly important where the embankment is in contact with structures; for example, culverts or bridge abutments, or where there are marked differences in foundation soils; for example, where Terrace Gravels give way to more compressible Alluvium.

The settlement of the structure at formation level (the top of the embankment) is the sum of the settlement of the foundation soil and the overlying embankment fill itself. Settlement estimates for clay foundation soils take into account primary settlement (ρ_c) and, for some clays, secondary compression (ρ_c'). To this is added immediate or 'elastic' settlement (ρ_i) which is complete at the end of construction. Total settlement is therefore:

$$\rho_t = \rho_i + \rho_c + \rho_c' \tag{12.2}$$

However, embankments are built to an elevation. As noted, immediate settlement is complete at the end of construction, so it is normally possible to 'build out' the immediate settlement by topping up the embankment with fill. This also applies to embankments on granular foundations, the settlements of which are normally complete at the end of construction. Therefore, in the case of embankments, it is usually possible to ignore immediate settlements. Total settlements for most forms of embankment construction on clays therefore become:

$$\rho_t = \rho_c + \rho_c' \tag{12.3}$$

The following concentrates on a primary and secondary settlements of clay soils and fill.

12.5.2 Primary settlement

Compressibility: As noted in Section 11.3.1, it is unlikely that many terrestrial deposits in British conditions are truly normally consolidated and most softer deposits are lightly overconsolidated to some degree. The critical property for settlement measurement in lightly overconsolidated soils is the pre-consolidation pressure (p_c). Defined as the maximum vertical effective pressure to which a sediment has been subjected in the past, it controls not only the magnitude but also the rate of settlement. Whilst a most important property in settlement estimates, it is critically dependent upon sample disturbance and graphical techniques to allow for such disturbance are provided in the standard texts. A good discussion of pre-consolidation pressure is given by Simons (1975).

Where the current *in situ* effective pressure p_o is less than p_c, and provided that the increment of applied stress Δp due to the embankment load is such that:

$$p_o + \Delta p < p_c \tag{12.4}$$

settlement of the clay bed will be small. On the other hand, where:

$$p_o + \Delta p > p_c \tag{12.5}$$

substantially greater settlements occur. This is because of the marked difference in compressibility either side of the pre-consolidation pressure, with the compressibility being much larger in stress ranges in excess of p_c.

For the case where equation 12.4 applies, the primary settlement of a clay of thickness H having a compression index C_{c1} under an increment of embankment load Δp is:

$$\rho = \frac{C_{c1}}{1 + e_o} H \log \left\{ \frac{p_o + \Delta p}{p_o} \right\} (m) \tag{12.6}$$

where e_o is the initial void ratio. Where equation 12.5 applies, the compression index for $p_o < p_c$ is C_{c1} and for $p_o > p_c$ is C_{c2}. For this case:

$$\rho = \frac{C_{c1}}{1 + e_o} H \log \frac{p_c}{p_o} + \frac{C_{c2}}{1 + e_o} H \log \left\{ \frac{p_o + \Delta p}{p_c} \right\} (m) \tag{12.7}$$

Schmertmann (1953) suggested that C_{c1} is equal to the coefficient of swelling C_s. For the more heavily overconsolidated British clays of Tertiary age and older, where the current *in situ* effective overburden pressure differs greatly from the pre-consolidation pressure, most engineers prefer to work with the coefficient of volume compressibility m_v rather than the compression index.

Compressibility characteristics of clay foundation soil may be determined using the conventional laboratory oedometer test (BS 1377: 1990: Part 5: Test 3) made on samples extracted from boreholes or trial pits. For most fill, particularly those containing coarse sand or gravel, compressibility characteristics may be obtained using larger diameter hydraulic (Rowe) cells (BS 1377: 1990: Part 6: Test 3).

Rate of settlement: The rate of settlement is governed by the coefficient of consolidation c_v. Like compressibility properties, it is also critically dependent upon the pre-consolidation pressure p_c. The expression for c_v is:

$$c_v = \frac{k}{m_v \gamma_w} (m)^2 (s) \tag{12.8}$$

where k is the coefficient of permeability and γ_w the unit weight of water. When a soil sample is loaded through the pre-consolidation pressure, k does not change but the coefficient of volume corresponding m_v increases substantially leading to a sharp reduction in c_v. As before, it is essential when measuring c_v to select the appropriate stress range, which will normally be the increment of applied embankment load Δp in excess of the current *in situ* effective overburden pressure p_o. As indicated in the appropriate British Standard (quoted above), the coefficient of consolidation may be derived using either the square root of time or the logarithm of time method. In a study of settlement and pore pressure dissipation of an embankment constructed from London Clay, Farrar (1978) found that the use of the logarithm of time method for deriving the coefficient of consolidation c_v was much more accurate than the alternative square root of time method. The possibility exists that this method will also be more accurate in the case of other overconsolidated clay fill.

The coefficient of consolidation is also particularly sensitive to sample disturbance and also sample size: continuous silt or sand layers which could have a substantial effect on drainage could be missed when sampling, or even when selecting the test specimen from the sample itself. For this reason, many engineers prefer to measure the permeability *in situ* and to use it, together with laboratory derived values of m_v and equation 12.8 to obtain c_v.

According to Davis and Poulos (1972), the assumption of one dimensional consolidation in the embankment foundation is satisfactory where the foundation thickness is less than the embankment width; in these circumstances, the results of conventional oedometer tests will be relevant. For foundation thicknesses which are large in comparison to bank widths, three dimensional flow (i.e. vertical and horizontal) becomes important and the results of oedometer tests are less relevant. Use of hydraulic cells which permit radial drainage should be considered in such cases.

12.5.3 Secondary compression

Primary settlement is directly related to drainage of pore water out of the soil under the weight of the overlying embankment fill. Another form of settlement common with soft (normally or lightly overconsolidated) clay, particularly when containing a significant organic component, is secondary compression ρ'_c, given by the expression:

$$\rho'_c = C_\alpha H \log (t_2/t_1) \tag{12.9}$$

where C_α is the coefficient of secondary compression, and t_1 and t_2 one the time periods under consideration. The time to the onset of secondary compression is normally believed to commence at about 90 per cent primary consolidation in the oedometer, but in thick consolidating beds, where the load increment due to embankment weight is small in comparison with the average effective stress in the deposit, the onset of secondary compression could be much sooner and 60 per cent primary consolidation is possible.

This form of settlement is believed due to the readjustment of the clay particles as a consequence of the decrease in void spaces brought about by drainage. It can be measured in the oedometer test (e.g. Craig, 1997) but a correlation of secondary compression (C_α) with water content is also available (Mesri, 1973).

12.5.4 Negative skin friction at structure locations

The possibility of negative skin friction acting on the back of bridge abutment walls should always be kept in mind, especially where the abutments are supported by piles and the adjoining embankment fill is placed upon compressible soil. Because of the support offered by the piles, the abutments may not settle by the same amount as the embankment fill and load may be shed from the fill on to the abutment walls, possibly overstressing the supporting piles unless they were designed for this condition.

12.6 Effect of shallow depth features on stability

12.6.1 General

A brief description of some of the more common shallow depth features and their effect on the stability of cut slopes was given in Section 11.5. In the following, examples of these features are given in connection with embankments, together with examples of possible ground improvement techniques. A good discussion of various ground improvement techniques for embankment foundations, together with references is given by O'Riordan and Seaman (1994).

12.6.2 Solifluction deposits and ancient failure surfaces

Chandler *et al.* (1973) described four case records of failures involving embankments built on ancient failure surfaces contained within former landslips or solifluction sheets. Three records showed delayed failure. The embankments were constructed safely but probably in the summer months when pore pressures on the ancient failure surfaces were low or negative. With time, after construction, and as the pore pressures on these surfaces increased due to seasonal effects, failure occurred. These records illustrate not only the importance of assigning correct residual shear strength ϕ'_r values to the ancient failure surfaces, but also the importance of adopting realistic pore water pressures for the foundation soils, i.e. those that reflect realistic permanent works conditions.

Where soils in which fissures, foliations and ancient failure surfaces are common at or near the surface, the 'toe dig-out' has been proposed (Garrett and Wale, 1985), illustrated in Fig. 12.5. The foundation soils at the

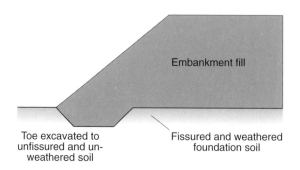

Toe excavated to
unfissured and un-
weathered soil

Fissured and weathered
foundation soil

Fig. 12.5   Example of toe dig-out (from Garrett and Wale, 1985)

embankment toe are excavated until stiff and intact materials are met and the excavated soils replaced by well-compacted granular soil or by other suitable materials. The depth of the toe dig-out and its lateral extent will be determined by the lateral resistance necessary to support the embankment slope.

12.6.3   Soft compressible soil
General

In soft compressible soil, embankment foundation stability may be enhanced by one of four principal methods:

- pre-loading or surcharging
- drainage
- structural elements
- excavation and replacement
- use of lightweight fill.

Some examples of these construction expedients are given in Fig. 12.6.

Pre-loading and surcharging

Pre-loading means that the embankment is raised at the earliest moment so that the underlying foundation soil can consolidate for as long as possible, thus increasing the soil's effective strength and reducing the settlements to be experienced during operation. Surcharging means the construction of the embankment to a height above its design level and removing the excess fill at as late a stage as possible; again with the intention of increasing the soil's effective strength and reducing the amount of settlement during operation. On weak soils, checks should be made that the additional load due to the surcharge will not fail the embankment.

A combination of both pre-loading and surcharging is very common. A method of calculating the surcharge necessary to eliminate primary consolidation under working load is given by Johnson (1970).

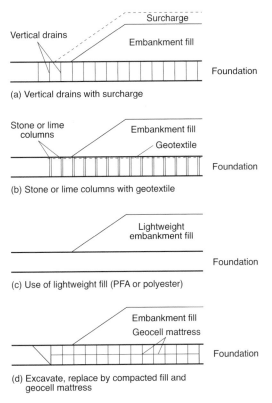

Fig. 12.6 Examples of various construction expedients to secure a soft clay foundation

Drainage

This approach includes the introduction of vertical plastic strip drains and staged construction (the controlled slow placement of fill); both methods permit pore pressures to dissipate in the foundation soil, thereby increasing its effective shear strength. These techniques are often adopted with pre-loading and/or surcharging.

Structural elements

Adding a structural element to the ground is a common method of strengthening the embankment foundation. Conventional piles, lime columns or stone columns are the most common techniques, usually with some sort of geotextile reinforcement laid at the surface. A piled raft was adopted for a section of the M60 Manchester ring road (*New Civil Engineer*, 2000). Instead of excavating nearly 200 000 m^3 of peat present at foundation level and replacing with imported fill, a 900 m long reinforced concrete raft supported by some 4500 pre-cast concrete piles was constructed. In this way, earthworks in the wet winter weather were avoided and the works proceeded to programme. Another reported advantage was the 72 000 lorry movements, through local roads, saved by the redesign.

This solution may also be considered for unstable sites such as former landslides, where the additional fill load placed directly upon the unstrengthened ground could provoke further instability. Snedker (1985) describes a trunk road running transverse to a slipped area in a hillside, formed from Etruria Marl, in which ancient failure surfaces to depths of 7 m had been discovered. Two rows of 915 mm diameter bored piles stabilised the hillside and permitted the up-slope cut and fill required by the highway construction.

Excavation and replacement

Another option favoured where embankments are to be raised on soft compressible soil, is to excavate and to replace by good quality fill, with or without a form of geocell mattress. However, excavation may have to take place below the groundwater table, as may placing and compacting the replacement fill. Such solutions may also require large volumes of unsuitable soil to be taken to tip and large quantities of fill to be imported, which are not environmentally attractive.

The consequences of excavation on the stability of adjoining buildings should be kept in mind.

Lightweight fill

Instead of devoting resources to strengthening the foundation soil, a different approach would be to reduce the load imposed by the embankment. This could be achieved by replacing some or all of the embankment fill by lightweight substances such as pulverized fuel ash or polyester foam. Nettleton *et al.* (1996) describe how the use of pulverized fuel ash fill for part of the A13 embankment reduced the calculated load on the foundation soils by some 25 per cent. A combination of various approaches may be considered. Note that polyester foam will be damaged if allowed to come in contact with fuel oils; consequently, drainage must be comprehensive and secure if foam is to be adopted. It is also known to be inflammable.

12.7 Construction aspects

12.7.1 Foundation excavation

Prior to placing the first layers of fill, the topsoil should be stripped and the embankment foundation checked to ensure that all weak, weathered or otherwise unsuitable material has been removed during excavation and that design formation level has been reached. The design formation level is that level to which the strength and compressibility data used in the design apply. Particular note should be taken of fissures, foliations and ancient failure surfaces, whether revealed by the site investigation or not. The designer must feel confident that the strength and compressibility characteristics adopted during design can be met in practice, and examination of the exposed soils in situ is essential.

If not already adopted at the design stage, a toe dig-out solution (Fig. 12.5) could be warranted if the inspection revealed more severe conditions than anticipated.

12.7.2 Non-uniform compaction and 'over-building'

Compaction may not be uniform across the whole cross-sectional area of the bank, because of the difficulty of securing full compactive effort at the edges. The requirement for uniform strength and compressibility characteristics throughout the embankment is consequently compromized. This unwelcome development may be avoided by 'overbuilding', or constructing the embankment wider than is necessary according to design geometrical requirements (Fig. 12.7(a)). Alternatively, and if the land is not available a slope steeper than the final design slope can be constructed and then trimmed back (Fig. 12.7(b)). If this latter procedure is adopted, foundation and embankment stability should be checked for the steeper side slopes. Whichever approach is employed, higher levels of compaction can be achieved up to the edge of the final embankment slope with beneficial consequences for stability, although less so for the approach shown in Fig. 12.7(b).

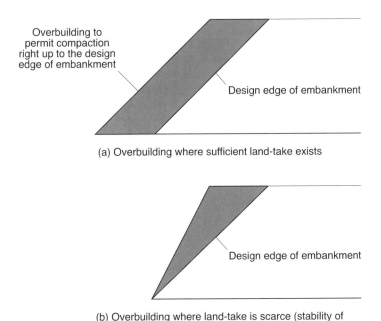

Overbuilding to permit compaction right up to the design edge of embankment

Design edge of embankment

(a) Overbuilding where sufficient land-take exists

Design edge of embankment

(b) Overbuilding where land-take is scarce (stability of temporary steeper profile to be checked)

Fig. 12.7 Increasing the degree of compaction at the embankment edge by 'overbuilding'

As already noted, overconsolidated clays at water contents well below their plastic limit are particularly difficult to compact, and chunks will at best be brought into contact but not kneaded together. This kind of under-compaction (see Section 3.4.3) taken together with non-uniform compaction provides excellent opportunities for water to enter the surface of an embankment, contributing to instability.

12.8 Drainage aspects

12.8.1 Carriageway

Studies of failed slopes in embankments raised from overconsolidated clays (Greenwood *et al.*, 1985) demonstrated the importance of proper detailing of drainage of the carriageway. For the slips investigated (in eastern England), the failed mass was very wet and extremely soft. It was concluded that water had entered the embankment via an extended granular sub-base, i.e. the carriageway sub-base had been extended outwards from the underside of the carriageway towards the embankment edges. Water had penetrated and the fill had been softened in this area. No indication was given as to whether the outer edges of the embankments had been compacted by overbuilding (see Section 12.7.2), the absence of which would have accounted for some of the softened state of the fill. Irrespective of the absence or otherwise of overbuilding during construction, water draining into the edges of embankment fill can only be deleterious and the proper detailing of carriageway drainage is essential.

12.8.2 Foundation

Basal drainage blankets are sometimes provided between the formation and the overlying embankment fill. Properly designed and installed, they can assist in lowering the pore pressures both in the fill and, if present, in the underlying foundation. However, if the incorrect particle size distribution is selected for the drainage blanket, or if otherwise appropriate material becomes contaminated, then basal drainage can have just the opposite effect. Flow of water from the embankment to atmosphere via the embankment side slopes may be encouraged and effective stresses in the base of the bank may be reduced (Fig. 12.8(a)). Finlayson *et al.* (1984) put down part of the reason for failure of a 10 m high embankment formed from clay till and London Clay to poorly functioning basal drains. Where their use is necessary, care is required in specifying layer thickness, falls and particle size distribution together with the method of installation so that clogging is avoided (Fig. 12.8(b)). It may be necessary to provide a separator between the drain and the foundation or the overlying fill, either as a graded filter or as some form of geotextile.

Note that the oxidation of pyrite in argillaceous fill (overconsolidated clay, shale, mudstone) may produce ferrous sulphate, which may in turn oxidise to ferric hydroxide. If precipitated in drains, it could cause blockages (*The Highways Agency Advice Note* HA 48/92).

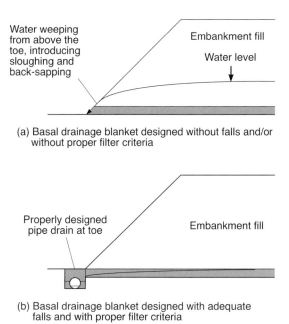

(a) Basal drainage blanket designed without falls and/or without proper filter criteria

(b) Basal drainage blanket designed with adequate falls and with proper filter criteria

Fig. 12.8 Effect of properly designed basal drainage blanket on embankment performance

Where embankments are constructed on side-long ground, water could back-up against the up-hill side of the embankment unless drainage is provided. Open ditch drainage is often used in these (and other) circumstances. However, there is evidence (Parsons and Perry, 1985) that open ditch drains promote instability of the embankment toe, which may be reflected in shallow depth movements in the overlying embankment itself. This could force the embankment sides to adopt a non-uniform profile and which, in turn, could disrupt gulley discharge drains, causing flow of drainage water on to the embankment slopes (Fig. 12.9(a)). The use of properly designed and constructed pipe drains may be preferable instead of open ditches, especially in softer and more compressible foundation soils, if this problem is to be reduced, if not avoided (Fig. 12.9(b)).

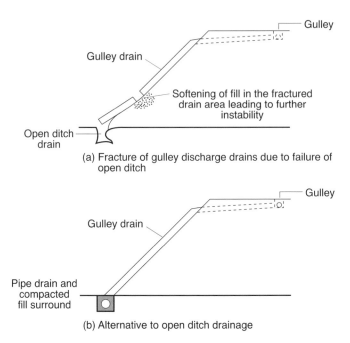

Gulley

Gulley drain

Softening of fill in the fractured
drain area leading to further
instability

Open ditch
drain

(a) Fracture of gulley discharge drains due to failure of
open ditch

Gulley

Gulley drain

Pipe drain and
compacted
fill surround

(b) Alternative to open ditch drainage

Fig. 12.9 Effect of improperly constructed toe-drain on embankment stability

13. Factor of safety of cuts and embankments

13.1 General

13.1.1 Definitions

A factor of safety is applied to a soil or rock parameter in order to yield a design value for further engineering analysis. There are two approaches (Nicholson *et al.*, 1999):

CIRIA Report 104: Design value = soil (or rock) parameter value

× (1/'lumped' factor of safety)

Eurocode 7 (1995): Design value = soil (or rock) characteristic value

× (1/partial factor)

In this book, the Construction Industry Research and Information Association CIRIA 104 (Padfield and Mair, 1984) or 'lumped' factor of safety method is adopted. This requires the establishment of a design value which is more conservative than the 'most probable' or probabilistic mean but is less conservative than the 'worst credible', or the worst value which the engineer believes could occur in practice. It may be termed the 'conservative best estimate' and may be regarded as being a cautious assessment of the data. Whether or not the engineer is entitled to draw the conclusion that the conservative best estimate has been made depends upon the amount and quality of the data available and on other factors considered below.

For a good discussion of the principles behind both the CIRIA 104 and the Eurocode 7 approaches, Nicholson *et al.* (1999) should be consulted.

A quite different concept of 'factor of safety' was introduced by Perry (1989) who considered designing to restrict failure to less than one percent of the length of an earthwork over a 25 year period. This is an interesting approach. By accepting that failure can occur, at a location which is unspecified, the engineer is clearly moving away from ideas of 'safety' to ideas of 'maintenance'. Essentially, these two ideas are mutually incompatible because with the 'maintenance approach' failure is perceived as being admissible; indeed, it is at the heart of the concept. Failure is designed to a time span, in this case 25 years. Thus the phenomena of pore pressure redistribution in overconsolidated clay and of softening of embankment fill are acknowledged, noting that both have a major bearing on earthwork stability. Therefore, it becomes a major economic consideration whether to design to sufficiently flat slopes to preserve stability at all times or whether to design to steeper slopes, in the knowledge that failure will probably occur a decade or so hence.

Nevertheless, when using the approach put forward by Perry, many engineers would wish to check using the more conventional definition of factor of safety, expanded upon below. This is particularly the case in high risk areas. However, the question remains, what is a high risk area in 25 years time? There is no easy answer to this question, apart from the obvious comment that one can only design on what is known or what is planned at the time the design is being prepared. Close co-operation, at the design stage, with the relevant authorities who would have to cope with the consequences of any failure a long way into the future would seem essential if this approach is to be adopted.

13.1.2   Category of data and effect on factor of safety

The factor of safety selected will usually depend upon two sets of circumstances:

- a technical assessment of the geotechnical data collected for the potential slip
- a judgement on the safety, environmental and economic costs of any failure.

An obvious difficulty in deciding the factor of safety to adopt for a particular structure is that the data corresponding to the above two sets of circumstances are of quite different categories: the technical assessment will be performed on data based on observation and experiment, like strata succession, groundwater conditions, strengths and densities; whilst the safety, environmental and economic costs will inevitably be based mainly on subjective judgements of matters such as lives at risk, amenity loss, pollution damage and cost to the promoter and to others who may be unwittingly caught up in the consequences of a failure.

Some engineers may prefer to lump these two matters together under the broad heading of 'experience' and this is essentially the approach of BS 6031: 1981. An alternative approach is given by the Geotechnical Engineering Office, Hong Kong (1984) which relates factors of safety for new slopes to risk to life and economic risk (for a ten year return period rainfall). This approach, in effect, distinguishes not only the technical category but also differentiates between loss of life and economic loss within the safety, environmental and economic category. It is considered that the Geotechnical Engineering Office approach allows an orderly progression of the selection of a factor of safety for both categories of data.

These two categories are discussed further, below.

13.1.3 Technical category

As already noted, the items for consideration under the heading 'technical category' are those obtained from observation and experiment usually, although by no means always, conducted at the site investigation stage. They include ground and groundwater conditions, laboratory and *in situ* tests, and the nature of the stability analysis.

Ground and groundwater conditions

Matters to note include:

- the complexity of the strata succession, its nature and the thickness and heterogeneity of the various layers
- the nature and degree of fabric or structure exhibited by the soils and rocks
- the presence of depositional or post-depositional features such as wash-outs, uncomformities, scour hollows, buried channels, solution holes, faults and folds
- the nature and complexity of the ground water table(s) or the pore pressure condition(s). This is particularly important if only limited standpipe or piezometer data are available on which to base the analysis, or where the hydrogeological conditions are complicated
- the presence of mine shafts or other old workings.

For embankments, the nature, heterogeneity and disposition of the fill is a major consideration affecting the confidence with which fill properties, pore pressure and groundwater conditions can be assessed. As discussed in Chapter 12, pore pressure conditions are particularly difficult to gauge in embankment fills.

Laboratory and *in situ* tests

Matters to note include:

- the number of tests, their representativeness and reliability with respect to the soils and rocks concerned
- the scatter of test results
- the availability of precedent information: important if information on adjoining failures is available, from which engineering properties may be 'back-analysed'.

Nature of the stability analysis

Matters to note include:

- whether total or effective stress procedures are adopted
- the accuracy of the stability analysis method employed
- the possibility of complicated failure mechanisms not normally treated by routine stability methods.

Except at unity, different methods of stability analysis will not necessarily yield the same factor of safety. Significant differences can occur, depending upon the assumptions made in the analysis. A summary of assumptions and some of the advantages and disadvantages of the most important methods of stability analysis is given in Table 11.1 (Chapter 11).

13.1.4 Safety, environmental and economic category

The subjective judgements necessary in this category are frequently informed by experts other than engineers; input might be necessary from environmental specialists, planners and economists, especially for the larger structures and the larger risks. For smaller structures, guidance can often be obtained from the relevant officials in the local or county authority in whose area the works are being constructed. Assistance in making these judgements may also be gained by employing a framework of risk analysis and management. Valuable guidance on the application of risk principles can be obtained from the RAMP (Risk Analysis and Management for Projects) report (1998); advice directed more specifically to geotechnical problems is given by Clayton (2001).

Unlike decisions made under the technical category which, as noted, normally await information from the site investigation, decisions made under the heading safety, environmental and economic category can be made well in advance of project implementation, thus permitting firmer control of budget and programme. However, major schemes can, and usually do, invite press speculation and adverse comment from those who consider themselves disadvantaged by the proposals. In this respect, it is essential for the engineer and others involved to understand the difference between risk as understood by the expert and the risk as perceived by the lay public. As it is the public who can, and often do, succeed in modifying original proposals in the light of its perception of the risk the proposals represent, such understanding is essential.

The approach given to assessing safety, environmental and economic risk in the following is similar to that of the Geotechnical Engineering Office, Hong Kong (1984). Its approach was to equate safety risk with the occupation density of the structure likely to be affected by failure. Examples of safety risk, with adaptations considered appropriate for the difference between Hong Kong and the United Kingdom, are reproduced in Table 13.1.

Environmental risk does not appear to have been considered by the Geotechnical Engineering Office. It has been added in Table 13.2, subdivided into amenity risk (loss of an exceptional established and mature environment) and pollution risk.

Highways Agency Advice Note HA 48/93 gives advice on the reinstatement of slope failures. There are five categories:

Table 13.1 Examples of safety risk (adapted from Geotechnical Engineering Office, Hong Kong, 1984)

	Example	Risk to life		
		negligible	*low*	*high*
(i)	open farmland	✓		
(ii)	country parks, lightly used recreation grounds	✓		
(iii)	country roads and low traffic density B roads	✓		
(iv)	storage compounds (non-hazardous goods)	✓		
(v)	town squares, sitting out areas, playgrounds and car parks		✓	
(vi)	high traffic density B roads		✓	
(vii)	public waiting areas (e.g. railway stations, bus stops)			✓
(viii)	occupied buildings (residential, commercial, industrial and educational)			✓
(ix)	all A roads, by-passes and motorways, including associated slip roads, petrol stations and service areas			✓
(x)	buildings storing hazardous goods, power stations (all types), nuclear, chemical and biological complexes			✓

Category (i): Those which require prompt action because of imminent danger of large movements affecting the carriageway and associated works, nearby structures, including those belonging to others, or statutory undertakers services

Category (ii.1): Likely to develop into Category (i) within a few weeks if weather conditions are adverse

Category (ii.2): Likely to be stable for a few weeks but may become unstable within a few months if weather conditions continue to be adverse

Category (ii.3): Tolerable for a year, unlikely to affect third parties

Category (iii): Most unlikely to affect areas outside the slope; will not affect carriageway, services or any property for many years.

The classification deals with the reinstatement of slope failures but it will be remembered that it is not only reinstatement which requires consideration; some first time failures of large cuts or embankments can be significant in themselves.

13.1.5 Temporary works (short term) and permanent works (long term) conditions

A further consideration to be taken into account in selecting a factor of safety is the nature of the works: whether the temporary (short term) or permanent (long term) condition. 'Temporary works' defines the period

Table 13.2 Examples of economic and environmental risk (adapted from Geotechnical Engineering Office, Hong Kong, 1984)

	Example	Economic and environmental risk		
		negligible	*low*	*high*
(i)	open farmland, country parks, lightly used recreation areas of low amenity value	✓		
(ii)	country and low traffic density B roads, open air car parks	✓		
(iii)	facilities whose failure would cause only slight pollution	✓		
(iv)	essential services (e.g. gas, electricity, water) whose failure would cause loss of service for a short period		✓	
(v)	facilities whose failure would cause significant pollution or severe loss of amenity (cultivated public gardens, with established and mature trees)		✓	
(vi)	high traffic density B and all A roads, residential and low rise commercial, industrial and educational properties		✓	
(vii)	facilities whose failure would cause heavy pollution			✓
(viii)	essential services whose failure would cause loss of service for a prolonged period			✓
(ix)	buildings whose failure would cause extensive structural damage			✓
(x)	all A roads, by-passes, motorways including associated slip roads, structures and service areas			✓
(xi)	buildings storing hazardous goods, power stations (all types), nuclear, chemical and biological complexes			✓

during which there are the construction activities necessary to build the structure; 'permanent works' defines the period when the structure is occupied or otherwise employed in discharging its design function. As such, temporary works are usually of short duration, varying from weeks to months, whilst the permanent works usually last several decades. Exceptionally, temporary works can last for years, not least because of factors such as project over-runs and industrial action. 'Short-term' and 'long-term' are geotechnical terms illustrating periods during which the assumption of undrained (total stress) and drained (effective stress) conditions can realistically be made; 'temporary works' and 'permanent works' are engineering terms of much broader significance, connoting amongst other things the engineer's perception of society's attitude to acceptable levels of risk.

Staff and operatives on site are qualified by experience and/or training to recognize the onset of failure in earthworks and to take appropriate actions to preserve their own safety and that of their colleagues. In this respect, they are unlike members of the lay public who cannot be expected to take such measures. Furthermore, temporary works are usually directly under the contractor's control and any failure is usually the contractor's own risk; the temporary works condition also offers the contractor an opportunity to use imagination and expertise to formulate a solution which will achieve (or improve on) both budget and programme. For these reasons, the convention has grown that the factor of safety for the temporary works condition may be substantially lower than that of the permanent works condition (Padfield and Mair, 1984, Table 5). This convention is followed here.

As always with factor of safety selection, the actual factors to be adopted depend upon the circumstances specific to the engineering problem in hand.

13.2 Possible approach to factor of safety selection
13.2.1 Cuts

Two conditions are normally treated for failures in cuts: first time failures, involving fresh cuts, and reactivation failures, involving ancient failure surfaces present in the soil mass. The factor of safety selected for the latter is almost invariably lower than for the former. Failure involving the reactivation of ancient failure surfaces usually takes place slowly, giving time for the appropriate warnings to be given to operatives and the public and frequently for remedial measures to be introduced. With fresh cuts, failure, were it to occur, could take place more quickly, possibly with dangerous consequences for the public. Different factors of safety are therefore applied for the two conditions. BS 6031: 1981 refers to factors of safety for cut slopes between 1.3 and 1.4 for first time failures and about 1.20 for failures involving ancient failure surfaces.

Table 13.3   Possible factors of safety for cut slopes*

Environmental and economic risk	Safety risk					
	Factor of safety (first time failure)			Factor of safety (reactivation failure)		
	negligible	*low*	*high*	*negligible*	*low*	*high*
negligible	1.30 (1.10)	1.35 (1.15)	1.40 (1.20)	1.10 (>1.0)	1.15 (1.05)	1.20 (1.10)
low	1.35 (1.15)	1.40 (1.20)	1.45 (1.25)	1.15 (1.05)	1.20 (1.10)	1.25 (1.15)
high	1.40 (1.20)	1.45 (1.25)	1.50 (1.30)	1.20 (1.10)	1.25 (1.15)	1.30 (1.20)

* Figures in brackets represent the factor of safety for the temporary works condition.

Possible factors of safety for cut slopes are given in Table 13.3 above: they are based on the values quoted by BS 6031 (1981) but take into account the safety risk on the one hand and the environmental and economic risk on the other. They also take into account the difference between the temporary works and permanent works conditions. The actual factor of safety to be adopted will depend upon the engineer's assessment of the structure and site specific conditions, including matters outlined in Sections 13.1.3 to 13.1.5.

Factors of safety may change depending upon the quality of the data to hand. A factor of safety less than 1.30 for negligible risk first time failure (permanent works condition) could be considered if very good information were available. However, if the quality of the information were poor, it might be necessary to increase the factor of safety for the stated risk; for example, instead of adopting a factor of safety of 1.40 for a low risk first time failure, a figure of 1.45 or even 1.50 might be necessary. For low risk reactivation failures (permanent works condition), a value of 1.10 rather than 1.20 could be adopted where there is very good information and monitoring will be performed (see Section 13.3).

For rocks where there are no traces of ancient failure surfaces, factors of safety appropriate to first time failure in soils may be considered.

Rather than increase the factor of safety, which at best is a step based on informed but qualitative judgements, the designer may feel that more technical data are needed. Contractual arrangements should be such that further geotechnical investigation may be undertaken, if necessary during construction, to achieve the desired level of knowledge and greater certainty in design.

Another alternative is to 'design out' the element of uncertainty surrounding a particular technical factor; for example, if the nature and extent of ancient failure surfaces and/or the appropriate residual shear strength values were in doubt, the designer might feel justified in adopting the toe dig-out approach (see Section 12.6.2). If little information were available about groundwater table rise, the designer could adopt a more comprehensive drainage than might have been necessary had more complete information been available. The designer should always inform the promoter of the possible cost savings to be gained by further geotechnical investigation.

13.2.2 Embankments
Embankment fill

In principle, there would appear to be no difference between the selection of factors of safety for a cut and for an embankment slope. However, in practice, differences may be substantial. Although soils can and do change rapidly throughout the length of a cut, they can be investigated before the main works and the implications for factor of safety selection determined.

This is unlikely to be the case for embankments where, unless the locations of the various fill types are specified, fill can vary markedly and unpredictably in distribution. Moreover, as has been seen, pore pressure response in embankments can be highly uncertain, particularly over the long term or permanent works condition.

Embankment performance also depends upon drainage, whose efficacy is controlled not only by the robustness of its design and construction but also by its maintenance. Design and construction on the one hand and maintenance on the other are often undertaken by different organizations, certainly at different times. Note that Bishop and Vaughan (1962) wrote: 'The principle uncertainty in the determination of factor of safety (of embankment dams) lies in the estimate of pore pressure represented by the term r_u'. This statement would probably be challenged by few engineers today, whether for embankment dams or for any other form of major embankment construction involving clay fill.

For these reasons, it is probably prudent to adopt somewhat higher factors of safety for embankment slopes than for cut slopes. A factor of safety of 1.4 is suggested (negligible risk), for the permanent works condition, which could be reduced if very good information were available, including experience from similar banks. Use of an enhanced factor of safety should also help to guard against delayed failure of embankment slopes and assist in keeping maintenance costs to a minimum.

Foundation

There are two foundation soil types requiring consideration for the temporary works condition: soft and 'other soil', because of the quite different order of deformations set up during construction. It is assumed that the shear strength of the embankment fill will be mobilised, as well as the foundation, although as noted in Section 12.3.2, some engineers analyse foundation stability without taking embankment strength into account. If this is the case, then a lower factor of safety than quoted below may be employed:

Other soil: deformation of the foundation during construction is not normally a problem and a factor of safety of 1.3 on the short term or temporary works condition (negligible risk) is probably acceptable.

Soft compressible soil: a factor of safety as low as 1.3 on the temporary works condition (negligible risk) could result in substantial deformation of the foundation soil during construction: whilst failure might not occur, there could be damage to services already installed in, or adjoining, the embankment, such as drainage lines or ditches. Furthermore, cracks could be produced in the fill which could have consequences for the bank's performance over the long term. Consequently, to obtain the factor of safety of a foundation comprising soft compressible soil, in the temporary works

Table 13.4 Possible factors of safety for embankment fill and foundation*

| Environmental and economic risk | Safety risk | | | | | |
| | embankment fill | | | foundation | | |
	negligible	low	high	negligible	low	high
negligible	1.40 (1.20)	1.45 (1.25)	1.50 (1.30)	1.30 (1.10)	1.35 (1.15)	1.40 (1.20)
low	1.45 (1.25)	1.50 (1.30)	1.55 (1.35)	1.35 (1.15)	1.40 (1.20)	1.45 (1.25)
high	1.50 (1.30)	1.55 (1.35)	1.60 (1.40)	1.40 (1.20)	1.45 (1.25)	1.50 (1.30)

* 1.40 denotes factors of safety for the stated risks for the permanent works condition (1.20) denotes factors of safety for the stated risks for the temporary works condition for 'other soil'. The temporary works factor of safety (foundations) to be increased by at least 15 per cent when constructing embankments on 'soft compressible soil'.

condition, it is suggested that the factors of safety recommended for 'other soils' should be increased by at least 15 per cent.

Settlement must also be checked (the total of embankment fill and foundation). If foundation settlement is unacceptably large, it might itself prompt the need for a higher factor of safety on embankment stability.

The various circumstances may be summarized in Table 13.4. As with cut slopes, the actual factor of safety employed will depend upon the engineer's assessment of the structure and site specific conditions, including the various matters outlined in Sections 13.1.3 to 13.1.5.

13.3 Use of instrumentation and the observational method
13.3.1 General

In addition to providing information necessary for design, instrumentation may provide assistance by yielding information to check safety:

- during the temporary works condition
- during the permanent works condition.

13.3.2 Temporary works

In Section 12.4.4, an approach to analysing and constructing an embankment on soft compressible soils in terms of effective stress was described. The embankment is raised until measured pore pressures reach such values that the factor of safety falls to an unacceptably low level. Construction then slows or is halted until pore pressures dissipate and construction can safely resume. This approach could benefit from application of the Observational Method (Nicholson *et al.*, 1999). *Eurocode 7* (1995), states: 'Because the prediction of geotechnical behaviour is often difficult, it is sometimes appropriate to adopt the approach known as the 'observational method', in which the design is reviewed during construction'. *Eurocode 7* continues by erecting four criteria which must be satisfied before construction commences:

- acceptable limits of behaviour should be established
- it must be shown that there is an acceptable probability that the actual behaviour will lie within these limits
- monitoring methods should reveal whether or not actual behaviour falls within acceptable limits, noting that the monitoring itself should be sufficiently frequent to enable contingency actions to be taken, and noting that the response time of the instruments and the time necessary to analyse them should also be sufficiently rapid
- contingency actions should be prepared which may be adopted if monitoring reveals behaviour outside the acceptable limits.

In the case of an embankment constructed on soft compressible soil, the acceptable limits of pore pressure rise would be established from the results of the laboratory tests. The acceptable probability that the actual behaviour would fall between the acceptable limits could be checked on the assumption that the actual behaviour follows the most probable or probabilistic mean of the data. The nature and extent of the instrumentation should be such that pore pressure rise is monitored at the most critical areas beneath the embankment and the monitoring process should be designed to generate the correct frequency of readings. A plan of campaign should be established in advance of the construction so that all concerned are aware of what should be done if actual behaviour falls outside the acceptable limits. This will normally entail halting or slowing construction until pore pressures have dissipated sufficiently to allow further work to carry on, when the above described procedure is repeated until construction is complete.

13.3.3 Permanent works

As has been seen, embankment failure may occur as a consequence of the increase of initially low or negative pore pressures (suctions); such failures are usually shallow depth and their onset can often be checked by visual observation of the bank slopes. More comprehensive instrumentation for both embankments and cuttings could include:

- monuments sited on berms and at the toe of the slope to permit measurements of both vertical and horizontal movements
- inclinometers
- crack-width measurements
- piezometers.

It is frequently advantageous to plot movements and pore pressure readings against time, with rainfall superimposed, so that any link can be established and conclusions drawn regarding the requirement or otherwise for further remedial action.

Simplicity and robustness should be the keynote of any instrumentation scheme and reference should be made to established texts such as Hanna (1985) and Dunnicliff (1988) to decide upon the best approach. However, note that instrumentation does not of itself guarantee safety or success: there must be a reliable system established to monitor the equipment and to interpret the results, as demanded of the Observational Method for temporary works. The cutting or embankment concerned may have a service life of decades and it may be difficult to ensure continuity of monitoring for anything like such a period. Nevertheless, even a few years monitoring after construction can provide valuable information to the designer and give confidence to the promoter.

14. Note on site safety considerations

14.1 General

Potentially, earthworks sites are amongst the most dangerous because of the variety of work being conducted and because of the speed at which some earth-moving plant can operate. Dangers include:

- falling objects from overhead plant and during demolition of existing structures
- contaminants (liquids, solids and gases) which may be found on brown-field sites and chemicals such as quicklime used to stabilize some fills (BS 890, 1995 and Smith, 1996)
- asphyxiating gases in confined spaces (old basements or other buried structures) during demolition
- collapse of excavations during site clearance
- unattended (open) excavations
- damage to (and from) public utilities such as electricity and gas mains
- falling rocks or rubble when working the face at a quarry (borrow), cutting or from higher benches
- blasting operations
- heavy earth-moving plant on haul roads and elsewhere
- heavy plant left at the edges of embankments or at part-completed retaining walls
- reversing plant all over the site.

Staff undertaking *in situ* tests (such as dry density determinations) are particularly at risk from earth-moving and compaction plant. They should be protected by warning lights and barriers.

Safety will be improved if plant is segregated into its own haul roads, away from private cars and pedestrians. Haul road surfaces should be well maintained because this improves braking distances; watering during dry weather helps to reduce dust nuisance. Plant should be restricted to travelling parallel to the dip of the slope, wherever possible. Tipping at the edge of a fill, without the use of chocks, should not be permitted.

14.2   Legislation and references

Organizations are obliged to have their own health and safety management plans and systems which should take into account legislation specific to construction sites, such as:

- Construction (Design and Management) Regulations 1994
- Construction (Health, Safety and Welfare) Regulations 1996
- Construction (Head Protection) Regulations 1989
- Confined Spaces Regulations 1997
- Manual Handling Operations Regulations 1992.

Depending upon the nature of the site, other regulations, e.g. The Control of Substances Hazardous to Health Regulations 1994 (COSHH) could be applicable, as could the Control of Asbestos at Work Regulations (1987). Further information and guidance on the subject can be obtained from:

- Construction Health and Safety: published by the Construction Industry Publications Ltd for the Building Employers Confederation
- Site Safety: CIRIA publication SP137
- CDM Regulations – Work Sector Guidance for Designers
- Managing Construction for Health and Safety – CDM Approved Code of Practice: published by the UK Health and Safety Commission.

The above list is not exhaustive. Much practical guidance on safety issues in earthworks engineering can be gained by reference to BS 6031: 1981.

14.3   Construction site safety: outline procedures

Before work commences, the project director must be satisfied that the staff, both at the office and on the site, thoroughly understand:

- the nature of the project and the risk to health and safety which it might bring in its train, and
- the legislation likely to control or impact upon site activities.

Also prior to project commencement, a risk assessment must be undertaken on all aspects of the work in order, so far as is reasonably practicable, to avoid or reduce the possibility of risk of injury and danger to health to all the workforce. The assessment should be done by, or with, somebody with a thorough understanding of the project and of the importance of each particular work activity. In such a way, the 'ownership' of the various risks, and how they can be mitigated or avoided, should become clear. With this information, and having regard to the various items of legislation, a safety plan may be formulated. which should:

- take account of the need to co-ordinate with other site users (including visitors)
- establish procedures for site training and induction for new-joiners

- ensure that copies of the relevant legislation are prominently displayed in work offices
- establish rules and emergency procedures, including those for first-aid
- establish measures for issuing appropriate protective clothing and safety equipment
- establish procedures for regular meetings between the senior personnel on site dealing with safety issues
- establish procedures for documenting and reporting accidents
- devise regular audits to compare site procedures with the safety plan.

Construction (Design and Management) Regulations 1994 will apply to all construction works classed as 'construction work' within the regulations and work involving demolition. Work of duration longer than 30 days or involving more than 500 staff days of construction work or involving demolition will also have to be notified to the Health and Safety Executive.

The requirements of the CDM regulations are onerous. As the majority of earthworks projects will fall within the scope of the regulations, the reader is referred to them and also to the Approved Code of Practice to the CDM regulations, quoted in Section 14.2, above.

For all projects, the organization's Health and Safety staff should be consulted to determine the sufficiency of the above for the particular problems in hand.

References

Al-Hussaini M. (1983). Effect of particle size and strain conditions on the strength of crushed basalt. *Can. Geotech. J.*, **20**, 706–717.

Al-Khafaji A.N. (1993). Estimation of soil compaction parameters by means of Atterberg limits. *Q.J. Engng Geol.*, **26**, No. 4, 359–368.

Anderson M.G. and Kneale P.E. (1980). Pore water pressure and stability conditions on a motorway embankment. *Earth Surface Processes*, **5**, 37–46.

Anderson M.G. and Kneale, P.E. (1982). The influence of shrinkage cracks on pore pressures within a clay embankment. *Q.J. Engng Geol.*, **15**, No. 1, 9–14.

Anon (1970). The logging of rock cores for engineering purposes. *Q.J. Engng Geol.*, **3**, No. 1, 1–24.

Anon (1977). The description of rock masses for engineering purposes. *Q.J. Engng Geol.*, **10**, No. 4, 355–388.

ASTM D 1557–91 (1997). *Test method for laboratory compaction characteristics of a soil using modified effort*. American Society for Testing and Materials, Philadelphia, PA.

ASTM D 5093–90 (1997). *Standard test method for field measurement of infiltration rate using a double ring infiltrometer with a sealed inner ring*. American Society for Testing and Materials, Philadelphia, PA.

Atkinson J.H. (1981). *Foundations and slopes: an introduction to applications of critical state soil mechanics*. London: McGraw-Hill.

Atkinson J.H. and Farrar D.M. (1985). Stress path tests to measure soil strength parameters for shallow landslips. *Proc. 12th Int. Conf. Soil Mechanics and Found. Engng, San Fransisco*, **4**, 983–986.

Atkinson M.F. (1993). *Structural foundations manual for low-rise buildings*. E and F.N. Spon, London.

Australian Standard AS 3798 (1990). *Guidelines on earthworks for commercial and residential developments*. Standards Australia, Sydney, New South Wales.

Barley A.D. (1996). Discussion on Ortigao *et al. Proc. Instn Civ. Engrs, Geotech. Engng*, **119**, Oct., 238–239.

Barnes G.E. and Staples S.G. (1988). The acceptability of clay fill as affected by stone content. *Ground Engineering*, January.

Barton M.E. and Thomson R.I. (1986). Interceptor drains for cliff-tops and above the crest of slopes and cuttings. In *Groundwater in Engineering Geology*, (ed. Cripps J.C., Bell F.G. and Culshaw M.G.) *Proc. 21 Conf. Engrg Group Geol. Soc.*, Sheffield, 387–394.

Bell, F.G. (1992). Open excavation in rock massess. In Bell, F.G. (ed.). *Engineering in rock masses*. Butterworth-Heinemann, Oxford, 400–422.

Bieniawski Z.T. (1979). The geomechanics classification in rock engineering application. *Proc. 4th Int. Congr. Rock Mech., ISRM, Montreux*, **2**, 51–58.

Bieniawski Z.T. (1989). *Engineering rock mass classifications*. John Wiley and Sons, London.

Binnie G.M. (1987). *Early dam builders in Britain*. Thomas Telford, London.

Bishop A.W. (1955). The use of the slip circle in the stability analysis of slopes. *Geotechnique*, **5**, No. 1, 7–17.

Bishop A.W. and Henkel D.J. (1962). *The measurement of soil properties in the triaxial test.* 2nd Edition, Edward Arnold, London: 119–121 and 104.

Bishop A.W. and Vaughan P.R. (1962). Selset reservoir: design and performance of the embankment. *Proc. Instn Civ. Engrs*, **21**, 305–346.

Bishop A.W. and Morgenstern N.R. (1960). Stability coefficients for earth slopes. *Geotechnique*, **10**, No. 4, 129–150.

Bjerrum L. (1972). Embankments on soft ground. *Proc. Speciality Conf. on Performance of Earth and Earth Supported Structures, Proc. ASCE*, **2**, 1–54.

Black W. and Lister N.W. (1978). The strength of clay fill subgrades: its prediction and relation to road performance. *Proc. Int. Conf. Clay Fills*. The Institution of Civil Engineers, London, 37–48.

Blanchfield R. and Anderson W.F. (2000). Wetting collapse in open-cast coalmine backfill. *Proc. Instn Civ. Engrs, Geotech. Engng*, **143**, July, 139–149.

Bolton M.D. and Lee D.M. (1993). Back analysis of a pilot scale shear test on coarse granular fill. *Proc. Conf. Engineered Fills, University of Newcastle upon Tyne*, 214–225.

Bridle R.J. and Davies M.C.R. (1996). Discussion on Ortigao *et al. Proc. Instn Civ. Engrs, Geotech. Engng*, **119**, Oct., 239–241.

Bromhead E.N, (1992). *The stability of slopes*, 2nd Edition, Surrey University Press, London.

BS 812 (1989). *Methods for sampling and testing mineral aggregates, sands and filters.* British Standards Institution, London.

BS 890 (1995). *Specification for building limes. Appendix J: Protective measures recommended when handling building limes.* British Standards Institution, London.

BS 1377 (1990). *Methods of test for soils for civil engineering purposes.* British Standards Institution, London.

BS 1924 (1990). *Stabilised materials for civil engineering purposes.* British Standards Institution, London.

BS 5930 (1981). *Code of practice for site investigations.* British Standards Institution, London.

BS 5930 (1999). *Code of practice for site investigations.* British Standards Institution, London.

BS 6031 (1981). *Code of practice for earthworks.* British Standards Institution, London.

BS 6543 (1990). *Use of industrial by-products and waste materials in building and civil engineering.* British Standards Institution, London.

BS 8004 (1994). *Code of practice for earth retaining structures.* British Standards Institution, London.

BS 8006 (1995). *Code of practice for strengthened/reinforced soils and other fills.* British Standards Institution, London.

BS 8081 (1989). *Code of practice for ground anchorages.* British Standards Institution, London.

BS ISO 5725-1 (1994). *Accuracy (trueness and precision) of measurement methods and results, Part 1: General principles and definitions.* British Standards Institution, London.

BS Eurocode 7 (1995). *Geotechnical Design, Part 1, General Rules.* British Standards Institution, London.

Building Research Establishment (BRE) (1996). *Sulphate and acid resistance of concrete in the ground.* Digest 363, January.

Burland J.B and Burbidge M.C. (1985). Settlement of foundations on sand and gravel. *Proc. Instn Civ. Engnrs*, **78**, Part 1, December, 1325–1381.

Cabrera J.G., Brain, M. and Rawcliffe, J. (1984). The use of pulverised fuel ash for the construction of structural fills. *AshTech '84, Second International Conference on Ash Technology and Marketing*. London, 529–533.

Caldwell J.A., Smith, A. and Wagner, J. (1984). Heave of coal shale fill. *Can. Geotech. J.*, **21**, 379–383.

Chandler R.J. (1969). Weathering effect on shear strength of Keuper Marl. *Geotechnique*, **19**, No. 3, 321–334.

Chandler R.J. (1978). Discussion. *Proc. Int Conf. Clay Fills*. The Institution of Civil Engineers, London, 234.

Chandler R.J. (1984). Recent European experience of landslides in over-consolidated clays and soft rocks. *Proc. 4th Int. Symp. on Landslides, Toronto*, **1**, 61–81.

Chandler R.J. and Davis A.G. (1973). *Further work on the engineering properties of Keuper Marl*, CIRIA Report 47. Construction Industry Research and Information Association, London.

Chandler R.J., Pachakis, M., Mercer, J. and Wrightman, J. (1973). Four long term failures of embankments founded on areas of landslip. *Q.J. Engng Geol.*, **6**, Nos 3–4, 405–422.

Chandler R.J. and Skempton A.W. (1974). The design of permanent cutting slopes in stiff fissured clays. *Geotechnique*, **24**, No. 4, 457–466.

Chandler R.J. and Peiris T.A. (1989). Further extension to the Bishop and Morgenstern slope stability charts. *Ground Engineering*, May, 33–38.

Charles J.A. (1978). General report: Methods of treatment of clay fills. *Proc. Int. Conf. Clay Fills*. The Institution of Civil Engineers, London, 315–321.

Charles J.A. (1993). *Building on fill: geotechnical aspects*. Building Research Establishment, Garston, Watford.

Charles J.A. and Burland J.B. (1982). Geotechnical considerations in the design of foundations for buildings on deep deposits of waste materials. *The Structural Engineer*, **60A**, No. 1, Jan., 8–14.

Charles J.A. and Penman A.D.M. (1988). The behaviour of embankment dams with bituminous watertight elements. *Trans. Int. Congr. Large Dams, San Francisco*, **2**, 693–705.

Charles J.A. and Watts K.W. (1980). The influence of confining pressure on the shear strength of compacted rockfill. *Geotechnique*, **30**, No. 4, 353–367.

Clarke B.G. and Coombes R. (1996). Specifying and using pulverised fuel ash as an engineered fill. *Waste Management*, **16**, Nos 1–3, 101–108.

Clayton C.R.I. (1980). The collapse of compacted chalk fill. *Proc. Int. Conf. on Compaction. Paris*, **1**, 119–124.

Clayton C.R.I. (2001). *Managing Geotechnical Risk*. Thomas Telford, London.

Clayton C.R.I., Symons, I.F. and Hiedra-Cobo, J.C. (1991). Pressure of clay backfill against retaining structures. *Can. Geotech. J.*, **28**, No. 2, 309–315.

Clayton C.R.I., Mathews, M.C. and Simons, N.E.. (1995). *Site investigations*, Blackwell Science, Oxford, 2nd Edition.

Cobbe M.I. and Threadgold L. (1988). Compaction control by the moisture condition test – a new approach. *J. Inst. Highways and Transportation*, Dec., 13–18.

Cole K.W. and Figg J. (1987). Improved rock paste: a slow hardening bulk infill based on colliery discard, pulverised fuel ash and lime. *Proc. 2nd Symposium on Reclamation Treatment of Coal Mining Wastes. University of Nottingham, 7–11 Sepember*.

Cox D.W. (1978). Volume change of compacted clay fill. *Proc. Int. Conf. Clay Fills*. The Institution of Civil Engineers, London, 79–86.

Crabb G.I and West G. (1986). Monitoring groundwater conditions in a highway embankment. In *Groundwater in Engineering Geology*, (ed. Cripps J.C., Bell F.G. and Culshaw M.G.) *Proc. 21 Conf. Engrg Group Geol. Soc.*, Sheffield, 387–394.

Crabb G.I. and Atkinson J.H. (1991). Determination of soil strength parameters for the analysis of highway slope failures. In *Slope Stability Engineering: Developments and Applications*. (ed. Chandler R.J.) 13–18.

Craig R..F. (1997). *Soil mechanics*. 6th Edition, Chapman and Hall, London.

Croney D. and Jacobs J.C. (1967). *The frost susceptibility of soils and road materials*. Road Research Report RRL LR 90, Transport Research Laboratory, Crowthorne, Berkshire.

Daniel D.E. (1993). *Geotechnical practice for waste disposal*. Chapman and Hall, London.

Davis E.H. and Poulos H.G. (1972). Rate of settlement under two- and three-dimensional conditions. *Geotechnique*, **22**, No. 1, 95–114.

Day R.W. (1989). Relative compaction of fill having oversize particles. *Proc. ASCE, J Geotech. Engng*, **115**, No. 10, 1487–1491.

Dennehy J.P. (1978). The remoulded undrained shear strength of cohesive soils and its influence on the suitability of embankment fill. *Proc. Int. Conf. Clay Fills*, The Institution of Civil Engineers, London, 87–94.

Design Manual for Roads and Bridges (DMBR): See *The Highways Agency Advice Note*.

DETR (1991). *Survey of derelict land in England*, (in two volumes). Her Majesty's Stationery Office, London.

DETR (1995). *Waste management paper 26B-landfill design, construction and operational practice*. Her Majesty's Stationery Office, London.

Dineen K., Colmenares, J.E., Ridley, A.M. and Burland, J.B. (1999). Suction and volume changes of a bentonite-enriched sand. *Proc. Instn Civ. Engrs, Geotech. Engng*, **137**, Oct., 197–201.

Dixon D.A., Gray, M.N. and Thomas, A.W. (1985). A study of the compaction properties of potential clay-sand buffer mixtures for use in nuclear fuel waste disposal. *Engineering Geology*, **21**, 247–255.

Dumbleton M.J. and West G. (1966). *The influence of the coarse fraction on the properties of clay soils*. Research Report LR306, Transport Research Laboratory, Crowthorne, Berkshire.

Dunnicliff J. (1988). *Geotechnical instrumentation for monitoring field performance*. Wiley-Interscience, New York.

Edelmann L., Hertweck, M. and Amann, P. (1999). Mechanical behaviour of landfill barrier systems. *Proc. Instn Civ. Engnrs, Geotech. Engng*, **137**, Oct, 215–224.

Edmonds C.N. and Kirkwood J.P. (1990). Suggested approach to ground investigation and the determination of suitable substructure solutions for sites underlain by chalk. *Proc. Int. Chalk Symp., Brighton, 1989*. Thomas Telford, London.

Ellis I.W. (1985). The use of reticulated *pali radice* structures to solve slope stability problems. *Proc. Symp. Failures in Earthworks*. The Institution of Civil Engineers, London, 432–435.

Elsbury B.R., David, D.E., Srader, G.A. and Anderson, D.C. (1990). Lessons learnt from compacted clay liner. *Proc. ASCE, J. Geotech. Eng.*, **116**, No. 11.

Eurocode 7 (1995): See BS Eurocode 7 (1995).

Farrar D.M. (1978). Settlement and pore-water pressure dissipation within an embankment built of London Clay. *Proc. Int. Conf. Clay fills*. The Institution of Civil Engineers, London, 101–106.

Farrar D.M. (1985). Slope drains in an old cutting in London Clay. *Proc. Symp. Failures in Earthworks*. The Institution of Civil Engineers, London, 448–450.

Farrar D.M. and Darley P. (1975). The operation of earthmoving plant on wet fill. *TRL Report LR 688*. Transport Research Laboratory, Crowthorne, Berkshire.

Finlayson D.M., Greenwood, J.R., Cooper, C.G. and Simons, N.E. (1984). Lessons to be learnt from an embankment failure. *Proc. Inst. Civil Engnrs*, Part 1, **76**, 207–220.

Fleming W.G.K., Weltman, A.J., Randolph, M.F. and Elson, W.K. (1985). *Piling Engineering*. Surrey University Press, London.

Franklin J.A., Broch, E. and Walton, G. (1971). Logging the mechanical character of rock. *Trans. Inst. Min. Metall. (Section A)*, **A80**, A1–A9.

Garrett C. and Wale J.H. (1985). Performance of embankments and cuttings in Gault Clay in Kent. *Proc. Symp. Failures in Earthworks*. The Institution of Civil Engineers, London, 93–112.

Geotechnical Engineering Office (1984). *Geotechnical Manual for Slopes*. Engineering Development Department, Hong Kong, 2nd Edition.

Gibson R.E. and Shefford G.C. (1968). The efficiency of horizontal drainage layers for accelerating consolidation of clay embankments. *Geotechnique*, **18**, No. 3, 327–335.

Gordon M.E. (1987). *Design and performance monitoring of clay-lined landfills. Geotechnical Practice for Waste Disposal '87.* (ed. Woods R.D.) Geotechnical Special Publication 13, ASCE, 500–514.

Grace H. and Green P.A. (1978). The use of wet fill for the construction of embankments for motorways. *Proc. Int. Conf. Clay Fills.* The Institution of Civil Engineers, London, 113–118.

Greenwood J.R. (1985). Wedge analysis of embankment instability during construction of the M25 motorway. *Proc. Symp. Failures in Earthworks.* The Institution of Civil Engineers, London, 403–405.

Greenwood J.R. (1993). Description, classification and specification of chalk for use in earthworks. *Proc. Conf. Engineered Fills.* University of Newcastle upon Tyne, 251–257.

Greenwood J.R., Holt, D.A. and Herrick, G.W. (1985). Shallow slips in highway embankments constructed of overconsolidated clay. *Proc. Symp. on Failures in Earthworks.* The Institution of Civil Engineers, London, 79–92.

Halcrow (1994). *Study of engineered fills for building purposes.* Report for the Building Research Establishment.

Hanna, T.H. (1985). *Field instrumentation in geotechnical engineering.* Trans Tech Publications, Clausthal-Zellerfeld.

Hawkins A.B. and Pinches G.M. (1987). Cause and significance of heave at Llandough Hospital, Cardiff – a case history of ground floor heave due to gypsum growth. *Q.J. Engng Geol.*, **20**, No. 1, 41–58.

Hawkins A.B. and Wilson S.L.S. (1990). Technical note: Sulphate increase in laboratory prepared samples. *Q.J. Engng Geol.*, **23**, No. 4, 383–386.

Head K.H. (1992). *Manual of soil laboratory testing*, Pentech Press, London, 2nd Edition, Vol. 1.

Head K.H. (1994). *Manual of soil laboratory testing*, Pentech Press, London, 2nd Edition, Vol. 2.

Heath D.C. (1966). Construction of the M40 High Wycombe bypass. *Proc. Symp. on Chalk in Earthworks and Construction, Session B discussion.* The Institution of Civil Engineers, London, 96–101.

Hencher S.R. and McNicholl D.P. (1995). Engineering in weathered rock. *Q.J. Engng Geol.*, **28**, Part 3, 253–266.

Hertford D. (1985). Properties and behaviour of Irish glacial till. *Proc. Int. Conf. on Construction in Glacial Tills and Boulder Clays, University of Edinburgh*, 93–98.

The Highways Agency Advice Note HA 30/87: *Backfilled retaining walls and bridge abutments.* Her Majesty's Stationery Office, London.

The Highways Agency Advice Note HA 43/91: *Geotechnical considerations and techniques for widening highway works.* Her Majesty's Stationery Office, London,

The Highways Agency Advice Note HA 44/91: *Earthworks-design and preparation of contract documents.* Her Majesty's Stationery Office, London.

The Highways Agency Advice Note HA 48/92: *Maintenance of highway earthworks and drainage.* Her Majesty's Stationery Office, London.

The Highways Agency Advice Note HA 68/94: *Design methods for the reinforcement of highway slopes by reinforced soil and soil nailing techniques.* Her Majesty's Stationery Office, London.

The Highways Agency Advice Note HA 70/94: *Construction of highway earthworks.* Her Majesty's Stationery Office, London.

The Highways Agency Advice Note HA 74/95: *Design and construction of lime stabilised capping.* Her Majesty's Stationery Office, London.

Hills C.W.W and Denby B. (1996). The predicition of opencast backfill settlement. *Proc. Instn Civ. Engrs, Geotech. Engng*, **119**, July, 167–176.

Hird C.C. and Jewel R.A. (1990). *Theory of reinforced embankments. Reinforced Embankments: theory and practice*. Thomas Telford, London.

Hird C.C., Smith, C.C. and Cripps, J.C. (1998). *Issues related to the use and specification of colliery spoil liners. Geotechnical Engineering of Landfills*. Thomas Telford, London.

Hodgetts S.J., Holden, J.M.W., Morgan, C.S. and Adams, J.N. (1993). Specifications for and performance of compacted open-cast backfills. *Proc. Conf. Engineered Fills, University of Newcastle upon Tyne*, 262–280.

Hoek E. and Bray J.W. (1997). *Rock slope engineering*, Institution of Mining and Metallurgy, London, 3rd Edition.

Horner P.C. (1988). *Earthworks, ICE Works Construction Guides*. Thomas Telford, London, 2nd Edition.

Hutchinson J.N. (1977). Assessment of the effectiveness of corrective measures in relation to geological conditions and types of slope movement. *Bull. Int. Assoc. Engnrg Geol.*, No. 16, 131–155.

Hutchinson J.N. (1991). *Periglacial and slope processes*. Quaternary Engineering Geology, Special Publication No. 7, The Geological Society, London, 283–331.

Ingold T.C. (1979). The effects of compaction on retaining walls. *Geotechnique*, **29**, No. 3, 265–283.

Ingoldby H.C. (1978). The classification of chalk for embankment construction. *Proc. Int. Conf. Clay Fills*. The Institution of Civil Engineers, London, 137–142.

Inter-Departmental Committee on the Redevelopment of Contaminated Land, ICRL 59/83 (2nd Edition).

International Union of Railways Design Code (1994). *Earthworks and trackbed layers for railway lines*. (UIC 719R), 2nd Edition.

Irfan T.Y. and Tang K.Y. (1993). *Effect of the coarse fractions on the shear strength of colluvium*. GEO Report No. 23. Geotechnical Engineering Office, Civil Engineering Department, Hong Kong.

Janbu N. (1972). Slope stability computations. In *Embankment Dam Engineering*, (ed. Hirschfield R.C. and Poulos S.J.) John Wiley, New York, 47–86.

Jewell R.A. (1996). *Soil reinforcement with geotextiles*. CIRIA Special Report 123. Construction Industry Research and Information Association, London.

Johnson S.J. (1970). Precompression for improving foundation soils. *J. Soil Mech. Found. Div.*, ASCE, **96**, SM1, 111–144.

Johnstone T.A. (1975). Discussion. *Proc. Symp. Engng Behaviour of Glacial Materials, University of Birmingham*, 69.

Jones C.J.F.P. (1996). *Earth reinforcement and soil structures*. Thomas Telford, London.

Jones R.L. and Keen D.H. (1993). *Pleistocene environments in the British Isles*. Chapman and Hall, London.

Kennard M.F. (1985). Discussion: The Carsington dam failure. *Proc. Symp. Failures in Earthworks*. The Institution of Civil Engineers, London, 233–235.

Kennard J. and Kennard M.F. (1962). Selset reservoir: design and construction. *Proc. Instn Civ. Engnrs*, **21**, Feb., 277–344.

Kennard M.F., Lovenbury, H.T., Chartres, F.R.D. and Hoskins, C.G. (1978). Shear strength specification for clay fills. *Proc. Int. Conf. Clay Fills*. The Institution of Civil Engineers, London, 143–148.

Kraus J.F., Benson, C.H., Erickson, A.E. and Chamberlin, E.J. (1997). Freeze-thaw cycling and hydraulic conductivity of bentonitic barriers. *Proc. ASCE, J Geotechnical Engineering*, **123**, No. 3, 229–238.

Lambe T.W. (1962). Soil stabilisation. In *Foundation Engineering*, (ed. Leonards G.A.) McGraw Hill, London, 351–437.

Lambe T.W. and Whitman R.V. (1969). *Soil Mechanics*. John Wiley and Sons, London.

Lizzi F. (1984). The *reticulo di pali radice* (reticulated root piles) for the improvement of soil resistance. *Proc. 8th European Conf. Soil Mech. and Found. Engng*, **2**. Balkema,

Rotterdam, 521–530.

Lunne T., Robertson, P.K. and Powell, J.J.M. (1997). *Cone penetration testing.* Blackie Academic and Professional, London.

Marsal R.J. and Fuentes de la Rosa (1976). Mechanical properties of rockfill soil mixtures. *Proc. 2nd Congress Large Dams, Mexico,* 179–209.

Matheson G.D. (1985). The stability of excavated slopes exposing rock. *Proc. Symp. Failures in Earthworks.* The Institution of Civil Engineers, London, 295–306.

Mathews M.C., Clayton, C.R.I. and Rigby-Jones, J. (2000). Locating dissolution features in chalk. *Q.J. Engng Geol.,* **33**, Part 2, May, 105–140.

McGinnity B.T. and Russell D. (1995). Investigation of London Underground earth structures. *Proc. Int. Conf. Advances in Site Investigation Practice.* Thomas Telford, London.

McGown A. (1975). *Genetic influences on the nature and properties of basal melt-out tills.* PhD Thesis, University of Strathclyde.

McGown A., Saldivar-Sali, A. and Radwan, A.M. (1974). Fissure patterns and slope failure in boulder clay at Hurlford, Ayrshire. *Q.J. Engng Geol.,* **7**, No. 1, 1–26.

McMillan P., Blair, A.R. and Nettleton, I.M. (1995). The use of down-hole CCTV for collection of quantitative discontinuity data. *Proc. Int. Conf. Advances in Site Investigation,* Thomas Telford, London.

Meigh A.C. (1987). *Cone penetration testing: methods and interpretation.* Construction Industry Research and Information Association, London.

Mesri G. (1973). Coefficient of secondary compression. *Proc. ASCE, J. Soil Mech. Found. Engng Div.,* **99**, No. SM1, 122–137.

Method of Measurement for Highway Works (1991). Her Majesty's Stationery Office, London.

Millmore J.P. and McNicol R. (1983). Geotechnical aspects of the Kielder dam. *Proc. Instn Civil Engrs.,* **74**, Part 1, 805–836.

Morgenstern N.R. and Price V.E. (1965). The analysis of the stability of general slip surfaces. *Geotechnique,* **15**, No. 1, 79–93.

Mudet M. (1993). Remblais ferroviaires en craie – methodologie. *Proc. Int. Conf. on Fills.* Paris, October.

Muir Wood D. (1990). *Soil behaviour and critical state soil mechanics.* Cambridge University Press, Cambridge.

Murray E.J. (1998). *Properties and testing of clay liners. Geotechnical Engineering of Landfills.* Thomas Telford, London.

Murray E.J., Rix, D.W. and Humphrey, R.D. (1992). Clay linings to landfill sites. *Q.J. Engng Geol.,* **29**, No. 3, 249–255.

NAVFAC DM 7.2. (1982). *Foundations and earth structures.* Department of the Navy, Naval Facilities Engineering Command, Alexandria, Va.

Nettleton A., Robertson, I. and Smith, J.H. (1996). Treatment of silt using lime and PFA to form embankment fill for the new A13. In *Lime Stabilisation,* (ed. Rogers *et al.*) Thomas Telford, London.

New B. (1986). *Ground vibrations caused by civil engineering works.* Research Report, RR 53, Transport Research Laboratory, Crowthorne, Berks.

New Civil Engineer (1984). Damage scares fails to halt steel slag use. Apr. 4–5.

New Civil Engineer (2000). Digging for victory. M60 supplement, Nov., viii–xix.

Nicholson D., Tse, C.M. and Penny, C. (1999). *The observation method in ground engineering: principles and applications.* CIRIA Report 185. Construction Industry Research and Information Association, London.

North West Water Regional Office NWWRO (1996). *Earthworks on landfill sites – a technical note on the design, construction and quality assurance of compacted clay liners.* Document No. NWTECH. 002.

NRA (1992). *Policy and practice for the protection of groundwaters.* National Rivers Authority, Bristol.

O'Riordan N.J. and Seaman J.W. (1994). *Highway embankments over soft compressible alluvial deposits: guidelines for design and construction*. Contractor Report 341, Transport Research Laboratory, Crowthorne, Berkshire.

O'Connor, M. and Mitchell, R.J. (1977). An extension of the Bishop and Morgenstern slope stability charts. *Can. Geotech. J.*, **14**, 144–151.

Ortigao J.A.R., Palmeira, E.M. and Zirlis, A.C. (1995). Experience with soil nailing in Brazil: 1970–1994. *Proc. Instn Civ. Engrs, Geotech. Engng*, **113**, Apr., 93–106.

Padfield C.J. and Mair R.J. (1984). *Design of retaining walls embedded in stiff clay*. CIRIA Report 104, Construction Industry Research and Information Association, London.

Paez J. (1980). Compaction energy and water content of remoulded cohesive soils and their influence on cohesion. *Proc. Int. Conf. on Compaction*, **1**, Paris, 181–187.

Pandian N.S., Nagaraj, T.S. and Manoj, M. (1997). Re-examination of compaction characteristics of fine grained soils. *Geotechnique*, **47**, No. 2, 363–373.

Pannel J.P.M. (1964). *An illustrated history of civil engineering*. Thames and Hudson, London.

Parkin A.K. (1988). *The calibration of cone penetrometers. Penetration Testing, IOPT -1*. Balkema, Rotterdam, 221–243.

Parsons A.W. (1978). General report: Construction and placement of clay fills. *Proc. Int. Conf. on Clay Fills*. The Institution of Civil Engineers, London, 307–314.

Parsons A.W. (1987). Compaction. In *Ground Engineering Reference Book*, Ch. 37, (ed. F.G. Bell). Butterworths, London, 1–15.

Parsons A.W. (1992). *Compaction of soils and granular materials. TRL State of the Art Report*. Her Majesty's Stationery Office, London.

Parsons A.W and Darley P. (1982). *The effect of soil conditions on the operation of earthmoving plant. TRL Report LR1034*, Transport Research Laboratory, Crowthorne, Berkshire.

Parsons A.W. and Perry J. (1985). Slope stability problems in ageing highway earthworks. *Proc. Symp. Failures in Earthworks*. The Institution of Civil Engineers, London, 63–78.

Penman A.D.M. (1971). Rockfill. *J. Instn Highway Engrs*, **18**, No. 12.

Penman A.D.M. (1986). The embankment dam. *Geotechnique*, **26**, No. 3, 303–348.

Penman A.D.M. (1995). Discussion: The failure of Carsington Dam. *Geotechnique*, **44**, No. 4, 719–721.

Penman A.D.M and Charles J.A. (1976). The quality and suitability of rockfill used in dam construction. *Trans. 12th Int. Congr. Large Dams, Mexico City*, **1**, 533–566.

Perry J. (1989). *A summary of slope conditions on motorway earthworks in England and Wales*. TRL Research Report 199, Transport Research Laboratory, Crowthorne, Berkshire.

Perry J. (1991). *The extent and analysis of shallow failures of highway slopes*. PhD Thesis, University of Durham.

Perry J., Snowdon, R.E. and Wilson, P.E. (1995). Site investigation for lime stabilisation of highway works. *Proc. Int Conf. Advances in Site Investigation Practice*. Thomas Telford, London.

Perry J. and West G. (1992). *Sources of information for site investigations in Britain. TRL Report LR 192*, Transport Research Laboratory, Crowthorne, Berkshire.

Petley D.J., Bromhead, E.N., Cooper, M.R. and Grant, D.I. (1991). Full scale slope failure at Selbourne, UK. In *Developments in Geotechnical Aspects of Embankments, Excavations and Buried Structures*. (ed Balasubramaniam *et al.*), Balkema, Rotterdam.

Pettifer G.S. and Fookes P.G. (1994). A revision of the graphical method of assessing the excavatability of rock. *Q.J. Engng Geol.*, **27**, No. 2, 145–164.

Pilot G. and Moreau M. (1973). *La stabilité des remblais sur sols mous; abaques des calcul*. Eyrolles, Paris.

Porter O.J. (1938). Preparation of subgrades. *Proc. Highway Res. Board, Washington*, **18**, No. 2, 324–331.

Powrie W. (1997). *Soil mechanics: concepts and applications*. E and FN Spon, London.

Privett K.D., Mathews, S.C. and Hodges, R.A. (1996). *Barriers, liners and cover systems for containment and control of land contamination.* CIRIA Special Publication 124, Construction Industry Research and Information Association, London.

Proctor R.R. (1933). The design and construction of rolled earth dams. *Engng News Record*, **111**, No. 9, 245–248; No. 10, 216–219; No. 12, 348–351; No. 13, 372–376.

Puiatti D. (1995). Lime treatment in earthworks and pavements – the French experience. *British Lime Association Seminar, Feb., Coventry.*

Pye K. and Miller J.A. (1990). Chemical and biochemical weathering of pyritic mudrocks in a shale embankment, *Q.J. Engng Geol.*, **23**, No. 4, 365–382.

Quigley R.M., Zajic, J.E., McKeyes, E. and Yong, R.N. (1973). Oxidation and heave of black shale. *Proc. ASCE*, **99**, SM5, May, 417–421.

RAMP (1998). *Risk Analysis and Management for Projects.* Thomas Telford, London.

Reichert J. (1980). Report 'various national specifications on control of compaction'. *Proc. Int. Conf on Compaction*, **3**. Paris, 181–203.

Rogers J.D. (1992). Long term behaviour of urban fill embankments. Stability and performance of slopes and embankments. *Proc. Speciality Conf., Berkeley, California.* Geotechnical Special Publication GSP 31, ASCE New York, **2**, 1258–1273.

Rogers C.D.F., Glendinning, S. and Roff. T.E.J. (1997). Lime modification of clay soils for construction expediency. *Proc. Instn Civ. Engrs, Geotech. Engng*, **125**, Oct., 242–249.

Rogers S.H. (1985). Slope failures in road cuttings through Coal Measures rocks. *Proc. Symp. Failures in Earthworks.* The Institution of Civil Engineers, London, 39–52.

Romana M. (1985). New adjustment rating for application of the Bieniawski classification to slopes. *Proc. Int. Symp. on Role of Rock Mechanics, ISRM, Zacatecas, Mexico*, 49–53.

Sarma S.K. (1979). Stability analysis of embankments and slopes. *Proc. ASCE., J. Geotech. Engng Div.*, **105**, 1511–1524.

Schmertmann J.H. (1953). Undisturbed consolidation behaviour of clay. *Trans. Am. Soc. Civ. Eng.*, **120**, 1201.

Scoble M.J. and Muftuoglu Y.V. (1984). Derivation of a diggability index for surface mine equipment selection. *Mining Science and Technology*, No. 1, 305–322.

Sharp B.N. (1996). Consolidation settlement of quay walls, quay aprons and crane rails involving rockfill. *Proc. Instn Civ. Engrs., Water Maritime and Energy*, **118**, Sept., 177–188.

Sherwood P.T. (1995). *Alternative materials in road construction.* Thomas Telford, London.

Simons N.E. (1975). Review paper: Normally consolidated and lightly overconsolidated cohesive materials. *Proc. Conf. Settlement of Structures*, Pentech Press, London, 500–530.

Simons N.E. and Menzies B.K. (1977). *A short course in foundation engineering.* Newnes-Butterworths, London.

Site investigation in construction (1993). The Institution of Civil Engineers, London.

Skempton A.W. (1976). The Quaternary history of the Lower Greensand escarpment and Weald Clay Vale near Sevenoaks, Kent. *Phil. Trans. R. Soc., Series A*, **283**, 493–526.

Skempton A.W. (1977). Slope stability of cuttings in brown London Clay. *Proc. 9th Int. Conf. Soil Mech. and Found. Engng, Tokyo*, **3**, 261–270.

Skempton A.W. (1979). Landmarks in early soil mechanics. *Proc. 7th Eur. Conf. Soil Mech. and Found. Engng, Brighton*, **5**, 1–26.

Skempton A.W. (1996). Embankments and cuttings on the early railways. *Construction History*, **11**, 33–49.

Skempton A.W. and De Lory F.A. (1952). Stability of natural slopes in London Clay. *Proc. 4th Int. Conf. Soil Mech. and Found. Engng*, **2**, 378–381.

Skempton A.W. and Brown J.D. (1961). A landslide in boulder clay at Selset, Yorkshire. *Geotechnique*, **11**, No. 4, 280–293.

Skempton A.W. and Coats D.J. (1985a). The Carsington dam failure. *Proc. Symp. Failures in Earthworks*, The Institution of Civil Engineers, London, 203–220.

Skempton A.W. and Coats D.J. (1985b). Discussion : The Carsington dam failure. *Proc. Symp.*

Failures in Earthworks, The Institution of Civil Engineers, London, 236–237.

Skempton A.W., Leadbetter, A.P. and Chandler, R.J. (1989). The Mam Tor landslide, north Derbyshire. *Phil. Trans. Royal Soc.*, **329**, No. 1607, 503–547.

Skermer N.A. and Hillis S.F. (1970). Gradation and shear characteristics of four cohesionless soils. *Can. Geotech. J.*, **7**, 62–68.

Skinner H.D. and Charles J.A. (1999). Problems associated with building on a variable depth of fill. *Ground Engineering*, July, 32–35.

Smith J.H. (1996). *Construction of lime or lime plus cement stabilised cohesive soils. Lime Stabilisation*. Thomas Telford, London, 13–26.

Smith M.R. and Collis L. (1993). *Aggregates: sand, gravel and crushed rock aggregates for construction purposes*. Geological Society Engineering Geology Special Publication No. 9. The Geological Society, London.

Snedker E.A. (1985). The stabilisation of a landslipped area to incorporate a highway by use of a system of bored piles. *Proc. Symp. Failures in Earthworks*. The Institution of Civil Engineers, London.

Snedker E.A. (1996). M40 lime stabilisation experiences. In *Lime stabilisation*, (ed. Rogers *et al.*), Thomas Telford, London.

Soil Mechanics for Road Engineers (1951). Her Majesty's Stationery Office, London.

Specification for Highway Works (1998). Manual of Contract Documents for Highway Works, Vol 1, Series 600, Her Majesty's Stationery Office, London.

Spencer E. (1967). A method of analysis of the stability of embankments assuming parallel interslice forces. *Geotechnique*, **17**, No. 1, 11–26.

Stewart D.I., Cousens, T.W., Studds, P.G. and Tay, Y.Y. (1999). Design parameters for bentonite-enhanced sand as landfill liner. *Proc. Instn Civ. Engrs, Geotech. Engng*, **137**, Oct., 189–195.

Taylor, D.W. (1948). *Fundamentals of soil mechanics*. John Wiley and Sons, New York.

Taylor R.K. (1984). *Composition and engineering properties of British colliery discards*. National Coal Board, Mining Department Report.

Terzaghi K., Peck, R.B. and Mesri, G. (1990). *Soil mechanics in engineering practice*, John Wiley and Sons, New York, 3rd Edition.

Threadgold L. (1978). Discussion, *Proc. Int. Conf. Clay Fills*. The Institution of Civil Engineers, London, 251–253.

Tomlinson M.J. (1994). *Pile design and construction practice*. E and F.N. Spon, London, 4th Edition.

Tomlinson M.J. *et al.* (1995). *Foundation design and construction*. Addison-Wesley Longman, London, 6th Edition.

Tomlinson M.J., Driscoll, R. and Burland, J.B. (1978). Foundations for low rise buildings. *Structural Engineer*, Part A, **56A**, No. 6, 161–173.

Trenter N.A. (1993). Compaction, monitoring and performance of engineered fill at the Dixon opencast site, Chesterfield, UK. *Proc. Conf. Engineered Fills. University of Newcastle upon Tyne*, 455–469.

Trenter N.A. (1999). *Engineering in glacial tills*, CIRIA Report C504, Construction Industry Research and Information Association, London.

Trenter N.A. and Charles J.A. (1996). A model specification for engineered fill for building purposes. *Proc. Instn Civil Engrs, Geotechnical Engineering*, **119**, Oct., 219–230.

Trenter N.A. and Warren C.J. (1996). Further investigations at the Folkestone Warren landslide. *Geotechnique*, **46**, No. 4, 589–620.

United States Bureau of Reclamation Earth Manual (1974). United States Department of the Interior. US Government Printing Office, Washington DC.

United States Environmental Protection Agency (1991). *Design and construction of RCRA/CERCLA final covers*. EPA/625/4-91/025. USEPA (ORD Cincinnati Ohio).

Upton N. (1975). *An illustrated history of civil engineering*. Heineman, London.

Vaughan P.R. (1978a). General Report: Engineering properties of clay fills. *Proc. Int. Conf. Clay Fills*, The Institution of Civil Engineers, London, 283–296.

Vaughan P.R. (1978b). Discussion. *Proc. Int. Conf. Clay Fills*, The Institution of Civil Engineers, London, 271–273.

Vaughan P.R. (1982). Design and construction with wet fills. *Proc. Assoc. Brazilian Soil Mechanics Engineers*, April, 1–6.

Vaughan P.R. (1994). Criteria for the use of weak and weathered rock for embankment fill and its compaction control. *Proc 13th Int. Conf. Soil Mech. and Found. Engng, Delhi*, 1, 195–206.

Vaughan P.R., Lovenbury, H.T. and Horswill, P. (1975). The design, construction and performance of the Cow Green embankment dam. *Geotechnique*, 25, No. 3, 555–580.

Vaughan P.R., Hight, D.W., Sodha, V.G. and Walbancke, H.J. (1978). Factors controlling the stability of fills in Britain. *Proc. Int. Conf. Clay Fills*, The Institution of Civil Engineers, London.

Vaughan P.R., Chandler, R.J., Apted, J.P., Maguire, W.M. and Sandroni, S.S. (1993). *Sampling disturbance-with particular reference to its effects on stiff clays*. Predictive Soil Mechanics, Thomas Telford, London, 685–708.

Wallace J. (1999). Strengthening thaumasite-affected concrete bridges. *Concrete Magazine*, September.

Walton G. and Wang H. (1993). *Aspects of diggability in weak rocks*. Presented at a meeting of the Engineering Group of the Geological Society on 9 November, 1993.

Webber I. and Gowan D. (1995). A new core orientation device. *Proc. Int. Conf. Advances in Site Investigation*. Thomas Telford, London.

Weeks A.G. (1969). The stability of natural slopes in south-east England as affected by periglacial activity. *Q.J. Engng Geol.*, 2, 49–61.

Whyte I.L. (1982). Soil plasticity and strength: a new approach using extrusion. *Ground Engineering*, 15, No. 1, Jan., 16–24.

Whyte I.L. and Vakalis I.G. (1988). Shear surfaces induced in clay fills by compaction plant. *Proc. Conf. Compaction Technology*. Thomas Telford, London, 125–137.

Williams C.E. (1987). Containment applications for earthen liners. *Proc. Speciality Conf. on Environmental Engineering*, (ed. Dietz J.D.), Proc. ASCE, 122–128.

Winter M.G. and Suhardi (1993). The effect of stone content on the determination of acceptability for earthworking. *Proc. Conf. Engineered Fills, University of Newcastle upon Tyne*, 312–319.

Winter M.G., Holmgeristottir, T.H. and Suhardi. (1998). The effect of large particles on acceptability determination for earthwork compaction. *Q.J. Engng Geol.*, 31, Part 3, 247–268.

Appendix I. End product specification for engineered fill supporting low-rise structures

(from N.A. Trenter and J.A. Charles, 1996)

This model specification is intended to be used in connection with the construction of low-rise buildings on engineered fill, typically no greater than $50\,000\,m^3$ in volume and no more than $5\,m$ in average depth. The specification is believed to be suitable for most purposes but there may be special conditions existing at some sites which are not treated in this document and which should be taken into account in arriving at a properly engineered fill. It is emphasized that clay fills can be at least as susceptible to settlement or heave due to climatic, vegetation or other effects, as naturally occurring cohesive soils.

This specification is for contracts which are designed, let and supervised by a consulting engineer. However, the appropriate wording may readily be adapted for other forms of contract, such as design-and-build. It is assumed that a site investigation will have been performed prior to the works and that the geotechnical properties of relevance to enforcing the specification will have been measured.

Guidance on the design of foundations for low-rise structures may be obtained from Tomlinson Driscoll and Burland (1978), Tomlinson (1995), Atkinson (1993), and from other authorities. Guidance on construction of earthworks may be obtained from BS 6031 (1981).

Note should be taken of the requirements of the Construction (Design and Management) Regulations (1994) to the extent that they may be relevant to the works.

A1. Engineered fill

[A1.1] Engineered fill is defined as fill which is selected, placed and compacted to an appropriate specification so that it will exhibit the required engineering behaviour.

[A1.2] Fill shall be classified as follows

(*a*) unsuitable fill
(*b*) general fill
(*c*) restricted fill
(*d*) special fill.

[A1.3]   Unsuitable fill shall comprise any material so designated by the Engineer and shall include

(*a*) cohesive soils having a liquid limit in excess of 90 per cent or plasticity index in excess of 65 per cent
(*b*) chalk having a fine fraction ($< 400 \ \mu$m) in excess of 10 per cent at the borrow pit
(*c*) any material containing topsoil, wood, peat or lignite
(*d*) any material containing biodegradables
(*e*) any material containing scrap metal
(*f*) frozen or waterlogged substances
(*g*) material from contaminated sites
(*h*) material which by virtue of its particle size or shape cannot be properly and effectively compacted (e.g. some slate wastes).

Unsuitable fill shall not be used at any location or part of the site, including landscaped areas.

[A1.4]   General fill shall comprise all fill except unsuitable fill, restricted fill and special fill.

[A1.5]   Restricted fill shall comprise material which would otherwise be classified as general fill but which contains minerals hostile to the built environment and shall include

(*a*) pyritic shales
(*b*) gypsiferous clays
(*c*) burnt colliery discard
(*d*) pulverized fuel ash
(*e*) steel slag
(*f*) spent oil shale
(*g*) incinerator waste
(*h*) some demolition and construction industry waste.

Such fill shall be precluded from use in designated zones, including locations where groundwater may rise to the level of the underside of the deepest foundation and where its use will be condemned by the appropriate authorities on pollution grounds. Such fill shall not be placed to a depth less than one metre from the underside of the deepest foundation.

[A1.6]   Special fill shall comprise material which would otherwise be classified as general fill but which contains durable well graded natural sand and natural gravel or crushed rock, other than argillaceous rock, or durable clean crushed demolition rubble of similar particle size and free from any contaminants. Such fill may be employed as capping layers beneath structure foundations, beneath roads or as backfill to retaining walls.

A2. Selection of end product requirements

[A2.1] On the basis of the results of a site investigation which shall have been carried out, the Engineer shall, at the time of tender, provide the Contractor with the following

(*a*) The results of the tests shown below
- (i)   natural water content (BS 1377: 1990, Part 2: Test 3)
- (ii) liquid and plastic limits for cohesive soils (BS 1377: 1990, Part 2: Tests 4 and 5)
- (iii) compaction tests to determine maximum dry density and optimum water content at the appropriate compactive effort (2.5 and 4.5 kg rammer) (BS 1377: 1990, Part 4: Test 3)
- (iv) particle density (specific gravity) to assist in evaluating the compaction test (BS 1377: 1990, Part 2: Test 8).

(*b*) A graph such as that illustrated in Fig. A1.1.

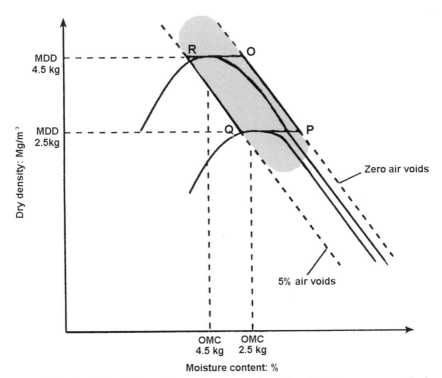

Fig. A1.1   Basis for design. Compaction curves for 2.5 and 4.5 kg rammer methods shown. Moisture contents and dry densities, when plotted, to fall within stippled area.

[A2.2] The graph will show the dry density plotted against water content for the 2.5 kg and 4.5 kg rammer method compaction tests; the corresponding optimum water contents and maximum dry densities; and the 5 per cent air voids line.

[A2.3] By reference to lines OPQR illustrated on Fig. A1.1, the required level of compaction will be indicated by selecting appropriate water content and dry density values. This level of compaction shall form the basis of the compaction specification.

A3. Preparation of site

[A3.1] On side-long ground, drainage grips or trenches shall be excavated uphill of the area to be filled and compacted. Drainage shall be effected without causing siltation or erosion and water shall be disposed of in a manner to be agreed by the Engineer.

[A3.2] The area to be filled, whether an existing excavation or otherwise undisturbed ground, shall be graded to falls, and sump pumping or other suitable dewatering facilities shall be provided by the Contractor to keep the base of the excavation dry at all times.

[A3.3] Where the area to be filled comprises an existing excavation, the excavation shall be inspected and subsequently monitored by the Contractor, to ensure that there is no danger of its collapse during the works with consequences for safety, for existing buildings or for other construction adjoining.

[A3.4] All topsoil shall be stripped and, where required for further use, stockpiled in an area provided by the Contractor and agreed by the Engineer.

[A3.5] All soft and compressible soils or existing fill shall be removed and run to spoil in dumps provided by the Contractor and agreed by the Engineer (including licensed tips in the case of certain contaminated materials). The work shall be accomplished in such a way that there is no undercutting of the sides of existing excavations.

[A3.6] Existing foundations or ledges of hard rock, roots of trees or former pipelines or services at the base of the area to be filled shall be excavated and replaced with compacted general fill which shall be compacted to the same specification as adopted for subsequent compaction works.

[A3.7] Where unsuitable material has been excavated, the underlying natural ground shall be compacted to the same specification as adopted for subsequent compaction works.

A4. Disposition of fill

[A4.1] Where construction is required upon fill placed over sloping natural ground, and where fill thickness is less than 5 m, the natural ground shall be benched, with the maximum vertical height of each bench not exceeding 500 mm (Fig. A1.2).

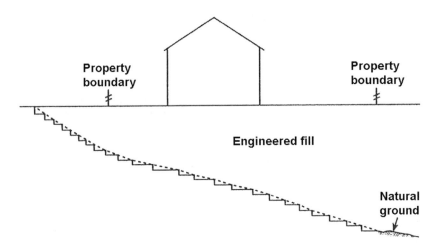

Fig. A1.2 Benching of sloping natural ground. Benching within engineered fill area only.

[A4.2] Where a development contains landscaped areas on which no structures will be built, the underlying fill shall be selected, placed and compacted in the same way as the engineered fill, unless otherwise directed by the Engineer. Where some relaxation of the specification for fill compaction underlying landscaped areas is permitted, there shall be a transition zone between the fill underlying the landscaped area and the fill underlying the structure. The dimensions of the transition zone will depend on the degree to which fill compaction was relaxed for the fill in the landscaped area (Fig. A1.3). The location and extent of fill placed to a reduced standard of compaction shall be recorded.

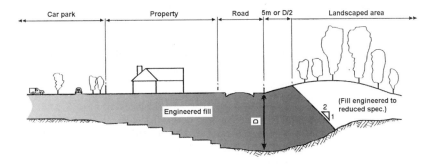

Fig. A1.3 Construction beneath buildings, hard standing and landscaped areas

A5.   Placing and compacting fill

[A5.1]   Fill shall be placed and compacted in near-horizontal layers of the thicknesses required to achieve the specified end product and shall, as far as practicable, be brought up at a uniform rate so that all parts of the site reach finished (formation) level at the same time.

[A5.2]   The compaction plant selected, the number of passes made and the fill layer thickness and water content used shall have regard to the specified end product and the means and manner of control testing.

[A5.3]   Where several different types of fill material (all meeting the requirements of Clause [A1] of this specification) are to be employed, they shall be deposited in such a way that all parts of the site receive roughly equal amounts of a given material, in roughly the same sequence, thus ensuring a uniform distribution of fill types over the whole fill thickness.

[A5.4]   The Contractor shall take all necessary steps to ensure that the fill is placed at the water content necessary to achieve the specified level of compaction and shall, where necessary, add water to or dry the fill, in order to obtain this value. Where it is necessary to add water, this shall be done as a fine spray and in such a way that there is time for the water to be absorbed into the fill before being rolled by the plant.

[A5.5]   Cobbles, boulders, rock or waste fragments whose largest dimension is greater than two-thirds of the loose layer thickness shall not be incorporated into the fill.

[A5.6]   No fill shall be placed and left uncompacted at the end of a working day. Compacted fill shall be graded to falls to ensure free runoff of rainwater without ponding.

[A5.7]   Compaction plant and compaction method shall be selected having regard to the proximity of existing trenches, excavations, retaining walls or other structures and all work shall be performed in such a way as to ensure that their existing stability is not impaired.

[A5.8]   If weather conditions are such that the specified water content and density values cannot be achieved, the Contractor shall cease work until such time that the fill can be placed and compacted to meet specification requirements.

[A5.9]   If the results of control tests (Clause [A6.3]) indicate that the fill is being placed and compacted in such a way that the desired level of compaction is not being achieved, the Contractor shall further compact or, if necessary, shall excavate the affected work and replace with new fill, compacted to meet the specification requirements.

[A5.10]   If the results of control tests (Clause [A6.3]) indicate that antecedent weather conditions (such as frost or heavy rain) have caused deterioration of finished work such that the work no longer meets the specification, the Contractor shall at its own cost take such steps as are necessary to bring the fill to specification requirements.

A6. Control testing

[A6.1]   The end product requirements selected in Clause [A2.1] shall be controlled by *in situ* and laboratory testing as follows

(*a*) *in situ* dry density (BS 1377: 1990, Part 9: Test 2) and water content determinations (BS 1377: 1990, Part 2: Test 3)

(*b*) where required these tests shall be augmented by water content–dry density relationships (BS 1377: 1990, Part 4: Test 3) and particle density (BS 1377: 1990, Part 2: Test 8).

[A6.2]   At least fourteen working days before the start of site work, the Contractor shall provide the Engineer, for approval, with a list of the equipment the Contractor proposes to use to undertake these tests.

[A6.3]   Control tests shall be performed throughout the fill at such frequency and at such locations as shall be directed by the Engineer.

[A6.4]   When requested by the Engineer, the Contractor shall make available a plot of *in situ* dry densities against *in situ* moisture content results on a graph such as illustrated in Fig. A1.1, showing that the results lie within or above the area OPQR or such area as has been selected by the Engineer. Should any results lie outside the selected area, the Contractor shall provide the Engineer with proposals for rectifying the existing situation and for improving future performance.

[A6.5]   The Engineer will, from time to time and with reasonable notice, request the Contractor to make available equipment to enable the Engineer to perform control tests. The results of these tests shall be used by the Engineer in assessing the Contractor's performance.

A7. Monitoring of fill performance

[A7.1]   If instructed by the Engineer, the Contractor shall make arrangements for the performance of the fill, once placed, to be monitored. Monitoring may take one or more of the following forms

(*a*) optical levelling of surface monuments

(*b*) standpipes or piezometers

(*c*) load tests

(*d*) other methods as directed by the Engineer.

[A7.2]   The Contractor shall, within twenty-one working days of receiving notification of the Engineer's intention to monitor fill performance, arrange for the procurement and supply of the equipment to the Engineer's written specification and shall inform the Engineer of the date on which the equipment installation shall commence. The specification shall include:

(*a*) a full description of the nature and type of instrument and the purpose it fulfils (*b*) the number required and the locations and or depths at which it is to be installed

(*c*) the frequency, accuracy and duration for which any readings are to be taken.

Appendix 2. Brief description of some earthmoving and compaction plant

(from P.C. Horner, 1988)

The following is a brief description of some of the plant commonly used in earthworks. *Manufacturers' catalogues may be consulted for further details.*

Excavation plant

Back-acter comprises a bucket on the end of an articulated boom, set on a pneumatic-tired or crawler tractor unit. The boom, bucket arm and bucket are usually controlled by hydraulic rams. Back-acters operate by digging towards the machine in an arc from a small distance above the surface on which the machine stands to a position vertically below the outer edge of the machine. The maximum depth of excavation is related to the length of the boom and machines with depth capacities between 2.5 and 6 m are in common use. Long reach machines are available for some of the work formerly carried out by draglines and which have nominal reach and depth capacities up to about 18 and 14 m, respectively. Buckets are available for back-acters in different sizes up to $3\,\text{m}^3$ (heaped) depending on the power of the machine and the use. Loading is generally carried out by lifting the bucket, and swinging the boom away from the working face to the awaiting haulage vehicle. Alternatively material can be dumped adjacent to the machine.

Face, front or loading shovel is constructed in a similar manner to a back-acter except that the boom, bucket arm and bucket operate in the opposite direction, i.e. up and away from the machine. Generally used for excavating faces up to about 8 m high and stockpiles, buckets are available in different sizes up to $4\,\text{m}^3$ (heaped) depending on the power of the machine. Loading is carried out in a similar manner to the back-acter, although some machines have bottom dump buckets to increase the speed of loading. It is useful in excavating soils, weak rock and blasted rock from faces in cuttings, etc. Some larger excavators can be converted from back-acters to face shovels.

Forward loader consists of a pneumatic-tired or crawler tractor at the front of which is mounted a wide bucket that can be moved in a vertical plane. Excavation is carried out by driving the machine towards, and the bucket into, the material; the bucket is then turned and lifted upwards thus catching and excavating the material. The hauling vehicle is loaded by driving the loader to, and emptying the bucket into the body of a vehicle. Loaders are generally used to excavate material at and for a distance above ground level (e.g. stockpiles, blasted rock) and can be used to push or haul material in the bucket over short distances. Modern loaders have hydraulically powered buckets and the smaller units may be equipped with a back-acter (i.e. a backhoe loader).

Dragline equipment is operated from cranes or similar plant with a long boom. Excavation is by pulling a bucket, suspended on a cable, towards the machine by a second cable. Thus draglines are especially suited for the excavation of soft and loose materials from a distance at a level beneath or slightly above their tracks, and may be used to excavate under water. Excavated material can be removed directly to a stockpile or loaded into haulage vehicles or conveyor hoppers by rotating the machine, with the bucket in the upright position.

Grab consists of a cable or hydraulically controlled bottom opening bucket suspended from a crane or a lifting arm. The bucket is opened and dropped on to the material to be removed; it is then closed and the material caught between the jaws lifted in the grab bucket and discharged on to stockpiles or into waiting haulage vehicles. Grabs are typically used for the excavation of pits or trenches, and loading to and from stockpiles.

Graders are used to spread fill and finely trim the sub-grade. They consist of a blade which can rotate in a circular arc about a sub-horizontal axis and which is supported beneath a longitudinal frame joining the front steering wheels and the rear drive wheels. The front wheels are generally articulated, whilst the rear wheels are set in tandem beneath the motor and control units. The blade is used to trim and redistribute soil and therefore graders usually operate in the forward direction.

Road lorries are available in varying sizes up to about 38 tonne gross vehicle weight and generally have steel or steel/aluminium sheeted bodies. Such vehicles require to be loaded by other plant but are generally unloaded by side or rear tipping.

Dump trucks and dumpers generally vary in size from one to about 80 tonne capacity; large capacity machines are available but are generally used in mines, quarries or opencast sites. In recent years articulated dump trucks with capacities up to about 35 tonne have become popular as they are versatile, and are especially suitable for hauling on softer sub-grades. Bodies of dump trucks may be heated by the exhaust from the engines and the sides are often splayed out to provide a large loading target. The speed of tipping is increased over a road lorry by the absence of a tailgate. Small dumper units are available for work on small sites and mounted dump trucks are also available with load capacities up to about 20 tonne.

Conveyors have been used with varying degrees of success on construction projects in the UK. They are built up with a number of units of endless flat belt conveyors placed in series and major changes in direction can be made at transfer points, where material from one belt falls and is channelled on to the next. Loading is generally carried out via a hopper which may be designed to screen out over-size material. The conveyor may end either above a stockpile or in a stacker which allows the material to be spread over a wide area. The capital costs to set up a conveyor system are often large in comparison with conventional plant, but operating costs may be lower. Conveyors are generally used in quarries and pits, in areas of very steep or poor access.

Plant that excavates, loads, hauls and deposits.

Bulldozer is a tractor equipped with a front pusher blade which can be raised and lowered by hydraulic rams. An angle dozer has a blade that is capable of being set at an angle to push material sideways whilst the tractor moves forward. The tractor unit is usually mounted on crawler tracks thus allowing it to travel over and push off a wide variety of ground conditions, although wheel-mounted units are available. Blades are manufactured in a variety of styles, but are all of heavy duty construction with a hardened steel basal leading edge, driven into the ground to cut and push the material to be excavated. Dozers have a wide variety of roles including excavating soils and weak rocks, ripping, moving excavated material over short distances, spreading materials, trimming earthworks, and acting as a pusher to boost the effective power of scrapers and other plant. A wide range of crawler units are available, ranging between about 45 and 575 kW. Dozer blades may be attached to other plant (such as self-propelled compactors) so that they can operate without the need for a dozer.

Scraper can excavate, load, haul and deposit material in one cycle and may be towed or self-propelled (motorised). It consists of a centrally-mounted bowl, the bottom, leading edge of which can be controlled. Both towed and self-propelled scrapers are effectively articulated between the front motorised or towing unit and the bowl, and larger self-propelled scrapers may have a second engine mounted at the rear. During excavation and loading and, as the machine moves forward, the cutting edge scrapes the top layer of soil into the bowl. On completion of loading the apron is lowered and the bowl raised. Deposition of the material is carried out by moving the ejector forward, with the apron raised and the bowl partially lowered. The thickness of the layer of deposited soil can be regulated by control of the ejector, apron and bowl. Ideally haulage should take place over well maintained haul roads with minimum of steep gradients or sharp turns.

Towed scrapers typically range in size from about 5 to $17 \, m^3$ struck capacity, and are generally towed by crawler tractors. They are limited to economic hauls of about 400 m each way.

Single and double engine motorized scrapers typically range in size from about 11 to $25 \, m^3$ struck capacity ($15 \, m^3$ to $34 \, m^3$ heaped). Motor scrapers can generally be economically operated on fast hauls of up to 2.6 km each way, with optimum performance on hauls of about 800 m.

Elevating and auger scrapers are similar to conventional scrapers except that a rotating elevator or auger moves the excavated material from the front of the bowl, breaks it down and deposits it within the bowl, thus reducing the resistance on, and increasing the speed of, loading. Elevating scrapers generally range in size from about 7 to $26 \, m^3$ and auger scrapers from 17 to $34 \, m^3$ (heaped) capacity.

The following is a brief description of some of the plant commonly used in earthworks compaction. Manufacturers' catalogues may be consulted for further details.

Smooth-wheeled rollers consist of smooth-wheeled drum rolls manufactured as three-roll or tanden-roll self-propelled units, or as a single towed roller. They generally range in size from 1.7 to 17 tonne deadweight, which may be increased by adding sand or water ballast to the rolls or by placing ballast weight on the frame of the roller. Where a roller has more than one axle, the higher mass per unit width is normally taken. Optimum speeds are generally from 2.5 to 5 km/h.

Pneumatic-tired rollers may be towed or self-propelled and may have one or two axles, on which are set a number of rubber-tired wheels. On two axle machines, one axle generally has one fewer wheel than the other and the tires are offset so that the weight of the roller can generally be increased by applying ballast to a box or platform mounted over or between the axles. The compactive effort can be further modified by adjusting the inflation pressures of the tires. Provision is usually made for a certain amount of vertical movement of individual or pairs of wheels, to enable the roller to negotiate uneven ground whilst exerting steady pressure on the soil. On the 'wobbly-wheel' roller, the wheels are set to wobble from side to side, providing more kneading action to the soil. These rollers are classified in terms of total mass of the roller divided by the number of wheels. Optimum speeds are generally between 1.6 and 24 km/h.

Grid rollers have a cylindrical heavy steel mesh roller and may be ballasted with concrete blocks. They are generally towed units and can operate at speeds between 5 and 24 km/h. Typical weights vary between 5.5 tonnes net and 15 tonnes ballasted.

Tamping rollers include sheepsfoot and pad rollers and consist of steel drums fitted with projecting feet. They may be self-propelled or towed, with single or multiple axles and the mass may be increased with ballast. The shape of the projecting feet varies considerably and may be circular, square or rectangular and are available in different lengths and tapers. Optimum speeds vary between 4 and 10 km/h.

Construction traffic is similar in effectiveness to pneumatic-tired rollers. In practice, it may be difficult to ensure complete and uniform coverage of the fill which in any case requires the plant to operate at less than normal speeds. Therefore compaction achieved by construction traffic is usually considered 'a bonus'. Excessive or concentrated trafficking can lead to extensive over-compaction, rutting and degradation of the fill.

Vibrating rollers generally range in size from about 0.5 to 17 tonne (static) and may be towed, self-propelled or manually guided. The former usually operate at speeds between 1.5 and 2.5 km/h, whereas manually guided machines typically operate between 0.5 and 1.0 km/h. Repeated passes at high speed are generally not as effective as fewer passes at lower speed. Where tandem rollers are used, both rolls can be considered to be applying compaction; the input of compacted effort is generally adjusted to that of the roll with the lesser mass per unit width; alternatively it can be considered as a single drum roller with higher weight per unit width. The frequency of vibration of a given machine is generally fixed by the manufacturer and typically varies from 20 to 35 Hz for larger rollers and from 45 to 75 Hz for smaller rollers. On some rollers the frequency can be varied. When the vibrating mechanism is not used the roller can be considered as a deadweight roller.

Vibrating plate compactors vary in weight from 100 kg to 2 tonne with plate areas between $0.16 m^2$ and $1.6 m^2$. Smaller versions are manually guided and therefore suitable for compacting small or awkwardly shaped areas. They usually travel at about 0.7 km/h. They are classified in terms of the mass divided by the area of the base in contact with the ground.

Vibro-tampers compaction is induced by vibrations set up in a base plate through a spring activated by an engine-driven reciprocating mechanism. They are usually manually guided and weigh between 50 and 100 kg. They are not suited to heavy compaction, but are frequently used in confined spaces. They are classified in terms of the static mass of the machine.

Power rammers are manually driven machines suitable for the compaction of small or awkwardly shaped areas. Explosions in an internal combustion engine cause the machine to be driven upwards and the subsequent impact of the base plate on the ground results in compaction. They generally weigh about 100 kg, although special larger versions are available. They are classified in terms of the static mass of the machine.

Dropping weight compactors consist of a weight of 500 kg or more which can be dropped from a controlled height, usually about 3 m.

Appendix 3. Examples of planning and construction for earthworks projects

(from P.C. Horner, 1988)

In the following, simplified examples of the planning of earthmoving and compaction projects are presented, together with brief reviews of some contracts.

Earthmoving

Example of the planning of an earthmoving scheme

A site 150 m wide and 250 m long is to be developed for warehousing units. This involves the stripping of topsoil, reducing the site level and removing the material off site. The following materials are to be excavated and disposed of

clay	$18\,125\,\text{m}^3$
topsoil	$10\,000\,\text{m}^3$
total	$28\,125\,\text{m}^3$

The site is reasonably flat and has good access. Tipping space is available 3.0 km distant. The work is to be carried out in the early summer and approximately 10 weeks are available on the provisional programme; production is limited to a 40 hour week.

During excavation, bulking of the soils will occur and this must be allowed for. Thus

$$\text{loose volume} = \text{bulking factor} \times \text{bank volume}$$

Therefore

loose volume clay $= 18\,125 \times 1.3 = 23\,562\,\text{m}^3$
loose volume topsoil $= 10\,000 \times 1.45 = 14\,500\,\text{m}^3$
total loose volume $= 38\,062\,\text{m}^3$

The estimator has chosen to investigate excavation using tracked forward loaders with $14\,\text{m}^3$ (20 tonne) road lorries. For a $1.53\,\text{m}^3$ capacity loader

bucket fill factor = 0.8 (80 per cent capacity)
load per cycle = $0.8 \times 1.53\,\text{m}^3 = 1.22\,\text{m}^3$
number of loads per $14\,\text{m}^3$ lorry = $14 \div 1.22$
$$= 11.5 \text{ (approx. 12)}$$
loading time of loader = 0.8 min/load (from manufacturer's tables)
total load time/lorry = 12×0.8 min = 9.6 min

Add 2.0 min for lorry to position. Therefore

total load time = 11.6 min
output per loader per 40 hour week working 50 min/h
$$= 40 \times 50/11.6 \text{ loads/week} = 172 \text{ loads/week}$$
$$= 2408\,\text{m}^3/\text{week}$$
total time required for one loader
$$= 38\,062 \div 2408 \text{ weeks}$$
$$= 15.8 \text{ weeks}$$

In order that the work can be completed within the allocation time period, two loaders will be required for 8 weeks each (thus allowing time for the establishment of the plant on site, etc.).

The lorries have the following working cycle

positioning at the loader	2.0 min
loading	9.6 min
moving on/off site	1.0 min
travel 2.5 km each way at 30 km/h	10.0 min
tipping time	3.0 min
total	25.6 min

Number of lorries required per loader = $25.6 \div 11.6 = 2.2$
Total number of lorries required = 4.4

Allowing for breakdowns, etc. 5 lorries will be required; thus the total plant required will be 2 loaders and 5 lorries.

Example of an earthmoving project

An example of a large earthmoving project can be well illustrated by a motorway that was constructed in South Wales, in which both soils and rock had to be excavated. Because of the scale of the project the example has been simplified without altering the fundamental pattern of the work.

The contract involved the excavation of three major and one minor cuttings, the construction of six embankments and the disposal of unsuitable and surplus suitable materials in off-site tips, as is shown in Fig. A3.1. In the middle of the works lay a large bridge which effectively limited the transport of fill along the line of motorway.

The mass haul indicated that short to medium hauls of up to 3 km and long hauls of up to 10 km would be required and that a mixed fleet of motor

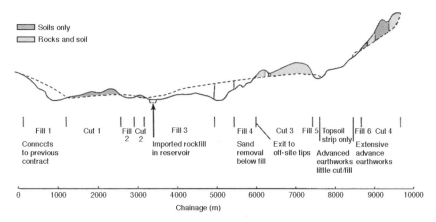

Fig. A3.1 Example of a large earthmoving project in South Wales

Table A3.1 Description of features, soil and rock types, and plant sequence for earth moving project in South Wales

Item	Fill 1	Cut 1	Fill 2	Cut 2	Fill 3	Bridges	Fill 4	Cut 3	Fill 5	Top soil strip area	Fill 6	Cut 4	Tips Adj. to Fill 4	Tips East of Cut 4
Feature	Rock-fill embankment	Major cutting	Minor fill	Major cutting	Major fill, part constructed of rock-fill	Two bridges providing limitations to cross-haul	Removal of sand dunes below fill in part	Major cutting	Minor fill	No fill-topsoil strip only	Minor fill	Major cut-advanced earthworks		
Soil/ rock types		Boulder clay sand and gravel		Boulder clay			Blown sand	Boulder clay, clay, marl, conglomerate, limestone				Boulder clay, clay, marl, sandstone, limestone		
Excavation techniques (soils)		Motor scrapers, dozers		Motor scrapers			Motor scrapers, tractor and box, dozers	Motor scrapers, dozers, back-acters				Draglines, face shovels, dozers, back-acters		
Excavation techniques (rock)							Drill and blast Dozers and rippers, Face-shovels, back-acters dropballs					Drill and blast Dozers and rippers, Face-shovels, back-acters dropballs		
Transport	Scrapers ⟶ ⟵ Scrapers ⟶ ⟵ Imported rockfill-road lorries ⟶ ⟵						⟵ Scrapers ⟶ ⟵ Dump ⟶ trucks ⟵ Scrapers ⟶ Road lorries					⟵ Dump ⟶ trucks ⟶		

scrapers, dump trucks and lorries would be necessary. Rock was known to be present within two of the cuttings and would need dump trucks or lorries for its transportation. This could be only partly accommodated by the requirements of the mass haul and consequently tended to reduce the amount of work that could be carried out by motor scrapers. In the event more rock was encountered than anticipated at the east end of the contract and further reduced the amount of work carried out by motor scrapers. In Table A3.1 the more important items of plant used to excavate, load and transport the rock and soil are shown together with the major hauls.

Compaction

Example of the planning of a compaction scheme

A series of embankments are to be constructed of rockfill and well graded granular soils. After the initial build up of plant, it is anticipated that between $15\,000\,m^3$ and $22\,000\,m^3$ of material is to be compacted per week. The types of rollers that should be used have to be determined. Rock fill and well graded granular soils can be treated similarly for compaction purposes and are generally best compacted by vibrating rollers. Therefore a study into whether a towed or self-propelled roller would be more suited is to be carried out.

For both types of roller the specification defines the number if passes for a given layer thickness of fill at an operational speed of 1.5 to 2.5 km/h (average 2.0 km/h), and an overlap of 0.15 m each side of the roll is to be taken on each pass. The sizes are as given in Table A3.2.

Table A3.2

	Towed roller	Self-propelled double drum roller
Roll width	2.08 m	2.03 m
Weight/m width of roller	5600 kg/m	3000 kg/m

The maximum thickness of compacted soil and minimum number of passes can be determined from the specification on compaction as shown in Table A3.3.

Table A3.3

	Towed roller	Self-propelled double drum roller
Maximum thickness of compacted soil	275 mm	200 mm
Minimum number of passes	4	2*

* For double drum rollers of equal mass/metre width the number of passes stated can be divided by two.

For towed rollers

$$\text{area covered/h} = \text{effective width of roller} \times \text{travel speed}$$
$$= (2.08 - 0.3) \times 2.0 \times 1000\,m^2/h$$
$$= 3560\,m^2/h$$

$$\text{total production/h} = \frac{3560 \times 0.275}{4}\,m^3/h = 244.75\,m^3/h$$

$$\text{total production/week} = 244.75 \times 54 = 13\,217\,m^3/\text{week}$$

This makes no allowance for working at less than peak efficiency, starting, turning, breakdowns, etc. A correction is required to allow for 60 per cent working efficiency

corrected weekly production $13\,217 \times 0.6\,m^3$/week
$$= 7930\,m^3/\text{week}$$

For self-propelled rollers

area covered/h $= (2.03 - 0.3) \times 2.0 \times 1000\,m^2$/h
$$= 3460\,m^2/\text{h}$$

total production/h $= \dfrac{3460 \times 0.2}{2}\,m^3$/h

$$= 18\,684 m^3/\text{week}$$

Allowing for the efficiency correction as before

corrected weekly production $= 18\,684 \times 0.6\,m^3$/week
$$= 11\,210\,m^3/\text{week}$$

To achieve peak production either 2 self-propelled tandem rollers or 3 towed vibrating rollers would be required. In this case the unit cost of operating a towed roller (including the crawler tractor) was 1.4 times that of the tandem roller and a significant saving could be made if two self-propelled tandem rollers were used. However, if the work had been spread over a number of embankments such that the rollers were required to be moved from area to area, it may have been more economical to use the three towed rollers.

Example on compaction practice

The example taken to illustrate compaction in practice concerns a motorway contract in south east England. The contract consisted of the construction of 2.25 km of motorway together with two roundabouts, their associated slip roads and a trunk road crossing the motorway. This involved the placing and compaction of over $700\,000\,m^3$ of bulk fill, selected backfill to structures, drainage blankets and fill for surcharging embankments and for landscaping purposes. The compaction of the fill was carried out with a number of different types of plant which were selected to suit the materials being compacted, the volumes and rate of placement of fill requiring compaction; and the environment in which compaction was being carried out. A summary of the plant used is given in Table A3.4.

The majority of the fill used consisted of Thanet Sand. Where motor scrapers were employed to deliver the sand at high output rates, towed vibrating rollers in tandem or self-propelled tamping rollers were used, whereas when lorries, dump trucks or tractor and boxes were employed,

Table A3.4 Description of features, soil conditions and plant for earthmoving project in South of England

Area	Fill type	Deposited by	Compacted by	Layer thickness: mm	Number of passes
Roundabout 1					
Slip roads	Thanet Sand	Lorries/ dump trucks	140 HP crawler tractor towing vibrating roller (3260 kg/m width)	275	8
Old chalk pits	Coarse sand–fine gravel (free draining)	Lorries	As above failed – then saturated material and compacted with tracks of 140 HP crawler tractor	As required	As required
Landscaping	Chalk, clay, rubble	Lorries	140 HP crawler tractor towing vibrating roller (3260 kg/m width)	200	2*
			As above without vibration on roller	150	2–4*
			140 HP crawler tractor towing 8000 kg smooth wheeled roller	150	2–4*
Motorway and Side Road Embankment					
Start to roundabout 1	Thanet Sand	Motor scrapers	300 HP crawler tractor towing 2 vibrating rollers in tandem (both 5600 kg/m width)	100	1
Roundabout 1 to viaduct	Thanet Sand	Motor scrapers	300 HP crawler tractor towing 2 vibrating rollers in tandem (5600 kg/m plus 3260 kg/m)	100	1–2
			30 740 kg self-propelled tamping roller	250	4
	Brickearth	Tractor and box	140 HP crawler tractor towing 5500 kg towed tamping roller	225	8
Old chalk pits	Thanet Sand	Motor scrapers	140 HP crawler tractor towing 5600 kg/m width vibrating roller	300	4

Table A3.4 Continued

Surcharge to embankments	Thanet Sand	Dump trucks	140 HP crawler tractor towing 3260 kg/m width vibrating roller	275	8
Roundabout 2					
Slip roads	Thanet Sand	Tractor and box	140 HP crawler tractor towing 5600 kg/m width vibrating roller	300	4
		Dump trucks	170 HP special rubber-tyred tractor towing 3260 kg/m vibrating roller	275	8
	Gravelly clay	Tractor and box	140 HP crawler tractor towing 3260 kg/m vibrating roller	200	4
		Motor scraper	30 740 kg self-propelled tamping roller	225/150	4/12
Clay seal to contaminated area	London Clay	Lorries	140 HP crawler tractor towing 5500 kg tamping roller	225	4
Trunk road embankments	Thanet Sand	Dump trucks	170 HP special rubber-tyred tractor towing 3260 kg/m vibrating roller	275	8
Structures					
Granular backfill	Sandy gravel	Lorries	140 HP crawler tractor towing 3260 kg/m vibrating roller	200	4
			Manual 664 kg/m vibrating roller	75	12

* Specification required compaction to be half of normal number of passes for landscaping fill.

single towed vibrating rollers were adopted. For other materials towed vibrating, smooth wheeled (deadweight) and towed or self-propelled tamping rollers were used, depending on the nature of the soil and rate of production required.

Appendix 4. Stability charts

(from Chandler and Peiris, 1989)

Further extensions to the Bishop & Morgenstern slope stability charts

Steep slopes in homogeneous soft rocks including chalk and marls can be analysed with this new extension to the Bishop Morgenstern charts.

The design charts for the effective stress stability analysis of slopes given by Bishop and Morgenstern (1960) and O'Connor and Mitchell (1977) are extended to slopes of inclination 0.5 : 1 (horizontal : vertical) and values of the dimensionless stability factor $c'/\gamma H$ up to 0.15. The present results are shown to agree with those of the earlier workers, whose results, included here, enable slopes to be designed in the range of inclination 0.5 : 1 to 5 : 1, for values of $c'/\gamma H = 0$ to 0.15, and $\phi' = 20°$ to 40°.

Introduction

Over the years the stability charts presented by Bishop and Morgenstern (1960) have proved very valuable for the preliminary design of slopes in terms of effective stresses. The range of strength and slope inclinations that they considered was, however, limited to values of the stability coefficient $c'/\gamma H$ no greater than 0.05 and slope inclinations in the range 2 : 1 to 5 : 1 (horizontal : vertical). The range of strengths was later extended by O'Connor and Mitchell (1977), who considered values of $c'/\gamma H$ up to 0.10.

We have extended further both the range of values of $c'/\gamma H$ (to 0.15) and the slope inclination (up to 0.5 : 1); following O'Connor and Mitchell we consider values of ϕ' between 20° and 40°. The results are presented here in tabular form. This further extension of the method not only allows steeper slopes to be considered, but the higher values of $c'/\gamma H$ enable the design of slopes composed of relatively homogeneous soft rocks such as chalk and Keuper Marl. The range of data which we provide is compared with those of the earlier publications in Fig. A4.1. We have included the results of Bishop and Morgenstern and O'Connor and Mitchell with our own results, so that the complete suite of stability coefficients is available to the potential user.

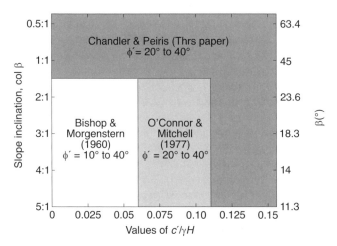

Fig. A4.1   Slope inclinations and values of $c'/\gamma H$ considered by the various authors

Methods

The analyses were carried out with a microcomputer, using the Bishop Simplified method for a circular arc failure surface (Bishop 1955), programmed to locate the most critical failure surface. As described by Bishop and Morgenstern (1960), the Bishop Simplified equation for the factor of safety, F, may be written in dimensionless terms. Thus F is dependant on the geometry of the particular problem, and on the parameters $c'/\gamma H$, ϕ' and $\bar{r}_u$, where c' and ϕ' are the effective stress strength parameters, γ is the unit weight of the soil, H the vertical height of the slope and $\bar{r}_u$ the average value of r_u within the slope. The pore pressure parameter r_u is defined in Fig. A4.2, as are the slope inclination, β, and the depth factor, D.

There is a linear relationship between F and r_u for given values of $c'/\gamma H$, ϕ', β and D, which may be given (Bishop and Morgenstern 1960) as:

$$F = m - nr_u \tag{1}$$

The results of the stability analyses may thus be expressed in terms of m and n.

Our computations followed similar procedures to both Bishop and Morgenstern and O'Connor and Mitchell. The former used 20 trial circular arcs to establish the critical arc, the latter 100. We used 24 (6 × 4 grid),

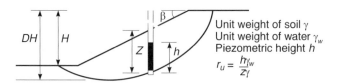

Fig. A4.2   Definitions of symbols used

guided by Spencer's observations (1967) that the contours of safety factor are approximately elliptical with their major axis normal to the surface of the slope, and that the centre of the critical arc is normally on or just upslope of the perpendicular bisector of the slope. A check was made that a minimum value of *F* lay within the grid; where necessary, the calculations were repeated with a new grid location so that a minimum value of *F* was obtained.

The values *m* and *n* in Equation (1) were computed using a regression analysis applied to the *F* versus r_u data.

Bishop and Morgenstern and O'Connor and Mitchell carried out their computations using values of $r_u = 0$, 0.3 and 0.7; we used 0, 0.3 and 0.6.

We also investigated the influence of the choice of 20 or 40 as the number of slices used in the analysis on the resulting value of *F*. For the case of $c'/\gamma H = 0.100$, $D = 1.5$, $\beta = 4:1$, with values of ϕ' in the range 20° to 40° and r_u to values of 0, 0.3 and 0.6, the variation in factor of safety lay between 0 and 1.53 per cent (average 0.4 per cent). In every instance the value of *F* obtained with 20 slices was the lower. We subsequently used 20 slices for all our analyses, so that in that respect our results will yield marginally conservative values of *F*.

Comparison with previous results

O'Connor and Mitchell compared their results with Bishop and Morgenstern's for $c'/\gamma H = 0.05$ and $D = 1.00$, and we have done the same. The results of this comparison are shown in Table A4.1, expressed as percentage differences from the original Bishop and Morgenstern *m* and *n* values. O'Connor and Mitchell's results show slightly closer agreement with Bishop and Morgenstern's than do ours, with their values of *m* and *n* being on average 0.26 per cent higher, while our results average 0.76 per cent

Table A4.1 Differences (±%) in values of *m* and *n* obtained by (1) O'Connor and Mitchell (1977) and (2) this paper, compared with Bishop and Morgenstern (1960), for $c'/\gamma H = 0.05$, $D = 1.0$

		\multicolumn{8}{c}{*Slope inclination*}							
ϕ'		2:1		3:1		4:1		5:1	
		m	*n*	*m*	*n*	*m*	*n*	*m*	*n*
20°	1	+0.1	+0.1	+1.0	+1.8	−0.2	−1.1	+0.3	+1.1
	2	+0.4	+2.0	+0.9	+2.8	−0.8	−1.0	+0.3	+0.9
30°	1	+0.1	+0.8	+0.3	+0.1	+0.4	+0.3	+0.4	+0.5
	2	+1.1	+2.4	+0.6	+1.4	+0.4	+2.0	−0.1	−0.2
40°	1	+0.2	−0.2	0	+0.1	−0.2	−1.0	+0.4	+1.0
	2	+1.2	+1.8	+0.6	+0.8	+0.2	−0.7	+0.4	+0.8

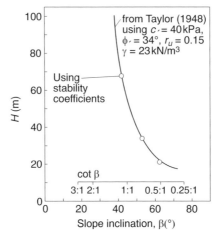

Fig. A4.3 Comparison of slope height versus inclination relationships calculated by different methods; curve from Chandler (1984)

higher. The use of such values in Eq. (1) will result in a corresponding percentage increase in F compared with the other worker's results. These differences are sufficiently small to be of no practical importance.

It is also possible to compare, indirectly, our results with those of Taylor (1948). Chandler (1984) used Taylor's work to construct a slope height versus inclination relationship for a slope having the soil properties $c' = 40$ kPa, $\phi' = 34°$, $\bar{r}_u = 0.15$ and $\gamma = 23$ kN/m³, obtaining the relationship shown in Fig. A4.3. Our extension of the Bishop and Morgenstern results enable this relationship, which involves slope inclinations in the range $1:1$ to $0.5:1$, to be checked. It is seen that the calculated points agree extremely well with the relationship obtained from Taylor's data.

Presentation of results

In the tables that follow (Tables A4.2 to A4.19), we present results of our computations, to which we have added for the user's convenience the results.

Table A4.2 $c'/\gamma H = 0$; all values of D.

Slope	0.5:1		1:1		2:1		3:1		4:1		5:1	
	m	*n*	*m*	*n*	*m*	*n*	*m*	*n*	*m*	*n*	*m*	*n*
ϕ'												
20°	0.182	0.910	0.364	0.728	0.728	0.910	1.092	1.213	1.456	1.547	1.820	1.892
25°	0.233	1.166	0.466	0.933	0.933	1.166	1.399	1.554	1.865	1.982	2.332	2.424
30°	0.289	1.443	0.577	1.155	1.155	1.443	1.732	1.924	2.309	2.454	2.887	3.001
35°	0.350	1.751	0.700	1.400	1.400	1.751	2.101	2.334	2.801	2.977	3.501	3.639
40°	0.420	2.098	0.839	1.678	1.678	2.098	2.517	2.797	3.356	3.566	4.196	4.362

Table A4.3 $c'/\gamma H = 0.025$; $D = 1.00$

Slope	0.5:1		1:1		2:1		3:1		4:1		5:1	
	m	n	m	n	m	n	m	n	m	n	m	n
ϕ'												
20°	0.523	0.733	0.707	0.764	1.124	1.022	1.542	1.347	1.962	*1.698*	2.380	*2.050*
25°	0.586	0.740	0.839	0.974	1.356	1.282	1.875	1.696	2.400	*2.141*	2.921	*2.596*
30°	0.667	0.875	0.983	1.202	1.606	1.567	2.235	2.078	2.873	*2.622*	3.508	*3.191*
35°	0.755	1.010	1.142	1.454	1.880	1.885	2.635	2.505	3.396	3.160	4.156	*3.849*
40°	0.857	1.183	1.318	1.731	2.190	2.247	3.090	2.993	3.984	3.778	4.885	*4.592*

Table A4.4 $c'/\gamma H = 0.025$; $D = 1.25$

Slope	0.5:1		1:1		2:1		3:1		4:1		5:1	
	m	n	m	n	m	n	m	n	m	n	m	n
ϕ'												
20°	0.996	0.943	1.076	1.036	1.309	1.216	1.618	1.478	1.961	1.775	2.334	2.090
25°	1.224	1.198	1.328	1.321	1.619	1.547	2.007	1.891	2.437	2.269	2.897	2.669
30°	1.472	1.483	1.602	1.631	1.956	1.915	2.431	2.342	2.953	2.806	3.511	3.299
35°	1.737	1.773	1.905	1.974	2.331	2.321	2.901	2.841	3.524	3.400	4.191	3.998
40°	2.045	2.118	2.242	2.362	2.753	2.775	3.431	3.399	4.164	4.064	4.958	4.784

Table A4.5 $c'/\gamma H = 0.050$; $D = 1.00$

Slope	0.5:1		1:1		2:1		3:1		4:1		5:1	
	m	n	m	n	m	n	m	n	m	n	m	n
ϕ'												
20°	0.688	0.783	0.912	0.818	1.380	1.071	1.840	*1.387*	2.333	*1.776*	2.783	*2.091*
25°	0.797	1.000	1.069	1.042	1.624	1.338	2.193	*1.757*	2.778	*2.211*	3.336	*2.651*
30°	0.908	1.217	1.222	1.247	1.888	1.630	2.574	*2.157*	3.261	*2.693*	3.934	*3.259*
35°	1.032	1.417	1.379	1.469	2.178	1.958	2.990	*2.592*	3.803	*3.253*	4.597	*3.927*
40°	1.148	1.617	1.559	1.755	2.505	2.332	3.451	*3.071*	4.425	*3.926*	5.344	*4.668*

Table A4.6 $c'/\gamma H = 0.050$; $D = 1.25$

Slope	0.5:1		1:1		2:1		3:1		4:1		5:1	
	m	n	m	n	m	n	m	n	m	n	m	n
ϕ'												
20°	1.172	0.988	1.253	1.084	1.509	1.266	1.834	1.493	2.230	1.799	2.643	*2.107*
25°	1.405	1.242	1.509	1.363	1.822	1.595	2.222	1.897	2.705	2.287	3.211	*2.690*
30°	1.656	1.518	1.783	1.669	2.161	1.950	2.645	2.342	3.221	2.819	3.829	3.324
35°	1.935	1.830	2.087	2.007	2.535	2.344	3.114	2.839	3.795	3.413	4.511	4.025
40°	2.245	2.174	2.429	2.390	2.953	2.791	*3.642*	3.400	4.442	4.090	5.273	4.806

Table A4.7 $c'/\gamma H = 0.050$; $D = 1.50$

Slope	0.5:1		1:1		2:1		3:1		4:1		5:1	
	m	n	m	n	m	n	m	n	m	n	m	n
ϕ'												
20°	1.491	1.289	1.561	1.343	1.752	1.501	2.011	1.705	2.337	1.993	2.690	2.280
25°	1.826	1.637	1.910	1.709	2.143	1.903	2.467	2.179	2.867	2.534	3.302	2.902
30°	2.187	2.015	2.287	2.104	2.568	2.342	2.964	2.696	3.443	3.120	3.967	3.577
35°	2.587	2.436	2.704	2.541	3.041	2.832	3.515	3.269	4.082	3.771	4.707	4.325
40°	3.040	2.915	3.175	3.036	3.574	3.389	4.136	3.915	4.803	4.507	5.543	5.171

Table A4.8 $c'/\gamma H = 0.075$; $D = 1.00$

Slope	0.5:1		1:1		2:1		3:1		4:1		5:1	
	m	n	m	n	m	n	m	n	m	n	m	n
ϕ'												
20°	0.845	0.800	1.088	0.837	1.610	*1.100*	2.141	*1.443*	2.664	*1.801*	3.173	*2.130*
25°	0.950	1.013	1.245	1.053	1.872	1.386	2.502	*1.815*	3.126	2.259	3.742	2.715
30°	1.064	1.238	1.416	1.296	2.142	1.686	2.884	*2.201*	3.623	2.758	4.357	*3.331*
35°	1.190	1.485	1.605	1.564	2.443	2.030	3.306	*2.659*	4.177	*3.331*	5.024	*4.001*
40°	1.332	1.762	1.798	1.824	2.772	2.386	3.775	*3.145*	4.785	*3.945*	5.776	*4.759*

Table A4.9 $c'/\gamma H = 0.075$; $D = 1.25$

Slope	0.5:1		1:1		2:1		3:1		4:1		5:1	
	m	n	m	n	m	n	m	n	m	n	m	n
ϕ'												
20°	1.336	1.023	1.387	1.087	1.688	1.285	2.071	1.543	2.492	1.815	2.954	2.173
25°	1.575	1.284	1.656	1.386	2.004	1.641	2.469	1.957	2.972	2.315	3.523	2.730
30°	1.830	1.560	1.943	1.701	2.352	2.015	2.888	2.385	3.499	2.857	4.149	3.357
35°	2.109	1.865	2.245	2.025	2.728	2.385	3.357	2.870	4.079	3.457	4.831	4.043
40°	2.424	2.210	2.583	2.403	3.154	2.841	3.889	3.428	4.729	4.128	5.603	4.830

Table A4.10 $c'/\gamma H = 0.075$; $D = 1.50$

Slope	0.5:1		1:1		2:1		3:1		4:1		5:1	
	m	n	m	n	m	n	m	n	m	n	m	n
ϕ'												
20°	1.637	1.305	1.706	1.349	1.918	1.514	2.199	1.728	2.548	1.985	2.931	2.272
25°	1.977	1.663	2.052	1.708	2.308	1.914	2.660	2.200	3.083	2.530	3.552	2.915
30°	2.340	2.041	2.426	2.100	2.735	2.355	3.158	2.714	3.659	3.128	4.218	3.585
35°	2.741	2.459	2.841	2.537	3.211	2.854	3.708	3.285	4.302	3.786	4.961	4.343
40°	3.193	2.931	3.310	3.031	3.742	3.397	4.332	3.926	5.026	4.527	5.788	5.185

Table A4.11 $c'/\gamma H = 0.100$; $D = 1.00$

Slope	0.5:1		1:1		2:1		3:1		4:1		5:1	
	m	*n*	*m*	*n*	*m*	*n*	*m*	*n*	*m*	*n*	*m*	*n*
ϕ'												
20°	0.993	0.797	1.263	0.871	1.841	*1.143*	2.421	*1.472*	2.982	*1.815*	3.549	*2.157*
25°	1.106	1.025	1.422	1.078	2.102	*1.430*	2.785	*1.845*	3.358	*2.303*	4.131	*2.743*
30°	1.222	1.259	1.592	1.306	2.378	1.714	3.183	*2.258*	3.973	*2.830*	4.751	*3.372*
35°	1.347	1.508	1.781	1.576	2.692	2.086	3.612	*2.715*	4.516	*3.359*	5.426	*4.059*
40°	1.489	1.788	1.995	1.879	3.025	2.445	4.103	*3.230*	5.144	*4.001*	6.187	*4.831*

Table A4.12 $c'/\gamma H = 0.100$; $D = 1.25$

Slope	0.5:1		1:1		2:1		3:1		4:1		5:1	
	m	*n*	*m*	*n*	*m*	*n*	*m*	*n*	*m*	*n*	*m*	*n*
ϕ'												
20°	1.489	1.036	1.529	1.095	1.874	1.301	2.283	1.558	2.751	*1.843*	3.253	*2.158*
25°	1.735	1.313	1.799	1.394	2.197	1.642	2.681	1.972	3.233	*2.330*	3.833	*2.758*
30°	1.997	1.602	2.091	1.718	2.540	2.000	3.112	2.415	3.753	*2.858*	4.451	*3.372*
35°	2.280	1.908	2.414	2.076	2.922	2.415	3.588	2.914	4.333	3.458	5.141	*4.072*
40°	2.597	2.253	2.763	2.453	3.345	2.855	4.119	3.457	4.987	4.142	5.921	*4.872*

Table A4.13 $c'/\gamma H = 0.100$; $D = 1.50$

Slope	0.5:1		1:1		2:1		3:1		4:1		5:1	
	m	*n*	*m*	*n*	*m*	*n*	*m*	*n*	*m*	*n*	*m*	*n*
ϕ'												
20°	1.778	1.314	1.863	1.371	2.079	1.528	2.387	1.742	2.768	2.014	3.158	2.285
25°	2.119	1.674	2.211	1.732	2.477	1.942	2.852	2.215	3.297	2.542	3.796	2.927
30°	2.489	2.063	2.586	2.122	2.908	2.385	3.349	2.728	3.881	3.143	4.468	3.614
35°	2.892	2.484	3.000	2.553	3.385	2.884	3.900	3.300	4.520	3.800	5.211	4.372
40°	3.347	2.957	3.469	3.046	3.924	3.441	4.524	3.941	5.247	4.542	6.040	5.200

Table A4.14 $c'/\gamma H = 0.125$; $D = 1.00$

Slope	0.5:1		1:1		2:1		3:1		4:1		5:1	
	m	*n*	*m*	*n*	*m*	*n*	*m*	*n*	*m*	*n*	*m*	*n*
ϕ'												
20°	1.121	0.808	1.425	0.881	2.042	*1.148*	2.689	*1.541*	3.263	*1.784*	3.868	*2.124*
25°	1.254	1.051	1.596	1.112	2.323	*1.447*	3.062	*1.908*	3.737	*2.271*	4.446	*2.721*
30°	1.376	1.267	1.769	1.337	2.618	*1.777*	3.457	*2.298*	4.253	*2.810*	5.073	*3.368*
35°	1.505	1.530	1.956	1.586	2.929	2.115	3.880	*2.705*	4.823	*3.407*	5.767	*4.048*
40°	1.612	1.743	2.171	1.891	3.272	2.483	4.356	*3.183*	5.457	*4.060*	6.551	*4.893*

Table A4.15 $c'/\gamma H = 0.125$; $D = 1.25$

Slope	0.5:1		1:1		2:1		3:1		4:1		5:1	
	m	n	m	n	m	n	m	n	m	n	m	n
ϕ'												
20°	1.642	1.057	1.671	1.102	2.054	1.324	2.492	*1.579*	2.983	*1.861*	3.496	*2.167*
25°	1.888	1.326	1.941	1.402	2.377	1.671	2.894	1.993	3.481	*2.379*	4.078	*2.753*
30°	2.156	1.626	2.234	1.727	2.727	2.042	3.324	2.431	4.009	*2.916*	4.712	*3.405*
35°	2.447	1.948	2.557	2.085	3.110	2.451	3.801	2.928	4.586	*3.500*	5.414	*4.128*
40°	2.767	2.295	2.922	2.490	3.542	2.913	4.338	3.494	5.237	4.161	6.207	*4.945*

Table A4.16 $c'/\gamma H = 0.125$; $D = 1.50$

Slope	0.5:1		1:1		2:1		3:1		4:1		5:1	
	m	n	m	n	m	n	m	n	m	n	m	n
ϕ'												
20°	1.920	1.322	2.015	1.385	2.234	1.545	2.565	1.749	2.963	2.004	3.400	2.287
25°	2.261	1.683	2.368	1.754	2.638	1.972	3.028	2.229	3.500	2.550	4.019	2.913
30°	2.631	2.073	2.745	2.145	3.072	2.425	3.529	2.749	4.083	3.149	4.692	3.598
35°	3.039	2.504	3.160	2.577	3.549	2.923	4.084	3.324	4.727	3.813	5.436	4.362
40°	3.497	2.982	3.628	3.065	4.089	3.485	4.712	3.980	5.456	4.566	6.278	5.226

Table A4.17 $c'/\gamma H = 0.150$; $D = 1.00$

Slope	0.5:1		1:1		2:1		3:1		4:1		5:1	
	m	n	m	n	m	n	m	n	m	n	m	n
ϕ'												
20°	1.248	0.813	1.585	0.886	2.261	*1.170*	2.895	*1.448*	3.579	*1.806*	4.230	*2.159*
25°	1.386	1.034	1.761	1.126	2.536	*1.462*	3.259	*1.814*	4.052	*2.280*	4.817	*2.765*
30°	1.525	1.260	1.944	1.370	2.836	*1.791*	3.657	*2.245*	4.567	*2.811*	5.451	*3.416*
35°	1.660	1.539	2.134	1.619	3.161	*2.153*	4.098	*2.721*	5.137	*3.408*	6.143	*4.117*
40°	1.805	1.832	2.346	1.901	3.512	2.535	4.597	*3.258*	5.782	*4.083*	6.913	*4.888*

Table A4.18 $c'/\gamma H = 0.150$; $D = 1.25$

Slope	0.5:1		1:1		2:1		3:1		4:1		5:1	
	m	n	m	n	m	n	m	n	m	n	m	n
ϕ'												
20°	1.796	1.079	1.813	1.107	2.229	1.334	2.701	1.600	3.225	1.873	3.780	2.182
25°	2.042	1.344	2.083	1.409	2.560	1.692	3.107	2.015	3.724	2.384	4.363	2.769
30°	2.309	1.639	2.377	1.734	2.909	2.065	3.542	2.464	4.262	2.941	5.995	3.406
35°	2.605	1.971	2.700	2.094	3.295	2.475	4.018	2.946	4.846	3.534	5.697	4.129
40°	2.934	2.335	3.066	2.499	3.728	2.938	4.556	3.509	5.498	4.195	6.490	4.947

Table A4.19 $c'/\gamma H = 0.150$; $D = 1.50$

Slope	0.5:1		1:1		2:1		3:1		4:1		5:1	
	m	*n*	*m*	*n*	*m*	*n*	*m*	*n*	*m*	*n*	*m*	*n*
ϕ'												
20°	2.061	1.335	2.164	1.391	2.394	1.550	2.748	1.756	3.174	2.020	3.641	2.308
25°	2.402	1.691	2.520	1.768	2.798	1.978	3.212	2.237	3.711	2.561	4.259	2.924
30°	2.772	2.082	2.902	2.168	3.236	2.441	3.718	2.758	4.293	3.156	4.931	3.604
35°	3.181	2.514	3.319	2.600	3.715	2.940	4.269	3.333	4.938	3.819	5.675	4.364
40°	3.643	3.000	3.788	3.088	4.255	3.503	4.896	3.983	5.667	4.569	6.517	5.228

We are thus able to give the stability coefficient for slopes in the range $0.5:1$ ($\beta = 64°$) to $1:5$ ($\beta = 11.3°$), for values of $c'/\gamma H = 0$ to 0.15, and $\phi' = 20°$ to 40°.

As Bishop and Morgenstern pointed out (p. 136), for the special case where $c' = 0$ the failure surface is a plane parallel to the slope surface (the 'infinite slope' case) and

$$F = \tan \phi'(1 - r_u \sec^2 \beta)/\tan \beta \tag{2}$$

Thus m and n (Table A4.2) may be easily evaluated as $m = \tan \phi'/\tan \beta$, and $n = m \sec^2 \beta$.

The previous authors presented their results in both tabulations and in chart form. We believe that the tabulations are used far more frequently than the charts, and therefore only include the tabulations. A particular benefit of the charts is that it is possible to show (for given values of β, ϕ', $c'/\gamma H$ and D) contours of values of $r_u(r_{ue})$ which yield the same value of F for values of $D = 1.00$ and 1.25; and also for $D = 1.25$ and 1.50. The value of r_u used for design can then be compared with the corresponding value of r_{ue}, to provide an immediate indication whether or not there is a more critical deeper slip surface. This is not so conveniently achieved with tables, but a partial solution, followed here, is outlined in the following section.

Use of tables

The tables give values of m and n to be inserted in the equation

$$F = m - nr_u \tag{1}$$

to obtain the factor of safety, F, of the slope for given values of $c'/\gamma H$, ϕ', r_u and slope inclination β, all of which are defined in Fig. A4.2. A method for obtaining a value of $\bar{r}_u$ within the slope for use in Eq. 1 is given by Bishop and Morgenstern (1960).

For values of n appearing in the tables in italics there is the possibility of a deeper, more critical failure surface if the design value of $\bar{r}_u$ is equal to or less than 0.5. The user should then check this possibility, using the table giving the next highest value of D for the same value of $c'/\gamma H$. It is also possible that a deeper critical surface may exist where the design r_u is greater than 0.5. No indication of this is given in the tables, so the user should also check this possibility at higher values of D. This problem does not occur when $c' = 0$ (Table A4.2); nor, as is often the case, when a stronger stratum lies at or close to the base of the slope.

Linear interpolation may be used, without significant loss of accuracy, for calculations involving intermediate values of $c'/\gamma H$, ϕ' and $\cot\beta$.

Worked example

The example chosen is that used by Bishop and Morgenstern (1960), an earth slope for which the relevant design parameters are $\phi' = 30°$, $c'/\gamma H = 0.035$, $\bar{r}_u = 0.5$, and which has a slope inclination $\cot\beta = 4:1$.

Referring to Table A4.3 ($c'/\gamma H = 0.025$; $D = 1.00$), it is seen that the value of n, *2.622*, is shown in italics. Since the design value of $\bar{r}_u$ (0.5) lies just within the range 0.5 to 0, there will be a deeper more critical failure surface. Thus it is necessary to turn to Table A4.4 ($c'/\gamma H = 0.025$, $D = 1.25$). This gives $m = 2.953$, $n = 2.806$, which when substituted into Eq. 1, along with $r_u = 0.5$, yields $F = 1.550$.

Similarly, from Table A4.5 ($c'/\gamma H = 0.050$, $D = 1.00$) a deeper more critical failure surface is again indicated. Thus Table A4.6 ($c'/\gamma H = 0.050$, $D = 1.25$) gives $m = 3.221$, $n = 2.819$, and Eq. 1 yields $F = 1.812$.

Interpolating linearly for $c'/\gamma H = 0.035$ gives

$$F = 1.550 + 0.4 \times 0.262$$
$$= 1.65.$$

Acknowledgements

We are grateful to the Institution of Civil Engineers and the Canadian Geotechnical Journal for allowing us to reprint the results previously obtained by Bishop and Morgenstern and O'Connor and Mitchell.

Appendix 4 reproduced from Ground Engineering with kind permission of the publisher Emap.

Index

The numbers in italics refer to figures.